D1256410

A

HANDBOOK
of RENAISSANCE
METEOROLOGY

With Particular Reference to Elizabethan and Jacobean Literature

S. K. HENINGER, JR.

GREENWOOD PRESS, PUBLISHERS
NEW YORK 1968

First Greenwood reprinting, 1968

Library of Congress catalogue card number: 69-10106

Printed in the United States of America

Preface

In accordance with Elizabethan usage the word "meteor" is used to cover all atmospheric phenomena; and therefore "meteorology," in terms of Elizabethan cosmology, deals with all mutations that occur in the region of Air between the earth's surface and the sphere of Fire. Until mid-seventeenth century this science was based on the natural philosophy of Aristotle, specifically his *Meteorologica.* Other strong influences affecting Renaissance concepts about meteors were the Holy Scriptures, classical mythology, and interrelated beliefs from astrology, magic, and folklore. My ruling purpose has been to provide a handy reference work which brings together all these ideas.

In reconstructing Elizabethan meteorology, I have begun with the authoritative scientific works best known in the period, such as Seneca's *Quaestiones naturales,* Pliny's *Historia naturalis,* Bartholomaeus' *De proprietatibus rerum* as edited by Stephen Batman, Du Bartas' *La Sepmaine,* and William Fulke's *Goodly Gallery.* For documentation I have relied mainly on books in English, since these obviously would have been most influential both in forming prevalent notions about meteors and in standardizing a vernacular vocabulary by which to express these notions.

I have taken at least first steps in determining Scriptural influences on meteorological concepts. In such matters I have found especially useful the work of Rabanus Maurus, the Biblical *Postilla* of Nicolas of Lyra, and the Protestant commentaries on Genesis by John Calvin, Gervase Babington, and Nicholas Gibbens.

When discussing meteorological ideas that derived from classical mythology, I have noted one or two passages from Greek and Latin literature which could have served as a source for Renaissance knowledge of the myth. Probably more influential than the classics themselves were such reference books as Boccaccio's *Genealogiae deorum gentilium,* Cartari's *Le imagini de i dei degli antichi,* and Natalis

Comes' *Mythologiae;* so I have also referred to pertinent passages in them. But most of the mythological material could easily have been found in any number of contemporary English writers.

Beliefs based upon folklore and popular hearsay have proved something of a problem. To cite specific authority for them is often impossible, so in many cases I can do little more than label the idea as commonplace and refer to a modern investigator in the field of folk-beliefs.

Wherever possible I have documented each factual statement with an instance of literary adaptation. This juxtaposition of scientific principle and literary application has a twofold aim: passages from the creative writers amplify the technical discussions about meteors, while conversely the quotations from technical writers elucidate many meteorological allusions in literature previously unexplained or misinterpreted. I have considered the illustrative material to be of equal importance with the scientific principles themselves, and consequently I have lingered over many literary passages for the sake of making purely critical remarks.

Most of my literary illustrations have been drawn from the better known writers: Spenser, Marlowe, Shakespeare, Jonson, Donne, and Chapman. There is perhaps a need to offer some explanation for the preponderance of material taken from Shakespeare, but the simple fact is that his works exhibit the highest concentration of meteorological matter. Because of the abundance of illustrative passages in his writings and because of his pre-eminence among his contemporaries, I have thought it proper to accord him a lion's share of attention.

In Part III the major creative writers are considered in the common light of Renaissance meteorology. I have sought fresh insight into their intellectual backgrounds and stylistic techniques by examining the various ways in which each author created imaginative poetry from the prosaic statements about meteors. Renaissance meteorology provides somewhat controlled conditions under which to compare poets because it is a relatively small, clearly stated body of beliefs from which all writers necessarily drew. It represents a common source available in equal degree to everyone, almost a common denominator.

All things of importance cannot be shown by this comparative method, but some significant points can be made.

At the time of completing this manuscript I did not have available Kester Svendsen's *Milton and Science.* We have worked several of the same mines, quite independently. My research provides a broader base for many of Dr. Svendsen's findings, especially in Chapter III, "This Vast Sublunar Vault"; while *Milton and Science* presents an impressive extension of my subject into a later period. Our two publications are supplementary, I believe, rather than repetitive. I have been gratified to find a kindred interest in Renaissance meteorology, and a kindred conviction that such knowledge is valuable in critical exegesis.

In quotations and titles I have expanded most abbreviations, normalized capitalization, and standardized the use of *i* and *j*, *u* and *v*, and similar orthographic details decided by the typesetter.

For financial aid, I am indebted to the Fulbright Commission and to the Research Council of Duke University. For gracious assistance in all matters, I wish to thank the staffs of the Bodleian Library, the British Museum, the Folger Shakespeare Library, the Bibliothèque Nationale, the Johns Hopkins University Library, and the Duke University Library. Finally, I should like to acknowledge my debt to Mrs. E. M. Simpson, Miss Helen Gardner, and Dr. D. C. Allen, all of whom have kindly read the manuscript at various stages of its preparation.

S.K.H.

Table of Contents

PART III

METEOROLOGICAL IMAGERY IN THE MAJOR CREATIVE WRITERS

APPENDIXES

Illustrations

FIGURES

HEADPIECES

PART I

BACKGROUND FOR THE STUDY OF METEORS IN RENAISSANCE ENGLAND

CHAPTER ONE

INTRODUCTION

THE intellectual revolution of the seventeenth century destroyed a complex of beliefs which now seem quite alien—or at best, quaint. The final rejection of geocentrism for heliocentrism reflected the fundamental change in man's conception of the universe. The traditional meteorology was of course also considered obsolete, and soon was reinterpreted in the new spirit of empiricism. Rain falls on the New Atlantis for reasons quite different from those which explained why divine grace showered the City of God.

In Elizabethan England, however, the study of atmospheric phenomena was a well-developed branch of knowledge as yet unthreatened by the iconoclasm of the seventeenth century. It was not a center of controversy, as were many of its sister sciences. For most atmospheric disturbances there were definite explanations which everyone accepted as obvious and indisputable, and references to them could be stated with a certainty that did not require elucidation or justification.

But modern readers, schooled only in post-Copernican science, are likely to be puzzled by early references to thunder and dew and the rainbow. We no longer believe that lightning and winds are formed from the same raw material, nor do we fear comets and earthquakes as dire portents of disaster. Furthermore, we no longer report many anomalies quite commonly mentioned in earlier centuries. Who today has seen a thunderstone, showers of blood, or a flying-dragon? Therefore we must reconstruct premodern meteorology to understand a world composed of four Elements.

The Renaissance use of the term "meteor" itself requires explanatory comments. The word was an exact transliteration of μετέωρον, which means literally "something raised up," from μετά+ἀείρειν. In Elizabethan usage the term included all atmospheric phenomena—

that is, all natural processes that occurred in the region of Air: clouds, dew, winds, lightning, comets, rainbows, and associated weather processes. "Meteorology" quite rightly designated the study of these phenomena, although this term was not so common as "meteor".[1]

A gradual refinement of the word "meteor" over many centuries has resulted in its present restricted use as an astronomical term for fragments from outer space which enter the earth's atmosphere. The restriction of the term proceeded first by its specific application to comets, which were at that time thought to be atmospheric phenomena. Already in the sixteenth century "meteor" could be employed in this limited sense, as instanced in Shakespeare's *Richard II*: "Meteors fright the fixed stars of heaven" (II.iv.9). Here, although there is intended the contrast between the lowly sublunary meteor and the noble celestial star, the image also largely depends upon the distinction between the ordered courses of the fixed stars and the erratic wanderings of disturbing comets. The restriction of "meteor" to its modern astronomical sense did not become completely effective until the present century, however, and to Renaissance Englishmen the term still covered all atmospheric processes and anomalies. In *Hymenaei* Jonson referred to "watrie *Meteors*" (line 658), and in *1 Tamburlaine* Marlowe spoke of "freezing meteors and conjealed colde" (line 19)—that is, sleet and snow.

Before the seventeenth century the science of meteorology (divorced from weather forecasting) was based almost exclusively on the natural philosophy of Aristotle. Meteors were imperfect mixtures of the four Elements. They were confined to the region of Air in the sublunary universe, since changing weather conditions could not conceivably transpire in the immutable region beyond the Moon. The contrast between the transitoriness of meteors and the permanence of the heavens provided the argument for Donne's reassurance of health to his mistress in a fever:

> These burning fits but meteors bee,
> Whose matter in thee is soone spent.

[1] In English writings the first instance of the word "meteorology" that I have found is in William Fulke, *A Goodly Gallery* (London: W. Griffith, 1563), fol. 51. This reference antedates the first recorded usage in the *NED* by fifty-seven years. Even earlier, "meteorologer" (meaning an authority on meteors) had been used by Leonard Digges, *A Prognostication of Right Good Effect* (London: T. Gemini, 1555), Biii.

> Thy beauty, and all parts, which are thee,
> Are unchangeable firmament.[2]
> ("A Feaver," 21-24)

Meteors, then, could occur only in the corruptible portion of the universe enclosed by the sphere of the Moon; and meteorology, in a strict sense, was limited to the study of these sublunary occurrences—their causes, their formation, their description, and their effects. Pierre de la Primaudaye precisely defined meteorology as "that part of natural philosophie, which entreateth of the aire, and of the things engendred therein, and appertayning thereto."[3]

The confinement of meteors to the mundane region determined the position of meteorology in the organization of knowledge. It was a distinct study, clearly dissociated from astronomy and astrology, whose sources of data were the celestial bodies. Medieval encyclopedists had normally dealt with meteors immediately following their discussion of the four Elements, and they had established a tradition of designating each meteor as Watery, Airy, Fiery, or Earthy. The Renaissance continued to classify meteorology with the studies of other mundane phenomena, such as the Elements, plants, and nonhuman animals. Conrad Gesner in his *Pandectae* (Zurich, 1548) organized all knowledge into twenty-one books, and he placed the chapters "De meteoris" in Liber XIV, *De naturali philosophia,* along with other chapters "De lapidibus," "De metallis," "De plantis," and "De animalibus." Gesner treated weather-prognostication, however, in Liber IX, *De astrologia,* indicating the association of forecasting with astrology. A separate book of the *Pandectae*, Liber VIII, was devoted to astronomy.

A similar classification of meteorology is offered by Sebastian Verro's *Physicorum libri .X.* (London, 1581). In this concise Latin encyclopedia for the natural sciences, Book V deals with meteors. It is immediately preceded by books "De elementis" and "De generatione," and it is followed by books "De fossilibus," "De stirpibus," and "De animalibus." Meteorology plainly was not a science of the heavens above the earth, but of the terrestrial sphere itself.

Contemporary scientific principles were the most consistent influ-

[2] Cf. Donne, "To the Countesse of Huntingdon," 5-8.
[3] *The Third Volume of the French Academie*, trans. R. Dolman (London: G. Bishop, 1601), pp. 203-204.

ence on Renaissance notions about meteors, but many other influences had also been at work. The mysteries of magic provided considerable commentary on many of the wondrous meteors, and folklore furnished even more. Scriptural references and their allegorical interpretation greatly increased the connotative value of meteors, so that the rainbow always brought to mind Jehovah's covenant with Noah after the Flood, and dew recalled His provision of manna for the Israelites in the desert. Classical mythology had personified several meteors (most notably the winds) and had recounted their individual stories. Moreover, poetical usage itself had established conventional imagery involving meteors, such as the rain:tears and the thunder: artillery comparisons.

For forecasting weather the Elizabethan layman could depend upon numerous weather signs based on a long popular tradition stretching back to the Greeks, or he could buy a printed prognostication prepared by an astrologer.[4] During the Middle Ages professional forecasting had become dominated by astrology, and this condition persisted into the Renaissance. The development of meteorology as an exact science was inevitably delayed until the seventeenth century, when the physical sciences were placed on a precise basis by the invention of dependable measuring instruments. In meteorology the use of a thermometer by Galileo in 1607 and of a barometer by Torricelli in 1643 heralded this new era,[5] which definitely arrived with the printing of Robert Hooke's "A Method for Making a History of the Weather."[6]

Although Renaissance meteorology has met the same fate as other Aristotelian sciences, some few remnants of the old notions about

[4] Appendix I briefly covers outstanding figures in the historical development of weather forecasting and summarizes the long lists of accepted weather signs available everywhere in almanacs and handbooks.

[5] See Abraham Wolf, *A History of Science, Technology, and Philosophy in the 16th and 17th Centuries* (London, 1935), pp. 82-98, 306-324. See also Lorenzo Magalotti, *Saggi di naturali esperienze fatte nell' Accademia del Cimento* (Florence, 1666); Magalotti, *Essayes of Natural Experiments Made in the Academie del Cimento*, trans. R. Waller (London, 1684); Gustav Hellmann, *Die Anfänge der meteorologischen Beobachtungen und Instrumente* (Berlin, 1890); and Hellmann, *Beiträge zur Erfindungsgeschichte meteorologischer Instrumente* (in *Abhandlungen der preussischen Akademie der Wissenschaften. Jahrgang 1920. Physikalisch-Mathematische Klasse*, nr. 1) (Berlin, 1920).

[6] An appendix to Thomas Sprat, *The History of the Royal-Society of London* (London, 1667), pp. 173-179.

meteors have been peculiarly persistent. Even today we speak of dew "falling" rather than condensing on the grass, and we think of lightning "striking" from the sky rather than being conducted up from or down to a grounded object. "Elements" as a metonym for "weather" —although the usage now sounds archaic—is another vestige of the old theory in which atmospheric conditions were closely linked with the supposed interactions between the four Elements.

CHAPTER TWO

THE STUDY OF METEORS BEFORE 1558

MOST primitive societies have made serious efforts to control the rain, the sunshine, and the wind;[1] and all polytheistic religions have included deities to preside over these natural phenomena. The Greeks explained changing weather conditions in terms of sophisticated mythology: the rainbow was the many-colored robe of Iris; excessive heat and drought were due to the carelessness of Phoebus, or possibly were a re-enactment of the Phaeton disaster; earthquakes and volcanoes resulted from the restlessness of Typhon in his underground prison; lightning was the impetuous wrath of Zeus. In the Hebraic-Christian tradition also there are numerous incidents involving similar meteors, such as the Rainbow of Promise, the drought to curse Egypt, and the earthquake and lightnings accompanying Moses' reception of the Ten Commandments. Always the natural processes of the atmosphere, both usual and unusual, have formed an integral part of the traditions within any culture that man has developed.

The meteorological traditions of Elizabethan England had their roots in the science of classical Greece. The first recorded attempt to explain atmospheric phenomena as various phases of an all-inclusive natural system was the *Meteorologica*[2] of Aristotle. Earlier philosophers had discussed isolated phenomena, and the *Meteorologica* itself alluded to many of these discussions—Hippocrates on comets, Democritus on the Milky Way, Anaxagoras on hail, Anaximenes on earthquakes, Empedocles on lightning. But these philosophers had not

[1] See Sir James G. Frazer, *The Golden Bough* (abridged ed.; London, 1923), pp. 60-83.

[2] The *Meteorologica* comprises four books, only the first three of which deal with meteors. Book IV concerns the chemistry of the Elements, and probably is spurious. Quite often Book IV is treated separately from the other books of the *Meteorologica*.

attempted to construct an atmospheric cycle which included these meteors as single phases of an integrated system, and their theories were cited in the *Meteorologica* only to be controverted by what Aristotle considered more plausible conclusions.

The system of atmospheric processes that Aristotle expounded was undeniably simple, yet all-embracing. In brief,[3] the Sun was thought to draw up two sorts of evaporations: (1) a hot and dry "exhalation," potentially like Fire, which rose from Elemental Earth; and (2) a warm and moist "vapor," potentially like Water, which rose from the Watery components of the earth's surface. The various meteors were formed as one (or possibly both) of these evaporations underwent temperature changes, either because of ascension through the three regions of the Air, because of variations in the intensity of heat from the Sun, or because of proximity to the sphere of Fire. From the dry exhalation came thunder and lightning, the winds, earthquakes, comets, and other fiery impressions; from the moist vapor developed clouds, rain, snow, hail, mist, dew, and frost. A third group of phenomena, which resulted from the reflection of various celestial bodies by sundry vapor formations, consisted of such displays as halos, rainbows, and multiple suns. This description of the atmosphere and its processes remained undisputed until mid-seventeenth century, and meteorological writings between Aristotle and Robert Hooke were largely attempts to amplify or adapt the *Meteorologica*.

Although each succeeding century adhered in general principle to Aristotle's atmospheric cycle, thinking men naturally wished to interpret the study in the light of their own observations. Consequently numerous commentaries were written throughout the Near Eastern and Christian worlds. The earlier commentators accorded the greatest respect during the Renaissance were Alexander of Aphrodisias (*fl.* 193-217); the Peripatetic philosopher Olympiodorus (*fl.* 6th century); John of Alexandria, called Philoponus (*fl.* 6th century); Averroës; the two great Schoolmen, Albertus Magnus and St. Thomas Aquinas; Themon Judaeus (d.>1361); and Gaetano da Thiene (1387-1465). Commentaries by these men frequently became integral parts of the Aristotelian text. In the late fifteenth and early sixteenth centuries, to meet the increased demand that followed the

[3] A detailed exposition of Aristotle's theory of the atmosphere is given in Part II, Chapter I, "General Principles."

invention of printing, many fresh commentaries were prepared, notably those by Johann Versor and Johann Eck in Germany, by Jacob van Amersfoort and Jan Dullaert in the Netherlands, by Thomas Bricot and Antoine Mizauld in France, and by Agostino Nifo and Francesco Vicomercato in Italy.

The *Meteorologica* had become available in Latin before the beginning of the thirteenth century, at the same time that the other scientific works of Aristotle were being recovered from their Arabic exile. Not only had Gerard of Cremona translated the first three books of the *Meteorologica* from the Arabic of the Moslems, but also about 1260 William of Moerbeke had made a translation directly from the Greek. By this time a vernacular rendition also was available in Mahieu le Vilain's translation of the first three books into French.[4] The *Meteorologica* was of course printed in the handsome Aldine edition of the complete works of Aristotle (in Greek) published in 1495-1498; but as early as 1474 a separate Latin edition of the treatise, with the commentary of Averroës, had been printed in Padua. In the early sixteenth century there were many important Latin translations, notably those by Pietro Alcionio, François Vatable, Giovanni Battista Camozzi, and Joachim Périon. A bibliography of the printed editions of the *Meteorologica* reveals the astonishing fact that more than 125 separate editions were published before 1601.[5]

The explanation of meteors elaborated in the *Meteorologica* was neatly summarized in the *De mundo*,[6] which is now known to be spurious. Until recently, however, it enjoyed the same authority as valid members of the Aristotelian canon. The *De mundo* was loosely paraphrased in Latin by Lucius Apuleius, and this text was printed in 1497. To correct Apuleius' version, Pietro Alcionio published in 1521 his fresh translation from the Greek. The most popular translation of the *De mundo*, however, was Guillaume Budé's text, first printed in 1526.

[4] George Sarton, *Introduction to the History of Science* (3 vols.; Baltimore, 1927-1948), II.509, 829-830. Mahieu le Vilain's translation has been edited by Rolf Edgren, *Les Meteores d'Aristote* (Uppsala, 1945).

[5] Gustav Hellmann, "Bibliographie der gedruckten Ausgaben, Übersetzungen und Auslegungen der Meteorologie des Aristoteles," *Beiträge zur Geschichte der Meteorologie*, II (1917), 3-45.

[6] The Aristotelian treatise known throughout the Middle Ages and Renaissance as *De caelo et mundo* is distinct from *De mundo* and should not be confused with it. *De caelo et mundo* is now usually called simply *De caelo*.

The *De mundo* incorporated information contained in a brief work on the winds, "Ventorum situs et cognomina." In manuscript this small treatise is an extract from the *De signis aquarum et ventorum*,[7] a pseudo-scientific formulation of weather-forecasting rules based on both verifiable observation and popular hearsay. The *De signis* and a supplementary work, the *De ventis*, are now attributed to Theophrastus, Aristotle's successor as head of the Lyceum. The complete works of Theophrastus were not published until 1541 in Basle, but the *De signis* and the *De ventis* had appeared under Theophrastus' name in the Aldine edition of Aristotle (1495-1498). A Latin translation of the *De signis* was included in a volume of pseudo-Aristotelia at least as early as 1501.

Another important Greek work on meteorology was the *Diosemea* by Aratus of Soli, a long didactic poem appended to the *Phaenomena* of the same author. The *Phaenomena* was intended to popularize recent astronomical discoveries, and the *Diosemea* was added to cover weather forecasting. The long list of weather signs was based upon Theophrastus, or perhaps upon an earlier common source.[8] Aratus' work proved extremely popular, especially with the Romans. It was the subject of a distinguished commentary by Theon of Alexandria (*fl.* 365-395), and fragments of it were rendered into Latin by no less eminent persons than Cicero, Germanicus Caesar, and Rufus Festus Avienus. The Latin fragments were printed with the *Opera* of Avienus in 1488. A major edition was an Aldine publication of 1499 (in *Scriptores astronomici veteres*), which included the Greek text with the three Latin fragments and the scholia of Theon of Alexandria. Before 1621 there were sixty-two other editions,[9] the most important being the *Syntagma Arateorum* of Hugo Grotius (Leyden, 1600).

The Roman interest in meteorology, indicated by the numerous adaptations of Aratus, was further shown by many other treatments of the subject, especially in the early manifestations of the encyclopedia

[7] See Aristotle, *Ventorum Situs et Cognomina*, trans. E. S. Forster (in *Works of Aristotle*, Vol. VI, ed. W. D. Ross; Oxford Univ. Press, 1913), preface.

[8] The complex problem of the relation between the *De signis* and Aratus' work, as well as the relation between these and lost works by Aristotle and Theophrastus, is discusssed by William E. Gillespie, *Vergil, Aratus and Others* (Princeton, 1938), pp. 9-31.

[9] See *Astronomy and Meteorology of Aratus*, trans. C. Leeson Prince (Lewes, 1895), pp. 1-16.

tradition. Vergil, writing largely under the influence of the *Diosemea,* included in Book I of his *Georgics* considerable information on weather signs; this work, in fact, established the tradition of furnishing forecasting rules in handbooks of husbandry. Lucretius devoted most of the last book of the *De rerum natura* to a lively explanation of meteors in atomist terms, a discussion which purported "to explain the true law of winds and storms, which men foolishly lay to the charge of the gods."[10] With no intention of originality *De placitis philosophorum* (commonly ascribed to Plutarch) recorded in digest form the opinions of ancient philosophers on "Meteores, that is to say, of such impressions as be engendred in the aire. . .betweene the circle of the Moone and the situation of the earth."[11] Seneca's *Quaestiones naturales* was likewise a collection of opinions mainly on meteorological topics, with moralistic conclusions drawn by the author. The *Quaestiones naturales,* written in A. D. 65, was the fullest discussion of meteors to have appeared.

But the Roman encyclopedist most widely read in the Renaissance was Pliny. By 1601 no less than 128 editions of the *Historia naturalis* had been published.[12] Book II contains "the discourse of the World, of coelestiall impressions and meteors,"[13] a discourse which deals with the many marvels that occur in the atmosphere between the earth and the heavens. Pliny accepted the fundamental principles of Aristotle's atmospheric system, but he embellished Aristotle's rational theory with many elements of wonder and even superstition. In Book XVIII Pliny gave a concise summary of "signes to prognosticate what weather is toward."[14]

Plutarch, Seneca, and Pliny were not great men of science in the sense that they made original contributions to knowledge. But they were men of inestimable influence whose encyclopedias remained

[10] Lucretius, *De Rerum Natura,* trans. H. A. J. Munro (2d. ed., 2 vols.; Cambridge, 1866), VI.47 ff. All references to Lucretius are made to this edition.

[11] Plutarch, *The Morals,* trans. Philemon Holland (London: A. Hatfield, 1603), p. 826 [III.proem]. All page references to Plutarch are quoted from this edition, with book and chapter references to the Teubner edition in square brackets.

[12] See E. W. Gudger, "Pliny's *Historia naturalis.* The Most Popular Natural History Ever Published," *Isis,* VI (1924), 269-281.

[13] Pliny, *Historie of the World,* trans. Philemon Holland (2 tomes, London: A. Islip, 1601), *a*ii. This phrase is an insertion by the translator. All page references to Pliny are quoted from Tome I of this edition, with book and chapter references to the Loeb Classical Library edition in square brackets.

[14] P. 610 [XVIII.lxxviii-lxxxix].

primary sources of scientific information well into the seventeenth century.

The encyclopedia tradition flourished in Europe throughout the Middle Ages, and almost without exception each new compilation of knowledge included extensive discussion on meteors. Isidore of Seville gathered a compendium of astronomy and meteorology under the title *De natura rerum* some time between 612 and 621.[15] His major work, the *Etymologiae,* written in succeeding years, was an even more comprehensive compilation of existing knowledge, and served as a model for later encyclopedias. The Venerable Bede soon followed Isidore's scientific compendium with a more concise *De natura rerum* of his own, but by no means stained Isidore's reputation as an authority. Meteors were discussed at length also in the important Latin encyclopedias of Rabanus Maurus (*ca.* 776-856), Alexander Neckam (1157-1217), Bartholomaeus Anglicus (*fl.* 1220-1250), Vincent de Beauvais (*ca.* 1190-1264), Thomas de Cantimpré (1201-<1280), and in the anonymous *Summa philosophiae* (*ca.* 1250) associated with Roger Bacon. Many of these encyclopedias were early translated into vernaculars; for example, Bartholomaeus' *De proprietatibus rerum* was translated into Italian in 1309, into French in 1372, into Provençal before 1391, into English in 1398, into Dutch in 1485, and into Spanish some time in the fifteenth century.[16] Meteorological information was also contained in other encyclopedias originally written in vernaculars, such as the long didactic poem *Image du Monde* (1245) by Gossouin (?),[17] Brunetto Latini's *Livres dou Trésor* (*ca.* 1265), and *Il Dottrinale* (<1349) by Jacopo di Dante Alighieri. All these popular compendia of learning drew freely from classical authors and from one another, and successfully disseminated considerable information to the large literate classes throughout Europe.

The renowned group of scientists who flourished in England in the thirteenth century, although usually praised for other achievements, wrote important treatises on various aspects of meteorology. The encyclopedist Bartholomaeus was an early member of this group,

[15] Sarton, *History of Science,* I.471.

[16] *Ibid.,* II.587.

[17] This work provided the original text of William Caxton's *Mirrour of the Worlde;* see p. 17, below.

as was also Alfred of Sareshel, who translated many Arabic texts into Latin and composed commentaries on much of Aristotle's work, including the *Meteorologica*. An Oxford don, identifiable only as John of London, lectured on astronomy and meteorology from about 1210 to at least 1252.[18] The two outstanding scientists of this group, Robert Grosseteste and Roger Bacon, were pioneers in the science of optics and consequently were active in the closely allied study of meteors.[19] Bacon composed a commentary on the *Meteorologica*, and Grosseteste wrote numerous meteorological essays, such as the "De cometis," "De iride," and "De aeris intemperia prognostica."

During the Middle Ages, when the validity of astrology was generally accepted, meteors became closely associated with the influence of the celestial bodies (a fact which Chaucer turned to comic advantage in "The Miller's Tale"). Authority for assigning domination of this world to the stars was explicit in Pliny, and could also be read into Aristotle.[20] The most direct influence which established astrology in Western Europe, however, was Arabic astronomy, especially the commentaries on Ptolemy's *Tetrabiblos*. By mid-century Leopold of Austria had gathered his *Compilatio de astrorum scientia*, which devoted Book VI of ten books to "De mutatione aeris." This was entirely astrological meteorology. Early works in the same tradition were the *Tractatus astronomiae* of the Italian astrologer Guido Bonatti da Forli, the *Pronosticon in mutationes aeris* of the French astrologer Firmin de Beauval, and the *Summa astrologiae iudicialis* of the English astrologer John Eschuid of Ashendon.

By the middle of the sixteenth century meteorology had thus developed along two divergent lines: the theoretical pure science

[18] Sarton, *History of Science*, II.582.

[19] In the thirteenth century the study of meteors had an offshoot: optics, or perspectives. This line of investigation, which began with Aristotle's attempts in the *Meteorologica* to explain atmospheric phenomena of reflection (such as rainbows and lunar halos), developed through Robert Grosseteste, Roger Bacon, and John Peckham in England, and Vitellio in Poland. See Sarton, *History of Science*, II. 761-763, 1024-1030; and Charles Singer, *Studies in the History and Method of Science* (Oxford Univ. Press, 1921), II.385-413.

[20] For example, in the *Meteorologica*: "Fire, earth and the kindred elements must therefore be regarded as the material cause of all sublunar events. . .while the driving power of the eternally moving bodies must be their [sublunar events'] cause in the sense of the ultimate source of their motion" (trans. H. D. P. Lee [Loeb Classical Library; London, 1952], 339[a]). All references to Aristotle are quoted from this edition. Vitruvius gives a list of Greek philosophers who had attempted to relate weather prognostication to astronomy (*De architectura*, IX.vi.3).

based on Aristotle, and the applied pseudo science of weather prognostication carried on by the astrologers. There seems to have been a movement among learned Protestants to liberate completely the science of meteors from astrology—at least William Fulke, who wrote the best Elizabethan handbook on meteors, also wrote the *Antiprognosticon* (1560) denouncing astrologers. But there is little evidence that astrology's control over weather prediction was seriously threatened until well into the seventeenth century. Here the important point to be noted is the abundance of authoritative opinion on meteorological questions when Elizabeth began her reign.[21]

[21] Appendix II lists the major authorities on meteors available in 1558.

CHAPTER THREE

METEOROLOGICAL WRITINGS IN ENGLISH TO 1625

THE learned works discussed in Chapter II set the pattern for technical books on meteorology in Renaissance England, and most writings prepared for a scholarly audience continued to appear in Latin. But the layman, not familiar with untranslated scientific works, necessarily formulated his notions about meteors either from hearsay or from books in English.

I. ENGLISH TRANSLATIONS OF CLASSICAL, MEDIEVAL, AND CONTEMPORARY WORKS

During the Elizabethan and Jacobean periods most of the earlier authorities on meteors were rendered into English by translators of varying abilities. The opinions of the Greek and Roman meteorologians were found everywhere, and the medieval encyclopedists were well represented by editions in English. The actual writings of the astrological meteorologians of the fourteenth and fifteenth centuries were not made available in popular form, but the practicing astrologers who carried on this tradition repeated the earlier authorities in their own treatises and almanacs. In addition to these adaptations of classical and medieval authorities, English readers could acquire translations of contemporary Continental works, such as *La Sepmaine* of Saluste du Bartas and *L'Académie Françoise* of La Primaudaye.

All of the major Roman authorities on meteors (with the exception of Lucretius) had become available to the English-reading public by 1625. Abraham Fleming's translation of the *Georgiks* of Vergil was printed with *The Bucoliks* at London in 1589. The first sixteen books of Pliny were briefly abstracted about 1566 by John Alday in a work entitled *A Summarie of the Antiquities and Wonders of the Worlde*, and Dr. Philemon Holland's excellent translation of the entire *Historie of the World* was handsomely printed in 1601. Dr. Holland's comparable translation of Plutarch, *The Philosophie, Commonlie Called, the Morals* (which contained the *Opinions of Philosophers*) appeared in 1603. *The Workes Both Morrall and Natural of Seneca*, competently rendered into English by Dr. Thomas Lodge, was printed in 1614.[1] In addition to their complete translations, these Roman authors were frequently quoted at length in English and even more frequently cited without acknowledgment.

The Greek authorities on meteors fared less well in translation than did the Roman. No avowed translation of Aristotle's *Meteorologica* was made, but the work was referred to directly or indirectly in every meteorological discussion. In his table of contents for *A Prognostication of Right Good Effect* (1555) Leonard Digges cited Aristotle as the authority for his theory of meteors, and this oft-reprinted handbook gave Aristotle's meteorological principles the widest possible circulation in England. Theophrastus and Aratus were less frequently drawn upon, although their names were always listed in any Renaissance roll of authorities. Aratus was seriously considered for a popular translation: Barnabe Googe tells how Urania tempted him to set forth "Aratus worthey bookes" rather than Palingenius' *Zodiake of Life*.[2]

By mid-sixteenth century, translations of two great medieval encyclopedias had already been published in English. William Caxton had translated the French *Image du Monde*, composed in 1245 probably by a cleric named Gossouin;[3] and in 1481 at Westminster, Caxton had prepared *The Mirrour of the Worlde*. He had printed another edition of this work in 1490, and yet a third edition had appeared from the press of Lawrence Andrewe about 1529. In this

[1] All page references to Seneca are quoted from this edition, with book and chapter references to the Teubner edition in square brackets.

[2] Marcellus Palingenius, *The Zodiake of Life* [1576], trans. Googe, ed. Rosemond Tuve (Scholars' Facsimiles; New York, 1947), "The Preface" to the 1560 ed.

[3] This work has been traditionally ascribed to Vincent de Beauvais, but modern scholars question his authorship. For a full discussion of the French original for Caxton's text, see *Caxton's Mirrour of the World*, ed. Oliver H. Prior (EETS; London, 1913).

encyclopedia the chapters on meteors appeared in their proper place, immediately following the chapter "of the Ayer and his nature" in the section which "declareth how the erthe is devided." The treatment of meteorology was rather cursory, however, compared with the more exhaustive discussions of astronomy and geography; and the author had omitted entirely the atmospheric phenomena of reflection.

The English layman had acquired an even richer mine of information in an English edition of another thirteenth-century encyclopedia, the *De proprietatibus rerum* of Bartholomaeus Anglicus. In 1495 Wynken de Worde had printed a translation made by John of Trevisa in 1398. Bartholomaeus' work was greatly popular in England, and a second edition was printed by Thomas Berthelet in 1535. Later in the century the learned clergyman Stephen Batman prepared a scholarly edition, which he "newly corrected, enlarged and amended." This edition was printed at London in 1582 under the title *Batman uppon Bartholome, His Booke De Proprietatibus Rerum.*[4]

In the *De proprietatibus rerum* Bartholomaeus had given detailed information on all meteors in their usual place in the organization of knowledge, in the book entitled "De aere et eius impressionibus." To Bartholomaeus' chapter on meteors, Batman made few additions and negligible emendations. The authorities drawn from most heavily were Isidore and Bede, and, in a less reverential manner, Aristotle and Pliny. But the long roll of authorities which Batman placed at the beginning of his edition included Theophrastus, Vergil, Averroës, and St. Thomas Aquinas.

Two Renaissance French works of encyclopedic scope likewise became available in English translation: Guillaume de Saluste du Bartas' *La Sepmaine* and Pierre de la Primaudaye's *L'Académie Françoise*. These works immediately gained a wide public in England, largely because of their Protestant leanings, and maintained their popularity far into the seventeenth century.

Du Bartas presented his poetic account of Creation in 1578, and within six years about thirty more editions were published. Joshua Sylvester gave this monumental poem a worthy rendering into English verse, which first appeared in 1605 under the title *Bartas His*

[4] All references to Bartholomaeus' *De proprietatibus rerum* are quoted from this edition prepared by Batman.

Devine Weekes & Workes. This book proved immensely popular, and other editions were issued in 1608, 1611, 1613, and 1621. Translated portions of du Bartas' work, however, had been published in London as early as 1595; and *The Second Day of the First Weeke,* the section dealing with meteors, had been printed separately in 1603.

In the Argument of the Second Day of the First Week, du Bartas stated his intention to discuss:

> . . .th'all-forming Elements;
> Their number, nature, use, and domination,
> Consent, excesse, continuance, scituation:
> Aires triple Regions; and their tempers change:
> Winds, exhalations, and all Meteors strange.[6]

In his text du Bartas treated successively atmospheric phenomena of vapors, of exhalations, and of reflection, and then drew a moral conclusion from the appearance of "prodigious signs." Earthquakes were discussed in the treatment of "Earth" on the Third Day of the First Week. Pliny seems to have been the major source of information for the meteorological sections, and much of Pliny's sense of wonder inheres in Sylvester's translation. Periodically du Bartas inserted a moralizing passage; but his intention of being pleasantly didactic was not perverted by too somber a religious tone, as occurred in La Primaudaye's slightly later prose encyclopedia, *L'Académie Françoise.*

Although La Primaudaye began to publish *L'Académie Françoise* in 1577, he did not finish his compendium until 1613. A full English translation of all four volumes did not appear until 1618. But R. Dolman's translation of *The Third Volume of the French Academie,* the section containing the meteorological discussions, had been printed at London in 1601.[7]

La Primaudye gave full, technical discussions, citing classical authorities, but showing no reluctance to uphold modern opinions. His ultimate, indisputable authority, however, was Holy Scripture. He employed an abundance of Biblical incidents and quotations, and sometimes attempted to correlate Biblical and classical explanations.

[5] All references to du Bartas' *Devine Weekes* are quoted from this translation by Sylvester.

[6] P. 31.

[7] All references to La Primaudaye's *French Academie* are quoted from this translation by Dolman, who should not be confused with Robert Persons, the Jesuit, who frequently published under the pseudonym "R. Doleman."

His range was encyclopedic, but his purpose was pointedly religious: to show the greatness and mercy of God manifested in the universe, and thus to bring his readers into the ways of the righteous. In his introduction to the section on meteors, La Primaudaye wrote:

Many excellent points of doctrine concerning the providence of God, as are taught us in the schoole of nature, by meanes of the meteors. . .of the cloudes, thunders, lightnings, stormes, flouds of water, windes, whirlewindes, and tempestes. . .will serve us. . .for preachers. . .to manifest unto us especially the judgements and heavie plagues of the almightie, and to make us oftner thinke thereupon then we doe.[8]

This point of view, an early expression of natural theology, commonly assailed the public both from pulpits held by enthusiastic divines and from bookstalls selling the produce of pious pamphleteers.

2. TECHNICAL TREATISES BY ENGLISH AUTHORS

All of the works discussed so far in this chapter have been either translations or adaptations of foreign authorities, works which were published under the name of the original author to enhance their salability to the reading public. But during the Renaissance a considerable body of meteorological writings was also prepared by native Englishmen. Although these English authors continued to lean heavily upon previous writers, they nonetheless presented their books under their own signatures without the crutch of a foreign authority on the title page. These books were usually prepared for the general public, while more erudite readers continued to rely upon the Latin texts pouring from Continental presses.

The most important work prepared by an Englishman for the English public was *A Goodly Gallery with a Most Pleasaunt Prospect, into the Garden of Naturall Contemplation, to Beholde the Naturall Causes of All Kind of Meteors*, first printed in 1563. This book was a youthful effort by William Fulke, the clergyman-don who, although he incurred much enmity through his vehement championing of the Protestant cause, eventually became vice-chancellor of Cambridge University. Other editions appeared in 1571, 1601, and 1602.

[8] P. 238.

r anye greate chaunge in the worlde, nother translations
er scarse anye falle of famous princes, no dearthe and
h and mortalitie, but GOD by the signes of heaven did
therof, to repent and beware betyme. . . .eclipses both of
ne. . .beside the appearing of sondrye Sonnes, and straunge
Moone. . .with rainbowes of mervailous formes, cometes of
and other wonderfull signes.[14]

emphasized the moral interpretation of such atmospheric
Indeed, Calvin had dogmatically claimed that "the in-
e of the aire, yce, thunders, unseasonable raines, drouthe,
what soever is extraordinarie in the world, are the fruites
[15]

this importance ascribed to the "signes of heaven"—and no
ned to be caught unprepared on Judgment Day—quite natu-
ach unusual meteor evoked lengthy commentary from the
leteers. These writings, although largely topical and religious
than technical, are pertinent here because they customarily
ned an explanation of the phenomenon under discussion; and
ly important, they maintained widespread interest in the study
eteors in general.

A prime example of the sort of natural phenomenon that rang
alarm for Elizabethans was the earthquake of 6 April 1580. This
quake was not violent—as Arthur Golding remarked, "rather shaking
Gods rod at us, than smiting us according to oure desertes."[16] Most
observers reported that it lasted just one minute, and that it did but
little damage except the felling of some few chimneys and towers.
The outstanding characteristic of this quake was its extensiveness, for
apparently it was felt throughout England.

Although this earthquake was comparatively harmless, it was con-
strued as a deadly portent of God's wrath, and the press catered to a

[14] (London: R. Wolfe, 1556), *av-av*v. This belief was ultimately based on Genesis 1:14. Many Scriptural commentators, however, especially those with Protestant sympathies, warned against the prognosticators' abuse of this passage; see, for example, John Calvin, *A Commentarie. . . upon . . . Genesis*, trans. T. Tymme (London: for J. Harrison and G. Bishop, 1578), pp. 35-36; Gervase Babington, *Certaine Plaine, Briefe, and Comfortable Notes upon Everie Chapter of Genesis* (London: for T. Charde, 1592), fol. 6v-7; and Nicholas Gibbens, *Questions and Disputations Concerning the Holy Scripture* (London: F. Kyngston, 1601), pp. 18-25.

[15] Calvin, *Commentarie upon Genesis*, p. 114. Cf. La Primaudaye, *French Academie*, p. 204.

[16] *A Discourse upon the Earthquake* (London: H. Bynneman, 1580), Cv.

As Fulke stated in his title, he intended to explain the "naturall causes" of meteors, as opposed to the causes assigned by the superstitious. This purpose was to be expected in a sixteenth-century Cambridge Puritan, and especially in the author of the *Antiprognosticon.* But natural explanations in no way precluded the assignment of religious significance to atmospheric phenomena; in fact, from the beginning of the *Goodly Gallery* Fulke quite clearly asserted:

The first and efficient cause [of meteors] is GoJ, the worker of all wonders, accordinge to that testimony of the Psalmist,[9] whiche sayeth. Fier, haile, snowe, yse, wynde and stones [i.e., thunderstones], do his will and commaundement.[10]

Fulke's attitude may best be described as "scientific" by Elizabethan standards: he sought rational explanations of the various irregularities in nature, and attempted to fit these apparent anomalies into a plan of natural order established by the Supreme Deity.

The atmospheric principles first postulated by Aristotle formed the system on which Fulke based his discussion, although he did not hestitate to question and sometimes to refute certain points in Aristotle's theory. Like a true Renaissance academician, Fulke cited most of the other classical authorities on meteors—Seneca, Plutarch, Posidonius, Vergil, Aratus, Theophrastus, and of course Pliny. The latter, though, was not accorded the usual deference; Fulke's purpose was to *explain* wonders in the heavens, not merely to describe them.

Fulke divided *A Goodly Gallery* into five books: an introductory book dealing with the general causes and usual location of meteors, and four books each of which discussed the meteors most closely associated with one of the four Elements. This division of meteors into Fiery, Airy, Watery, and Earthy had been inherited from the Middle Ages, and in itself is a good example of the tendency to adapt rather than wholly to accept or reject Aristotle's meteorological theory.

In the last four books of *A Goodly Gallery* Fulke systematically devoted a section to each meteor. In treating a specific phenomenon he normally gave a judicious review of all controversial opinions, and then stated his own conclusions and his reasons for accepting this

[9] Psalms 148:8.

[10] Fol. 3v. All references to Fulke's *Goodly Gallery* are quoted from the 1571 edition, which is merely the sheets of the 1563 edition with a new title page and dedicatory epistle.

authority and rejecting that one. Fulke's discussion of the Milky Way exemplifies his method. First he noted explanations for this phenomenon by Pythagoras, Anaxagoras and Democritus, Cardano, "the Poets" (four mythological accounts), Theophrastus, Diodorus Siculus, Posidonius, and Aristotle. Fulke could accept none of these opinions, but instead offered an uncommon thesis postulated by Parmenides:

> [The Milky Way] is of the nature of heaven, thycker in substaunce then other partes of heaven be, having some lykenes to the substance of the Moone, which being lightned by the same, as al the starres be, apereth whight.[11]

Even though Fulke was wrong in his conclusion, he performed a valuable service in listing the many alternative explanations and in weighing the plausibility of each.

Thomas Hill's *A Contemplation of Mysteries* (1571) was a book within its scope as useful as Fulke's *Goodly Gallery*. Hill was a London translator and compiler who within his lifetime turned out calendars and prognostications as well as elementary handbooks for such sciences as physiognomy, gardening, and astronomy.[12] *A Contemplation of Mysteries* was a comparable manual describing and explaining all the meteors deriving from hot and dry exhalations—that is, comets, fiery impressions, thunder and lightning, winds, and earthquakes. Hill also included chapters on the rainbow, on multiple suns and multiple moons, and on marvelous springs and rivers. Obviously this popular writer wished to treat only those meteors that were most wondrous and fearful; his book was a contemplation of "mysteries." He noted on his title page that this "matter [will be] delectable both for the Saylor and Husbandman." But the book, with its informative illustrations, would have been useful to anyone seeking enlightenment on meteors, or seeking only titillating horror in the shelter of his closet.

The information that Hill gave was complete and sound. He cited most of the authoritative writers on meteors, usually with acknowledgment. Hill drew most heavily from Fulke's *Goodly Gal-*

[11] Fol. 39ᵛ.

[12] The literary activity of Thomas Hill (*ca.* 1528-*ca.* 1573), with a bibliography of his works, is presented by F. R. Johnson, "Thomas Hill: An Elizabethan Huxley," *Huntington Library Quarterly*, VII (1943-1944), 329-351.

lery, however, and this greatest debt was un
Hill's method was quite similar to that o
popular writer compiling his material at gre
did less sifting and weighing. Hill included n
hearsay, with long lists of "prodigious tokens"
events that followed—material that the more c

In a tradition entirely different from Fulk
and Hill's *Contemplation of Mysteries* is *A N*
Mery of the Nature of the .iiii. Elements. T
drama, printed about 1525, is usually ascribed to
introductory material includes a table of "dyvers m
in this interlude conteynyd":

> Of the sytuacyon of the .iiii. elements that is to sey the
> the ayre and fyre /& of theyr qualytese and propertese / an
> acyon & corrupcyon of thyngs made of the commyxton of t
>
> . . . .
>
> Of the cause of rayne snowe and hayle
> Of the cause of the wyndys and thonder
> Of the cause of the lyghtnynge of blasyng sterrys and flamy
> the ayre[13]

Unfortunately, the unique extant copy is imperfect and th
dealing with these meteors is missing, so it is impossible t
mine precisely what meteorological information *The .iiii. El*
did contain. Perhaps it was comparable to the long passage on A
its impressions in Gower's *Confessio Amantis* (VII.254-374).
tainly Rastell drew upon Aristotle, as indicated by the inclusio
"generacyon & corrupcyon" in the table of contents.

3. TOPICAL WRITINGS OCCASIONED BY THE APPEARANCE OF SPECIFIC METEORS

Numerous pamphlets were prompted by the actual occurrence of some fearful meteor, for most Renaissance Englishmen maintained unshakable faith in heavenly portents. The prevailing attitude was expressed by the level-headed Robert Recorde in his textbook of mathematical astronomy, *The Castle of Knowledge:*

[13] Reproduced for Tudor Facsimile Texts (London, 1908), *A*1-*A*1ᵛ.

curious and frightened public with voluminous writings on earthquakes.[17] Typical of such treatises was a short work by Thomas Twyne, which is best described by its own title page:

A shorte and pithie discourse, concerning the engendring, tokens, and effects of all Earthquakes in generall: particularly applyed and conferred with that most strange and terrible worke of the Lord in shaking the Earth, not only within the Citie of London, but also in most partes of all Englande: which hapned upon Wensday in Easter weeke last past, which was the sixt day of April, almost at sixe a clocke in the evening, in the yeare of our Lord GOD. 1580.

This timely pamphlet included the complete theory of earthquakes based on Aristotle, a full description of various types of earthquakes and of the accompanying forewarnings and effects, and an attempt to correlate this information with observations made during the recent earthquake. All of this ended with a lengthily documented admonition to righteousness as the only means of preventing future catastrophes. Aristotle and Seneca were the authorities openly cited, but quite obviously Twyne had read much on his subject.

Abraham Fleming's *A Bright Burning Beacon,* a pamphlet similar to Twyne's *Discourse Concerning. . .Earthquakes,* was also occasioned by the earthquake of 1580. This treatise, as the author stated in the epistle dedicatory, was largely a translation of a work by Frederick Nausea (*ca.* 1480-1552), Bishop of Vienna. But Fleming added an exemplary account of all earthquakes in England, Ireland, and Scotland from the time of William the Conqueror to the present day. There was the customary morbidness concerning an imminent ending of the world, and the expected injunction to appease God's supposed wrath by repentance.

Of all the pamphlets following the earthquake of 1580, Arthur Golding's *A Discourse upon the Earthquake. . .the Sixt of Aprill*

[17] At the end of the table of contents to *A Bright Burning Beacon* (London: H. Denham, 1580), Abraham Fleming listed eight writers besides himself "whose reportes of our late Easter earthquake, &c. are printed and published": Francis Shakelton, Arthur Golding, Thomas Twyne, Thomas Churchyard, Richard Tarlton, John Phillips, Robert Gittins, and John Grafton. The *STC* records publications during 1580 for only the first four authors, and Richard Tarlton's short work was printed in the same volume as that of Thomas Churchyard (see Lily B. Campbell, "Richard Tarlton and the Earthquake of 1580," *HLQ,* IV [1940-41], 293-301). The pamphlets written by the last three men are no longer extant, a fact that suggests the large number of ephemeral writings on prodigious meteors which have been lost.

.*1580.* most strongly sounded the call to a more godly existence. The Privy Council ordered that this treatise (under the title "A Godly Admonition for the Time Present") be appended to the Order of Prayer for use in all parish churches.[18] In this beautifully written sermon, Golding cited many historical examples of "dreadful wonders" preceding visitations by Divine fury; and while attempting to show that the causes of this quake were not natural but miraculous, he listed all the signs and characteristics expected of an earthquake.

The writing on the earthquake of 1580 most familiar now is Gabriel Harvey's letter to Spenser on the following day.[19] With his usual thoroughness Harvey considered the technical explanation for earthquakes, and also subjoined a section in which he dealt with the question "whether you counte of earthquakes, as naturall, or supernaturall motions."[20] As authorities he specifically mentioned Aristotle, Dionysius the Areopagite, Pliny, Ovid, and Pico della Mirandola. Although Harvey agreed that earthquakes might be portents of grave events, he hesitated to claim that an earthquake was "necessarily, and undoubtedly a supernaturall, and immediate fatall action of God. . .there may be a sufficient naturall, eyther necessarie or contingent cause in the very earth it selfe."[21] This cautious statement of the relationship between meteor and Divine will may be taken as a common opinion held by the university men of the period. Certainly Harvey's point of view was shared by William Fulke, his fellow don at Cambridge.

Comets were considered to be as ominous as earthquakes, so the occurrence of a comet also was quickly followed by many explanations and prognostications. The tradition for this sort of literature was continuous from the time of Pliny. Treatises on the several Renaissance comets were similar in scope, method, and purpose to the pamphlets evoked by the earthquake of 1580, and were just as pessimistic in their outlook for man's future.

The most notable of the Elizabethan essays on comets was Abraham Fleming's *A Treatise of Blazing Starres in Generall,* occasioned

[18] See *Liturgical Services of the Reign of Queen Elizabeth,* ed. Rev. William K. Clay (Parker Society; Cambridge Univ. Press, 1847), pp. 562 ff.

[19] Printed in *Three Proper, and Wittie, Familiar Letters* (London: H. Bynneman, 1580).

[20] *Ibid.,* p. 16.

[21] *Ibid.,* p. 19.

by the blazing star which appeared about 10 November 1577.[22] This work was adapted from Latin writings by Frederick Nausea, as was also Fleming's treatise on earthquakes. In his long-winded discussion Fleming mediated between the divines who explained comets only as "immediate messengers and ministers of His will" and the philosophers who assigned them only natural causes. He concluded intelligently that "*Blasing-Starres* doe arise of causes naturall, albeit the Lord God is the principall author and worker of them."[23] Fleming referred to Aristotle, Vergil, and Pliny; and following the latter, he gave much space to terrifying events presaged by comets. In fact, the treatise was primarily descriptive rather than explanatory, and there were, of course, moral conclusions about the wickedness of man. Some verses of Pontano on comets were translated at the beginning.

Thomas Twyne was another to produce an interesting pamphlet on the comet of 1577: *A View of Certain Wonderful Effects. . .of the Comete* (1578). This was a nonscientific discussion on the appearance of the comet, and an attempt to attribute the calamities of the intervening year to its influence. There was an unusually somber tone throughout, and at the end the inevitable exhortation to contrition.

A small comet which appeared 8 or 9 October 1580[24] and continued through November prompted Francis Shakelton to write *A Blazyng Starre or Burnyng Beacon* (1580). On the title page Shakelton labeled himself a "minister and preacher of the words of God," and he proceeded with vehemence to propound his thesis that the recent meteor was a divine messenger. For dire incidents portended by blazing stars this author drew heavily from the Holy Scriptures, and much less heavily from classical sources. The comet of 1580 also brought forth a short discussion *Of the Crinitall*[25] *Starre, Which*

[22] This book was republished in 1618 (thirteen years after Fleming's death) because of a comet which appeared that year. Reference here is to the 1618 edition. C. Doris Hellman has collected a bibliography of 160 items written on the comet of 1577 (*The Comet of 1577: Its Place in the History of Astronomy* [Columbia Studies in History, Economics, and Public Law; Columbia Univ. Press, 1944], pp. 318-430; and "Additional Tracts on the Comet of 1577," *Isis*, XXXIX [1948], 172-174).

[23] *B*3v-*B*4.

[24] A technical history of this comet and also the comet of 10 November 1577 was given by William Bourne, *An Almanacke and Prognostication for X. Yeeres* (London: R. Watkins and J. Roberts, 1581), *F*viii-*F*viiiv.

[25] From Latin, *crinitus*, "having long hair"; in use most likely through Pliny, who had employed the term in connection with comets (*Historie of World*, p. 15 [II.xxii]).

Appeareth This October and November. 1580, written by an unidentified "F. K." This pamphlet was a combined warning to repentance and prognostication for three years—all based on the appearance of the comet. Whoever "F. K." may have been, he knew that his readers wanted sensationalism, and he did not stint the miseries and calamities that he foretold.

Comparable to the timely pamphlets on earthquakes and comets was a competent *Discourse of the Severall Kinds and Causes of Lightnings*, written by Simon Harward.[26] Although this treatise repeated the moral admonition common to all such pamphlets on prodigious meteors, its basic purpose was to give authoritative information on thunder and lightning. Consequently it presented an admirable array of authorities: Aristotle, Seneca, Pontano, the Scriptures, Bede, Hermes Trismegistus, Gartze, and others. Harward's work was a definitive compilation of prevailing opinions on lightnings, and it maintained a commendable balance between the factual and the hearsay.

On a yet more popular level, broadsides and ballads provided commentary on current meteorological events. The lightning that destroyed the steeple of St. Paul's on 4 June 1561, the comets of 1577 and 1580, the harsh blizzard during the winter of 1578-79, the greatly disturbing earthquake of 1580, the heavy frost of 1608, the disastrous winds and storms during the winter of 1612-13—all were irresistible topics for the ballad-mongers.[27] But these ballads, which made capital of the fleeting interests of the multitude, are relevant to this discussion only by reflecting the universal attention to meteors

[26] This treatise was prompted by the "occasion of a fearefull lightning which on the 17. day of this instant November, *Anno Domini* 1606. did in a very short time burne up the spire steeple of *Blechingley* in *Surrey*" (London: J. Windet, 1607), title page.

[27] See Hyder E. Rollins, "An Analytical Index to the Ballad-Entries in the Registers of the Company of Stationers of London," *SP*, XXI (1924), 1-324; for ballads on the destruction of St. Paul's steeple, note entries 586, 1250, 2925; on the comet of 1577, entry 296; on the comet of 1580, entries 22, 807, 2630; on the earthquake of 1580, entries 327, 663, 1838, 2224, 2630, 2714; on the winter of 1578-79, entries 1967, 2596; on the great frost of 1608, entry 1474; and on the tempestuous winter of 1612-13, entry 1551. See also Matthias A. Shaaber, *Some Forerunners of the Newspaper in England, 1476-1622* (Philadelphia, 1929), pp. 162-165. For a discussion of other popular writings dealing with anomalous meteors, see Eva G. R. Taylor, *Late Tudor and Early Stuart Geography, 1583-1650* (London, 1934), pp. 93-99.

of all sorts and by recording the actual phenomena that most prominently influenced common conceptions of such occurrences.

4. POPULAR LITERATURE INCIDENTALLY DEALING WITH METEORS

In addition to the topical treatments of particular meteors, many popular books contained meteorological information incidental to their main subjects. These books—compilations of assorted wonders, professional handbooks, almanacs and prognostications—were also important agents in spreading information on meteors.

Typical of the collection of wondrous incidents was *Certaine Secrete Wonders of Nature* (1569)[28] by Edward Fenton, the Elizabethan navigator and soldier of fortune. In the course of describing a wide variety of prodigies, Fenton included chapters on "sundry sortes of lightnings, with wonderful thunders and tempests happening in our time" (fol. 19 ff.), on "wonders of certaine horrible earthquakes" (fol. 33 ff.), on "divers figures, comets, dragones and flames, which appeared in heaven" (fol. 56 ff.), and on "thre Sunnes sene at one time" (fol. 145). Although Fenton stressed the sensation value of these anomalies, he always noted the natural causes of the meteorological wonders, openly basing the explanations on theories of Aristotle and Pliny.

A wonder-book similar to Fenton's was prepared by Bartholomaeus' editor, Stephen Batman, under the title *The Doome Warning All Men to Judgemente* (1581).[29] The aim of this work was explicit in its title. In form the book was a chronological listing of "all the straunge prodigies hapned in the Worlde," beginning with the Creation and ending in 1580. The meteorological theory contained in Batman's wonder-book was much scantier than in Fenton's, but such prodigies as earthquakes, comets, and torrential rains were described in considerable detail.

[28] Translated (with a few additions) from the contemporary French of Pierre Boaistuau. See n. 29, below.

[29] This book and Fenton's *Certaine Secrete Wonders* were both printed under the supervision of Henry Bynneman, and the same woodcuts illustrate both. These woodcuts had previously appeared in the original text of Pierre Boaistuau, *Histoires Prodigieuses* ([Paris]: Annet Briere for Vincent Sertenas *et al.*, 1560 [and several subsequent editions]).

Another source of incidental information on meteors was the numerous technical manuals for such occupations as navigation and husbandry. For example, *The Cosmographical Glasse* (1559)—William Cuningham's concise introduction to the fundamentals of astronomy, cartography, and navigation—included a paragraph on the distribution of meteors through the three regions of the Air (p. 42) and a longer description of the winds (pp. 157-160). The immensely popular *Arte of Navigation*[30] by Martin Cortes contained even fuller discourses on meteors for perusal by "the wyse Christian Mariner" (fol. 53^{v}). In the course of comprehensively describing the Aristotelian universe, this book discussed the three regions of Air (fol. 7); and later while setting forth practical rules of navigation it dealt with "signes whiche prognosticate tempestes or fayre weather" (fol. 50-51^{v}), Saint Elmo's fire (fol. 51^{v}-53^{v}), and the winds (fol. 54-56).

Since knowledge of meteorology was essential to successful farming, handbooks of husbandry likewise contained frequent references to meteors, their causes and effects. The perennial *Five Hundreth Pointes of Good Husbandrie*[31] compiled by Thomas Tusser included a homely poem which outlined "the properties of winds all the times of the yeere" (pp. 26-27). Less artfully, Thomas Hill in *The Profitable Arte of Gardening*[32] noted several tokens to protect the garden from lightning, hail, and tempests (pp. 24-26). In an appended treatise entitled "Certaine Husbandly Conjectures of Dearth and Plentie for Ever," Hill gave an unusual discourse on the ill effects that various sorts of weather have upon plants and men (pp. 45-50), and listed a full catalogue of accepted weather signs (pp. 65-74). Although the reader bought such manuals primarily for information on either husbandry or navigation, the books served a subordinate function by propagating knowledge of meteors and interest in their observation.

The most salable of all writings, however, were still the ephemer-

[30] Translated by Richard Eden from the Spanish of Cortes, and first printed in London in 1561. Other editions appeared in 1572, 1579, 1584, 1589, 1596, 1609, and 1615. References here are to the 1561 edition.

[31] Reference here is to the 1597 edition.

[32] This work was first printed in 1563 under the title *Howe to Dress a Garden*, but the numerous later editions were entitled *The Profitable Arte of Gardening*. References here are to the 1574 edition.

ides, and here most probably may be found the major source of meteorological notions held by the multitude. The annual calendars and prognostications, prepared for a single year, contained little actual theory of meteors because brevity was requisite in producing a pamphlet to sell for a penny or two. Their discussion of meteors was therefore restricted to citations of recent phenomena and prognostications of dire meteorological events to come. But the almanac intended for use over a number of years could be sold at a higher price, and such publications often included full treatment of meteors. For example, a complete summary of meteorological theory appeared in Leonard Digges's *A Prognostication of Right Good Effect.*[33] In this work Digges gave terse statements of the theoretical explanation and the signification of each of the major meteors: the rainbow, rain, frost and dew, snow, hail, winds, earthquakes, thunder and lightning, comets, and multiple suns and moons. This discussion was avowedly based on Aristotle, but Pliny also was often cited in the marginal glosses. Although designed for readers more intelligent than anticipated for most almanacs, *A Prognostication of Right Good Effect* and its successors reached all intellectual strata and became easily available to anyone seeking authoritative information on meteors.

Many other multiannual almanacs were published, and to help their readers through the trying years most of them included advice based on meteors. To lend this counsel a semblance of authority, many of them more or less accurately reproduced prevailing scientific ideas. *The Kalender of Sheepeherds*[34] discussed the three regions of Air and the distribution of meteors through them, and later described "divers impressions that Sheepheards see in the night in the ayre" (*Mi*ᵛ-*Mi*i), including flying-dragons, fiery lances, pillars of flame, and the Milky Way.[35] Philip Moore's *A Fourtie Yeres Almanacke* (*ca.* 1567),[36] William Bourne's *An Almanacke and Prognostication for X. Yeeres* (1581), and the *Perpetuall and Naturall Prognostications of the Change of Weather* (1591)[37] all contained

[33] First printed in 1553 and republished with various additions at least eleven times before 1605. References here are to the 1555 edition.

[34] Reference here is to the 1560 edition.

[35] Note Figure 3.

[36] Other editions in 1570 and 1573.

[37] Translated from Italian by I. F[armery?]. Another edition in 1598.

full lists of weather signs. In his almanac for 1604, as well as in his many subsequent almanacs, Edward Pond announced "a briefe, plaine, and true description of the foure Elements. . . .As also the natural cause of Ayerie Meteors" ($C5^v$), and then he recited a doggerel poem of some sixty-eight lines, adapted from du Bartas.

In addition to the almanacs designed to cover several years the astrologers produced other writings, aimed at a more sophisticated audience, which may best be described as introductory handbooks to astrology. These more theoretical approaches to the occult science also contained their share of meteorological principles. Godfridus' *Boke of Knowledge of Thynges Unknowen* (1530?),[38] for instance, discussed "what the thunder signifieth in every moneth of the yeere" (pp. 18-19) and "the 12 winds with their names and properties" (pp. 91-93). Furthermore, "The Husbandmans Practise" (appended to the 1619 edition) was fundamentally a list of weather signs based largely on the appearance of various meteors.

Another example of the introductory handbook to astrology was *The Diall of Destiny* compiled by John Maplet, who dealt with the "course, disposition, qualities, effectes and influence" of each of the seven planets in turn.[39] In his discussion of the Sun, Maplet included discourses on multiple suns (fol. 30^v-31^v), halos around the Sun (fol. 32-32^v), and the rainbow (fol. 33-34^v); in dealing with the Moon he gave an account of multiple moons (fol. 9) and lunar halos (fol. 12); and in various other sections he included digressions on fiery impressions (fol. 9^v-11^v), the Milky Way (fol. 12^v-13^v), comets (fol. 35-36^v), and earthquakes (fol. 70-73^v). Maplet described each of these meteors in detail, and usually discussed how they were engendered, when they were seen, and what they prognosticated. In consequence, *The Diall of Destiny* contained considerable meteorological information, theoretical as well as astrological and descriptive.

The growing general concern with science during the Elizabethan and Jacobean periods resulted in an ever-increasing number of technical books. But even though part of this larger trend, the quantity and variety of specifically meteorological writings attest to the widespread interest in meteorology. Discussions on meteors ranged from

[38] Other editions in 1585 and 1619. References here are to the 1619 edition.
[39] (London: T. Marsh, 1581), title page.

William Fulke's largely theoretical *Goodly Gallery* to the largely descriptive wonder-book of Stephen Batman, from standard classical works such as Philemon Holland's translation of Pliny to the numerous ephemerides, from detailed expositions in Thomas Hill's *Contemplation of Mysteries* to casual references in handbooks for navigators and farmers. The press provided texts to suit all intellectual needs and tastes, and thereby assured the greatest diffusion of recognized theories. Meteorological notions of all sorts, regardless of their wide variety, were easily accessible to everyone; and even those conceived in a scientific spirit had readily passed into the commonplaces of everyday life.

PART II

METEOROLOGICAL THEORY AND ITS LITERARY PARAPHRASE

CHAPTER ONE

GENERAL PRINCIPLES

RENAISSANCE meteorology had evolved within the theory of four Elements. Edward Pond in his almanac for 1604 presented a summary of representative opinion, which, as a matter of course, was based upon the Aristotelian arrangement of the universe:

> There are foure Elements, viz. Fire, Ayre, Water, and Earth: The Fire is hot and drie, very light, aspyring, bright and cleare, placed above the Ayre, next under the orbe of the Moone. . . .The Ayre hotte and moyst, ascending, light and cleare, by his heate joyned to the fire, and by his moisture joyned to the water. The Water moyst and colde, descending, waightie, and mixt: by his moisture joyned to the Ayre: and by his coldnesse joyned to the Earth. The Earth colde and drie, falling, heavie and thicke, the lowest of the foure Elements. . . .Now these foure Elements are the simples, whereof all things under the orbe of the Moone are made.[1]

The region of Air was the most important Element for meteorology, since within its limits all meteors occurred. But Earth and Water provided the raw material for meteors, and the sphere of Fire had great influence on their development or dissipation, especially in the case of fiery impressions.

There was thought to be constant interaction, even transmutation, between the four Elements. Aristotle had formulated the law that "fire, air, water and earth are transformable one into another, and that each is potentially latent in the others";[2] and this law provided the foundation for Aristotelian meteorology. When the heat of the Sun reached the earth's surface, it was believed to meddle with the cold and moist Water to form a new substance, warm and moist, essentially like Air. The Sun's heat similarly acted upon the cold and dry Earth to produce another new substance, warm and dry, essentially like Fire. On Aristotle's authority these new substances were visualized as evaporations from the Watery and Earthy com-

[1] *Enchiridion. . .1604*, *C5*ᵛ.
[2] *Meteorologica*, 339ᵇ. Cf. Spenser, *F. Q.*, VII.vii.25.1-9.

ponents of the earth's surface.[3] It was generally agreed, therefore, that the Sun drew up[4] two sorts of evaporations: (1) the hot and dry "exhalations," which provided the source material for the wide variety of windy and fiery impressions; and (2) the wet and usually warm "vapors," from which developed all moist meteors.[5] William Fulke in *A Goodly Gallery* provided a clear-cut distinction between the two:

> *Vapors*. . .be as it were fumes or smokes, warme & moist, whiche will easely be resolved into water. . . .
>
> *Exhalations* are as smokes that be hoat and drie. . .they be thinne, & lyghter then *vapors*.[6]

Du Bartas' poetical account of the generation of evaporations, though more fanciful, is equally accurate:

> . . .the swift Coach-man whose bright flaming haire
> Doth every day guild either *Hemispheare*,
> Two sorts of Vapours[7] by his heat exhales
> From floating deepes, and from the flowerie dales;
> Th'one somewhat hot, but heavie, moist and thick,
> The other light, dry, burning, pure and quick.[8]

Meteors which formed from these vapors and exhalations were composed of the four Elements, as indeed were all sublunary things; and frequently the phenomena were classified according to their most abundant Element, so that Renaissance meteorologians, following the practice of the medieval encyclopedists, spoke of Watery, Earthy, Airy, and Fiery meteors.

Many authorities ascribed the power of exhaling evaporations not only to the Sun, but also to the other planets and stars. For this

[3] *Meteorologica*, 341[b] and 360[a].

[4] "Exhale" was the usual Elizabethan term (*NED*, sense 4).

[5] Seneca explicitly based his meteorology on Aristotle's atmospheric cycle; cf. *Naturall Questions*, p. 759 [I.i]. Pliny, the other great Roman authority on meteorology, also accepted this fundamental hypothesis: "Certaine it is, how there is sent forth from the earth a mist sometimes moist, otherwhiles smokie, by reason of hote vapours and exhalations" (*Historie of World*, p. 20 [II.xlii]).

[6] Fol. 2-2[v].

[7] The term "vapors," following vulgate practice, was here used to include "exhalations" as well as vapors proper. It is not surprising to find that "evaporation," "vapor," and "exhalation" were commonly employed almost as synonyms, and that only the most careful writers, such as Fulke, maintained a rigid distinction between them. At this initial point, however, I shall repeat Fulke's admonition that these "termes must be well noted, because they must be much used" (fol. 2).

[8] *Devine Weekes*, p. 48.

reason, during the Middle Ages planetary influence on meteorology had been easily broadened to planetary dominance. The Sun, however, was always rightly considered the most important agent in the eduction of meteors.

Usually vapors and exhalations were drawn up simultaneously and indiscriminately, and the sort of meteor into which they developed depended largely upon the proportions in which they were mixed. For instance, rain with some little thunder and no lightning resulted from a moist vapor which contained a small amount of dry exhalation; but summer clouds that lightninged without producing rain were preponderantly formed of the hot, dry evaporation. The proportion of exhalation to vapor seemed to be determined by the terrain from which they were drawn. Areas possessing large bodies of water naturally provided abundant vapors, with the consequent moist meteors; desert areas produced but a dearth of vapors, so their characteristic meteor was the hot and dry wind.

Evaporations from fens were thought to incorporate the infectious qualities inherent in such places, so that Caliban means precisely what he says when he calls down upon Prospero "all the infections that the sun sucks up / From bogs, fens, flats" (*Tempest*, II.ii.1-2). Since pestilential vapors were considered a real possibility, the phrase "cloud of infection" had a literal meaning (Beaumont and Fletcher, *Philaster*, II.iv.142-143). For example, Hamlet expresses the prevalent evil with which he feels himself surrounded as "a foul and pestilent congregation of vapours" which has contaminated "this most excellent canopy, the air" (II.ii.311 ff.).

After the vapors and exhalations had been formed, they were subject to a multitude of powers. Heat and Cold were the most important of these, since a fundamental law (derived from Aristotle) held that Heat and Cold, being opposites, repulsed one another and forced one another to draw more closely together. Therefore Heat and Cold were the controlling agents in the actual formation of meteors from the evaporations. Temperature changes determined whether a potential meteor would develop, remain quiescent, or dissipate. Alterations in temperature resulted from passage through the strata of Air, from the increase or decrease of radiation from the Sun, and from the direct absorption of heat because of contiguity with

Figure 1. The three regions of Air: (1) the lowest heated by reflection of the Sun's beams, (2) the cold middle region with its congealed Watery meteors, and (3) the uppermost warmed by proximity to the sphere of Fire.

Gregor Reisch, *Margarita Philosophica* ([Strasbourg], 1515), fol. Si.

the orb of Fire. These critical influences will now be discussed in turn.

Unless unusual conditions prevented them, evaporations tended to rise because of some power of the Sun and planets to attract them upward. In some authors this power of attraction may be interpreted as little more than the buoyancy of the evaporation in the heavier Air, or as the characteristic motion of the four Elements either up from or down toward the earth's center. In pure terms of Aristotelian cosmology, the heavy Elements of Water and Earth had been transmuted by Heat of the Sun to lighter substances that naturally sought a position in the arrangement of Elements consonant with their new characteristics.

In any case, however, during their normal upward course the evaporations successively passed through the three distinct "regions" into which the Air was believed to be stratified. These regions, sharply defined as areas of Heat or Cold, were bounded by temperature contrasts for the reasons clearly presented by William Cuningham:

> The hier part of the Aëre. . .[is] nere to the orbe of the Fier, and is daylie caried about. . .and is made more hoote then the middle region is: againe, the lower region next us. . .is thorowe the reflextion of the Sonne beames rebounding from th'earth also made hoote, therefore the middle region. . .beynge voide of heate, is alway coulde: yea and so much the coulder, howe much the heate is more vehement in th'other two regions.[9]

The highest region was heated by proximity to the sphere of Fire and by the friction of the rotating spheres of heaven. The lowest region was warmed by reflection of the Sun's radiation from the earth's surface, and in this layer was implied a diurnal variation of temperature dependent upon the position of the Sun in the sky. The middle region of the Air, having no direct source of heat, was consequently Cold, and this coldness was compressed and intensified by the Heat of the two layers on either side. Again du Bartas transmuted this information into rather pleasing verse:

> . . .our elder Sages
> Have fitly parted it [the Air] into three stages:
> Whereof, because the highest still is driven
> With violence of the *First-moving* Heaven,
> From East to West; and from the West returning
> To th'honoured cradle of the rosiall Morning:

[9] *Cosmographical Glasse,* p. 42. Note Figure 1.

And also seated next the Fierie vault,
It by the learned very hot is thought.
That, which we touch, with times doth variate,
Now hot, now cold, and sometimes temperate;
. . . .
. . .the fields. . .reflect
The sparkling rayes of thousand starres aspect,
And chiefly *Phoebus*, to whose arrowes bright,
Our Globie Grandame serves for butt and white.
But now, because the middle-region's set
Farre from the Fierie seelings flagrant heat,
And also from the warme reverberation
Which aye the Earth reflects in divers fashion;
The circle shivers with eternal cold:
. . . .
The mid-most Aire redoubleth all his Froasts;
Being besieged by two mighty hoasts
Of heat, more fierce 'gainst his cold force then ever,
Calls from all quarters his chill troupes together,
T'incounter them with his united power.[10]

Du Bartas emphasized the strife between the cold middle region and its two warm neighbors, and he saw this battle as a requisite condition for the formation of meteors.[11]

Many other factors, of course, conditioned the influence of the Air in the formation of meteors. Batman in his edition of Bartholomaeus noted several: "rising and downe going of starres," "divers disposition place and stead of the earth [i.e., latitudinal variation]," "highnesse or lownesse of the earth [i.e., altitude]," "nighnesse of the sea," and "nighnesse of carrion."[12] But next to the temperature contrasts provided by the three regions of Air, the diurnal and seasonal variations in intensity of the Sun's radiation were the most important factors in the development of meteors.

Anyone could prove by simple observation that the Sun's rising and setting resulted in a diurnal temperature variation in the lowest region of Air. Fulke clearly stated the principles involved:

The region of Air next the earth by *repercussion* or striking back of the

[10] *Devine Weekes*, pp. 45-46.

[11] Meteors had previously been expressed in terms of the strife between counterforces in the universe by Pliny; see *Historie of World*, p. 19 [II.xxxviii]. This idea was more fully developed by La Primaudaye, *French Academie*, p. 199.

[12] *De proprietatibus rerum*, fol. 157-157ᵛ.

sunne beames waxeth hoate, and by absence of them is made colde. . . . For the water and the earthe being both colde elementes, after the sunne-setting in the nighte season dooe coole the aire, even to the midle region. But in the morning the sunne rysing warmeth the ayre, so farre as his beames whiche are beaten back from the earth & the water, can extende and reache, whiche is not so highe as the midle region.[13]

As a result, the lowest region of the Air cooled rapidly after sunset and tended to coagulate into meteors any evaporation which had not ascended above it; therefore night was considered the period of dampness and vapor phenomena. That explains why Bajazeth, shortly before he brains himself, utters this imprecation:

. . . ugly darknesse with her rusty coach
Engyrt with tempests wrapt in pitchy clouds,
Smother the earth with never fading mistes.
(Marlowe, *1 Tamb.*, 2075-2077)

Or here is a blunter statement of the belief: "Day is gone; / Clouds, dews, and dangers come" (Shakespeare, *Caesar*, V.iii.63-64). Conversely, the Sun's rising in the morning cleared the lowest region of evaporations, particularly of vapors. The dispelling of vapor accumulations was simply one aspect of the Sun's general beneficence.

The strength of the Sun varied not only according to its daily rising and setting, but also according to the season of the year. The fact was often noted that although the Sun was the ultimate source of life itself, it was also a threat of excessive heat and drought. Fulke, with commendable perception, stated that the Sun is "meane & temperate. . . .[or] vehement & burning. . . .either in respect of the place, or the tyme, but moste properly according to the casting of his beames either directly or undirectly"[14]—that is, according to the angle at which the Sun's rays strike the earth. This angle, of course, depends upon the season.

Fulke applied this principle to meteorology and distinguished two extreme atmospheric conditions which the Sun could produce by its heat. First Fulke noted that when the Sun shone at "the meane":

He draweth vapors out of the water and exhalations out of the earth, and not onely draweth them out, but also lifteth them up very high from the earth, into the ayer, where they ar torned into diverse kinde of *Meteores*.

[13] *Goodly Gallery*, fol. 5^{v}. Note Figure 1.
[14] *Goodly Gallery*, fol. 4.

As a result of these circumstances, "often is his gold complexion dimm'd." But conversely, "sometime too hot the eye of heaven shines" (Shakespeare, *Sonnets*, xviii.5-6). This other condition was described by Fulke as "the burning heate of the Sunne"; and then "he burneth, dissipateth and consumeth the vapors and exhalations before he draweth them up, so that of them no *Meteors* can be generated." Excessive heat from the Sun was therefore a check on itself in the generation of meteors: although a larger quantity of evaporations would be exhaled by the Sun's increased activity, a greater than average proportion of the evaporations would be dissipated by the abnormal heat.

Evaporations which rose through all three regions to the uppermost stratum of Air were subjected to the intense heat of the neighboring sphere of Fire. This was yet another temperature change which affected potential meteors, for at this place the evaporations were either dissipated by the great heat or ignited by the presence of Fire.

The optimum conditions for the development of meteors may now be summarized as follows: (1) an abundant source of evaporations in the Watery and Earthy components of the earth's surface; (2) moderate heat from the Sun of sufficient strength and duration to exhale a goodly amount of the evaporations, but not so strong as to dissipate them; and (3) temperature contrasts, usually provided by the supposed vertical stratification of the Air, by variations of the Sun's heat, or by proximity to the sphere of Fire. The temperature contrasts coagulated (by Cold) or ignited (by Heat) the evaporations, thereby changing them into meteors as they rose in the atmosphere.

The distance above the earth at which the various meteors formed was determined both by the type of evaporation involved and by the inherent qualities of each of the three Airy regions. The hot and dry evaporations, being lighter than the moist, strove to reach the uppermost limit of the Air. There they mingled with Elemental Fire, which Aristotle had described "as extending round the outside of the terrestrial sphere like a kind of inflammable material, which often needs only a little motion to make it burst into flames."[15] The circular motion of the celestial spheres tended to agitate this mixture of exhalation and Fire so that it burned at its most inflammable point.

[15] *Meteorologica*, 341^{b}.

The result was the Milky Way, comets, and various other fiery impressions.

The Watery vapors never appeared above the middle region of Air because of their own grossness and because of the Heat in the topmost stratum, which would dissipate them. So in the middle region developed the meteors resulting from the congelation of vapors by sudden contact with Cold—such as clouds and the subsequent rain, snow, hail, and thunder and lightning. Phenomena of reflection (rainbows, halos, and mock suns), because they depended upon cloud formations, also were usually placed in the middle region of Air.

The home of the winds was the lowest Airy region, although some authorities believed they could venture higher. Also in the nethermost stratum appeared various meteors which formed from evaporations drawn up by the Sun during the day but deserted by the Sun at its setting. Thereby bereft of further power to rise and soon congealed by the cold of night, these evaporations were coagulated into dew or frost (depending upon the temperature), mist, and a wide assortment of fiery impressions, such as *ignis fatuus* and falling stars.

The three distinct strata of the Air, the Sun and the sphere of Fire as sources of heat, the formation of meteors at the level most favorable to each sort—all this complicated mechanism of the atmosphere was believed to be in constant operation. And the atmospheric machine was envisaged as having a very definite form. The preciseness of Renaissance views on the matter is plainly shown in Jonson's masque *Hymenaei*, which at one point presented this spectacle:

A cortine of painted clouds. . .reach'd to the upmost roofe of the hall; and sodainely opening, reveal'd the three *Regions* of *Ayre:* in the highest of which, sate JUNO, in a glorious throne of gold, circled with *Comets,* and fierie *Meteors,* engendred in that hot and drie *Region;* her feet reaching to the lowest: where was made a *Rainebow,* and within it *Musicians* seated, figuring *airie* spirits, their habits various, and resembling the severall colours caused in that part of the *aire* by reflexion. The midst was all of darke and condensed clouds, as being the proper place where *Raine, Haile,* and other watrie *Meteors* are made. . . .

. . .(as above in place, so in the beautie). . .was the *sphere* of *fire,* in the top of all, encompassing the *ayre.*

(lines 647-658, 668-670)

Classical tradition had ascribed control of the weather to Juno,[16] and here she properly holds sway over "the three *Regions* of *Ayre*." A superficial imposition of mythology was necessary to suit the needs of a court masque, but the details of the stage mechanism derived from technical meteorology. There were "*Comets*, and fierie *Meteors*, engendred in that hot and drie *Region*" just below the sphere of Fire. The musicians, dressed as spirits of the lowest region of Air, were enlivened "by reflexion" of sunbeams. And between the two colorful, brilliant layers was the middle region, "all of darke and condensed clouds," where "*Raine*, *Haile* and other watrie *Meteors*" were placed in their dull costumes of grey and white.[17] A more clear-cut and detailed representation of the atmosphere could not be given.

Now that some preliminary statement of the general theory has been made, a more specialized discussion of the individual meteors may be presented. In accordance with Elizabethan practice, this study is organized on an outline of the atmospheric system proposed by Aristotle; and following him, the meteors are classified as phenomena of vapors, of exhalations, and of reflection.

[16] Cf. *Hymenaei*, 218 (and Jonson's gloss), and *Chloridia*, 195 ff. See Allan H. Gilbert, *The Symbolic Persons in the Masques of Ben Jonson* (Duke Univ. Press, 1948), pp. 148-151. The identification of Juno with the atmosphere goes back to the Greek philosophers; cf. Plato, *Cratylus*, 404C, and Diogenes Laertius, *Lives of Philosophers*, VII.147, both of whom note that ἀήρ is an anagram of Ἥρα. See also Macrobius, *Somnium Scipionis*, I.xvii.15. Abraham Fraunce stated that "allegorically *Jupiter* noteth the celestiall and fierie region, *Juno* the ayrie and inferior" (*Third Part of Countesse of Pembrokes Ivychurch* [London: for T. Woodcock, 1592], *D*3^v^). Furthermore, "her [Juno's] nymphs and handmayds expresse the variable change & alteration of the ayre, portending either fair or fowle weather, windes, stormes, rayne, hayle and such like" (*ibid.*, *E*1^v^). See Spenser, *F. Q.*, VII. vii.26.6; and Jonson, *Hymenaei*, 215 (gloss).

[17] For a suggestion of their costumes, see Jonson, *Chloridia*, 185-192.

CHAPTER TWO

PHENOMENA OF VAPORS

METEORS of this classification formed from warm and moist vapors which Cold changed back to a cold and moist substance —i.e., water. They developed either when the vapor was congealed to mist, dew, or frost by the coldness of night, or when the vapor, after entering the cold middle region of Air, was condensed to cloud, or possibly further condensed to rain, hail, or snow.

1. CLOUDS

Clouds formed from moist vapors which were congealed to a thicker consistency by the sudden drop in temperature when they passed into the cold middle region of Air. No author explained the process more succinctly than did du Bartas:

> But if the vapour bravely can adventure
> Up to th'eternall seat of shivering Winter,
> The small thin humour by the cold is prest
> Into a cloud.[1]

The Cold of the middle region, coming in contact with the warm evaporation, concentrated the Heat until the subtle, invisible vapor was compressed into a cloud. According to Pliny, clouds were "thicke, grosse, and of a bodily consistence."[2]

As coagulated vapors, clouds effectively blocked the Sun's brilliance from reaching the earth, and "a clowde sette betweene us and

[1] *Devine Weekes,* p. 49.
[2] *Historie of World,* p. 20 [II.xlii].

the Sunne, swageth and bateth the heate thereof."[3] Conversely, the heat of the Sun tended to dissipate clouds. Meteorological writings formalized this constant opposition between Sun and cloud; and poets, stimulated by personal observation as well as by the technical exposition of the process, often based their images on it. One eminent example of the resultant poetry occurs in Shakespeare's *1 Henry IV:* after a clownish scene with Poins and Falstaff, Prince Hal confides to the audience:

> . . . herein will I imitate the sun,
> Who doth permit the base contagious clouds
> To smother up his beauty from the world,
> That, when he please again to be himself,
> Being wanted, he may be more wonder'd at,
> By breaking through the foul and ugly mists
> Of vapours that did seem to strangle him.
> (I.ii.221-227)

Prince Hal sees himself as a Sun-king surrounded temporarily by "the base contagious clouds" of low companions. But he promises that at the proper time he will break forth in the full glory of his regal magnificence and thereby diffuse his beneficial powers to all his people.

If the congelation process was sufficiently strong when the cloud entered the cold region of Air, or if the cloud was progressively augmented by fresh vapor drawn up by the Sun, the cloud was eventually condensed into the Watery meteors of rain, snow, or hail. In this way the atmosphere was cleared of vapors and other impurities. Caxton had described the atmosphere's complete aqueous cycle in *The Mirrour of the Worlde:*

> Whan the sonne spredeth his rayes upon therthe & upon the mareys, he. . .draweth up. . .a moisture subtyl whiche appereth but lytyl and is named vapour / and it mounteth into the myddle of thayer and there it assembleth. . . .And lytil & lytil it encreceth that it cometh thycke and derke in suche wise that it taketh fro us the sight of the sonne. And this thynge is the clowde. . . .
>
> And whan it groweth over thycke it becometh water whiche falleth on the erthe. . . .
>
> Thenne apperith the cloude clere and whyte whiche thenne is lyght and mounteth on hye somoche that in thende she faylleth and is deffeted by

[3] Bartholomaeus, *De proprietatibus rerum,* fol. 160.

the hete of the sonne on hye whiche all dreyeth up / Thenne thayer wexeth agayn pure & clere / and the heven as blew as Azure.[4]

In Spenser's translation of du Bellay's *Antiquitez de Rome*, the rise and decline of Rome is described as a development analogous to the formation and condensation of clouds:

> No otherwise than raynie cloud, first fed
> With earthly vapours gathered in the ayre,
> Eftsoones in compas arch't, to steepe his hed,
> Doth plonge himselfe in *Thetys* bosome faire;
> And mounting up againe, from whence he came,
> With his great bellie spreds the dimmed world,
> Till at the last dissolving his moist frame,
> In raine, or snowe, or haile he forth is horld.
> (*Ruines of Rome*, 267-274)

And the dissipation of Roman power, comparable to the dissipation of clouds, was demonstration "that all in th'end to nought shall fade"[5] (line 280).

The purifying effect of condensing clouds was the phase of the congelation process emphasized by Thomas Nashe in *Christs Teares over Jerusalem*:

> And had I [Christ] been in Heaven as I was on Earth, the Sunne shoulde have exhaled from thee all thy trespasses as meteors, which the clowdes, his cofferers, receiving, might foorth-with have conduited downe into the Sea, and drowned for ever.
> (II.37-38)

This image is unusually fanciful, with Christ (commonly conceived as light or the Sun) drawing up vaporous meteors (frequently described metaphorically as sins) to the clouds, which would wash them down into the shoreless sea of eternity, thus cleansing both earth and heaven of evil.

The ever-changing variety of cloud shapes had forced itself upon the imagination of all eras, and Bartholomaeus had risen to the occasion of providing an explanation of this phenomenon:

> A cloud is kindly hollow, with many holes as a spoung. . . .And therfore by entring and incomming of the Sunne beames, a cloude representeth and sheweth diverse formes & shapes and coulours.[6]

[4] II.xxv.

[5] The cloud as a figure of transitoriness occurs in the Bible: see Job 30:15, and Hosea 6:4.

[6] *De proprietatibus rerum*, fol. 160.

Not surprisingly, the constant transformation of clouds from one suggestive form to another is noted by a host of characters in Renaissance fiction. Hamlet uses the progression of cloud shapes to toy with Polonius (III.ii.393 ff.); and Antony, considering his rapidly changing fortunes in Egypt, compares himself to a succession of alterations in "black vesper's pageants":

> Sometime we see a cloud that's dragonish;[7]
> A vapour sometime like a bear or lion,
> A tower'd citadel, a pendent rock,
> A forked mountain, or blue promontory
> With trees upon't, that nod unto the world,
> And mock our eyes with air.
> (IV.xiv.2-7)

Antony sees the incessant transformation of clouds as a visual comparison for mutability. In a different context, equally effective, Bussy d'Ambois refers to the phenomenon as an example of man's credulity: in a long digression on sin, Bussy persuades Tamyra that sin's "shadows. . .[are] like empty clouds, / In which our faulty apprehensions forge / The forms of dragons, lions, elephants" (*Bussy d'Ambois,* III.i.23-25). Therefore, Bussy implies, man's fear of sin is largely self-induced, or at least the result of self-delusion.

Metaphorically, clouds functioned in innumerable ways, usually in the fundamental sense of overshadowing or darkening something bright. Death was frequently depicted as a cloud dimming the vital spark, as in "Dark cloudy death o'ershades his beams of life" (*3 Henry VI,* II.vi.62). Sin also was expressed in terms of clouds, so that Daniel's Rosamond woefully admits that "sinne did cloude my brow" (*Complaint of Rosamond,* 76). Often the body's sinfulness, symbolized by the flesh, was described as clouds masking the beauty of the soul. Tamyra begins a lengthy passage rationalizing her infatuation with Bussy by observing that "our bodies are but thick clouds to our souls" (*Bussy d'Ambois,* III.i.78); and Sir John Davies humbly warns his soul, "Know that thou canst know nothing perfectly / While thou art clouded with this flesh of mine" (*Nosce Teipsum,* "Of the Soule of Man," p. 116). Moreover, cloud imagery was used to express a wide range of emotions. Poets spoke of "cloudy

[7] A sublimated reference to "flying-dragons"; note pp. 95-96, below.

wrath" (Shakespeare, *Richard III*, I.iii.268), "envies cloud" (Spenser, *F. Q.*, V.xii.27.7), "cloudy melancholy" (Shakespeare, *T. Andron.* II.iii.33), "that cloud of pryde" (Spenser, *Amoretti*, lxxxi.7), a "cloud of sorrow" (Shakespeare, *L.L.L.*, V.ii.758), "this black cloud [of jealousy]" (Jonson, *E.M.I.H.H.*, II.iii.73)—and one character's "cloudy brow [discloses] his stormy hate" (*2 Henry VI*, III.i.155).

2. RAIN

Rain was an integral phase in the natural cycle which began with vapor, continued through cloud, and ended with a return of the moisture to earth in the form of rain, snow, or hail. Bartholomaeus, citing Bede, had written:

> Fumosities. . .be drawen out of the waters & of earth by strength of heate of heaven, be drawn to the nethermost part of the middle space of the aire, & there by coldenesse of the place they bee made thick, & then by heat dissolving and departing the moisture therof, & not wasting all, these fumosities be resolved & fallen & turne into reine and showers.[8]

The actual condensation of cloud into rain was usually explained as the result of some heat source acting upon the cold congealed vapor. As the most common agent of the required heat, William Fulke suggested "the Southerne wynde, or any other wynde of hotte temper."[9] Spenser described the process by which cloud was transformed to rain, noting specifically the essential part played by the south wind:

> . . .when a foggy mist hath overcast
> The face of heaven. . .
>
> . . . .
>
> The watry Southwinde from the seabord cost
> Upblowing, doth disperse the vapour lo'st,
> And poures it selfe forth in a stormy showre.
> (*F. Q.*, III.iv.13.1-2, 4-6)

[8] *De proprietatibus rerum*, fol. 162. The reference to Bede is *De natura rerum*, chap. xxxii.

[9] *Goodly Gallery*, fol. 49.

Du Bartas simplified all this theory of rain formation into the bare statement that the cloud "wanders East and West / Upon the Winds wings, till in drops of raine / It fall into his Grandames lap againe."[10]

As Caxton had noted,[11] the phase of rain in the natural atmospheric cycle had the incidental function of purifying the Air. Moreover, authorities ascribed certain beneficial qualities to rain water itself. Fulke, remembering that the Sun initiated the drawing up of vapors, suggested that rain water "reteineth much of the sunns heate in it,"[12] and consequently stimulated growing things. Bartholomaeus had asserted specifically that rain "is more fresh and sweet then other waters. . . .[and it] maketh the lande to beare fruit".[13] Sir Philip Sidney echoes Bartholomaeus' statement of this commonplace in the opening sonnet of *Astrophel and Stella*: he recounts the mental throes of finding suitable subject matter and style for his love sonnets, and he describes the painful process of "oft turning others leaves, to see if thence would flowe, / Some fresh and fruitfull showre, upon my Sunne-burnt braine" (i.7-8).

The Holy Scriptures frequently speak of Jehovah or His influence as a shower strengthening and refreshing the plants and creatures on earth.[14] Following this precedent La Primaudaye characteristically employed for a religious purpose the belief that land unwatered by heaven is infertile, and he expressed Divine grace in terms of rain: "as the earth waxeth barren, if it be not watred by raine from heaven; so men cannot performe any thing, if God powre not downe his grace upon them."[15] In this spirit, Prospero prays that the "Heavens rain grace" on the match between Miranda and Ferdinand (*Tempest*, III.i.75).

Rain was a paradox, however, and from experience meteorologians knew that rain storms wrought disaster as well as good. If rain deserted the desirable mean and became "distemperate. . . .[it]

[10] *Devine Weekes*, p. 49.

[11] *Mirrour of Worlde*, II.xxv; quoted pp. 48-49, above.

[12] *Goodly Gallery*, fol. 49^{v}.

[13] *De proprietatibus rerum*, fol. 162. In his *Naturall Questions*, Plutarch had considered the problem: "What might the reason be, that trees and seeds are nourished better with raine, than any other water" (printed in *The Morals*, trans. Holland, pp. 1003-1004).

[14] See as examples, Deuteronomy 32:2; Psalms 71:6; and Isaiah 55:10-11. See Gervase Babington's comment on Genesis 2:5-6 (*Notes upon Genesis*, fol. 8^{v}).

[15] *French Academie*, p. 231.

bringeth forth much unprofitable hearbes and grasse, and corrupteth and destroyeth fruites and seedes, and quencheth in seeds the naturall heat."[16] This is the complaint that Titania makes to Oberon. The King of Fairies controls the weather, she says; and in his jealousy over her small Indian favorite, Oberon has disturbed the natural progress of the seasons. Among other anomalies, the winds "have suck'd up from the sea / Contagious fogs" (*M.N.D.*, II.i.89-90), which have fallen upon the land in such great quantity that floods have followed:

> The ox hath therefore stretch'd his yoke in vain,
> The ploughman lost his sweat, and the green corn
> Hath rotted ere his youth attain'd a beard.
> (II.i.93-95)

But among nonscientific writers this threat of a corruptive excess of rain was seldom considered, except possibly in a tenuous connection with the destructiveness of tempests,[17] where the heavy rain's physical force rather than its power to induce decay was emphasized. Spenser, for instance, stressed the ferocity of rain in this description: "In his shield, as thicke as stormie showre, / Their strokes did raine" (*F. Q.*, II.viii.35.5-6). The resultant simile parallels Spenser's image where hail represents sword strokes;[18] and it evokes not only a mental picture of rapidly repeated blows, but also a mental echo of the clatter of rain drops pounding on metal.

As a purely poetical conception, tears were often described as rain. Although tears:rain images were relatively consistent in their purpose of conveying sorrow, their forms varied greatly, ranging from the simple statement, "Mine eyes rain" (Beaumont and Fletcher, *Maids Tragedie*, II.i.133), to this elaborate conceit:

> . . .the storme so rumbled in her brest,
> As Eolus could never roare the like,
> And showers downe rayned from her iyen so fast,
> That all bedreynt the place, till at the last
> Well eased they the dolour of her minde,
> As rage of rayne doth swage the stormy wynde.
> (Sackville, "Induction," *Mir. for Magis.*, 142-147)

[16] Bartholomaeus, *De proprietatibus rerum*, fol. 162.
[17] For a discussion of summer tempests, see pp. 56-57, below.
[18] See p. 57, below.

Quite commonly, as in this passage, when rain represented tears, sighs became winds. Venus' alternating expressions of her anguish on the death of Adonis are " like a stormy day, now wind, now rain, / Sighs dry her cheeks, tears make them wet again" (Shakespeare, *Venus*, 965-966); in *A Lover's Complaint* the maiden deserted by her swain enters "storming her world with sorrow's wind and rain" (line 7); and in *As You Like It* love-sick Silvius follows disdainful Phoebe "like foggy south puffing with wind and rain" (III.v.50). In fact, the correspondence of rain to tears and of winds to sighs had been so over used that Donne scoffed gently at the hackneyed convention and begged his mistress at their parting to cause "no teare-floods, nor sigh-tempests" ("Valediction: Forbidding Mourning," 6).

Used in the opposite direction, the tears:rain and sighs:wind analogies could express pathetic fallacy, as in Joseph Hall's short poem "Upon. . .the Unseasonable Death of. . .Prince *Henry*." Here Nature mourns the untimely death of the Prince, and "the *Windes* are Sighes: the *Raine* is Heavens Teares" (line 6). In "An Eglogue upon the Death of. . .Sir Francis Walsingham," Thomas Watson calls upon "*Aire*. . . / . . .to lament great *Meliboeus* death"; and recalling the condensation of clouds by warm winds, he begs: "Let clouds of teares with sighs be turnd to raine."[19]

Popular hearsay seems to have accounted for the notion that rain water fattened fishes, while actual observation of the progress of thunder showers may have prompted the beliefs that "after strong heat commeth strong raine" and that rain "ceaseth & stinteth windes."[20] In Shakespeare's *Troilus and Cressida* Pandarus alludes to the latter belief when the lovers must be separated by Cressida's departure for the Greek camp. Sadly he then asks, "Where are my tears?"; and he commands that they "rain, to lay this wind [his sighs], or my heart will be blown up by the root" (IV.iv.55-56).

Renaissance Englishmen could read numerous accounts of prodigious rains—marvelous not only because of quantity, but also because of substance. Pliny had recorded historical incidents accompanied by rains of "milke, blood, flesh, iron, wooll, tyles, and brickes";[21] and other Biblical, classical, and medieval precedents for prodigies of

[19] *Poems*, ed. Edward Arber (London, 1870), p. 161.

[20] Bartholomaeus, *De proprietatibus rerum*, fol. 162. Cf. Aristotle, *Meteorologica*, 360^b.

[21] *Historie of World*, p. 27 [II.lvii]. See also *ibid.*, p. 17 [II.xxvii].

rain were abundant. Du Bartas mentioned a rain of frogs, and then quite seriously offered two alternative explanations:

> Eyther because the floating cloud doth fold
> Within itselfe both moist, drie, hot, and cold,
> Whence all things heere are made: or else, for that
> The active windes sweeping this dustie flat,
> Sometimes in th'aire some fruitfull dust doo heape,
> Whence these new-formed ugly creatures leape.[22]

This argument was sincere and clever; and particularly the first explanation, entailing combination of the four Elements, manifested du Bartas' underlying interest in a rational account of the universe. Similarly in a scientific spirit, Bartholomaeus had suggested an explanation for equally terrifying showers of blood:

> Sometime is so great generation of heate by gathering of beames, & by rebounding therof about the clowds, that the vapour is as it wer burnt: & by strong burning heat it turneth into red choler. And therefore sometime the people thinke that it raineth bloud.[23]

Rather desperately Fulke attempted explanations of all these purported prodigies of rain, as well as showers of worms, wheat, quicksilver, and chalk.[24]

3. HAIL

Authorities on meteors unanimously agreed that hail was merely frozen rain. Echoing Aristotle,[25] Pliny had asserted that "haile is ingendred of rain congealed into an ice";[26] Bartholomaeus had concurred that "haile is freesing of drops of rain";[27] and La Primaudaye reiterated that "haile is made of raine frozen in the aire."[28] But Bartholomaeus had pursued the inquiry further; and de-

[22] *Devine Weekes*, p. 50.
[23] *De proprietatibus rerum*, fol. 162.
[24] *Goodly Gallery*, fol. 51^{v}-53.
[25] *Meteorologica*, 348^{b}.
[26] *Historie of World*, p. 29 [II.lxi].
[27] *De proprietatibus rerum*, fol. 162^{v}.
[28] *French Academie*, p. 210.

spite a certain vagueness, his detailed explanation of the hail-forming process is impressive if only for its intricacy. According to him, the process began with the congelation of warm and moist vapors in the cold middle region of Air. These condensed vapors, now cold and moist, reacted to Heat in the Air by withdrawing tightly into themselves; and if the Heat was sufficiently strong, they were finally compressed into a solid. In Bartholomaeus' words, the cold and moist vapors "flye heate of the aire, & come togethers into the inner parts of the clowde, and there. . .[the compressed Cold within the cloud] congealeth and freeseth them into the substance of haile." Hail therefore depended upon the presence of immoderate Heat in the Air to force the compression of the potentially hail-forming vapor, and consequently there was "ofter haile in summer then in winter."[29] This specious argument shrewdly anticipated any incongruity in the empirical fact that "frozen rain" occurred most frequently in summer, the hottest season.

This theory of the generation of hail illuminates an obscure passage in *Antony and Cleopatra*. After the defeat at Actium, Cleopatra entertains a messenger from Caesar; and Antony in anger rebukes her with the pointed question, "Cold-hearted toward me?" (III.xiii.158). Cleopatra replies, "Ah, dear, if I be so, / From my cold heart let heaven engender hail." If her heart be cold, Cleopatra says, within her body would exist a situation analagous to the atmospheric conditions which produce hail: her heart would compare to a cold cloud, and the great heat of her love for Antony (suffused throughout her body) would act to compress her heart into hail. Cleopatra's ingenious response deftly turns Antony's accusation into a statement of her fervent devotion to him.

William Caxton was another technical authority who had noted that moisture in the Air was "assembled and amassed, for the hete that chaceth after it," and thereby frozen into hail. He had identified this meteor with "the tempeste whiche falleth ofte in the somer."[30] Du Bartas very prettily described hail as "a dropping shower, / [Which] th'excessive cold of the mid-Aire, anon / Candies. . .all in balles of icie stone,"[31] and likewise associated it with the destructive

[29] *De proprietatibus rerum*, fol. 162^{v}. This argument loosely follows Aristotle, *Meteorologica*, 348^{b}.

[30] *Mirrour of Worlde*, II.xxvii.

[31] *Devine Weekes*, p. 50. Cf.: "the discandying of this pelleted storm" (Shakespeare, *Antony*, III.xiii.165).

summer tempest. With a mixture of reproval and respect, he commented:

> . . .violent-stormes, sometimes (alas) doo proine
> Without a knife, our orchard and our vine;
> Reape without sickle, beat downe birds and cattle,
> Disgrace our woods, and make our roofes to rattle.

The mental picture evoked by this description of the tempest's fury and its resultant havoc was effectively utilized in a dramatic context by Webster in *The Dutchesse of Malfy*. When the Cardinal and Ferdinand learn of their sister's supposedly illegitimate child, the choleric Ferdinand furiously expresses the wish that his rage might turn into a tempest:

> That I might tosse her pallace 'bout her eares,
> Roote up her goodly forrests, blast her meades,
> And lay her generall territory as wast,
> As she hath done her honors.
> (II.v.26-29)

Since the formation of hail most frequently accompanied the summer storm, it was inevitably associated with wanton violence. This connotation was supplemented by the punitive use of hail in the Bible to plague Egypt.[32] As a result, the dropping of hail was normally considered an event "horrible and dred" (Spenser, *F. Q.*, III.ix.11.6).

The pounding rapidity of falling hail had given rise to the popular simile "as thick as hail" to convey a sense of continuous quantity or number. Ross informs Macbeth that messengers bearing news of his recent victories came to the King "as thick as hail" (I.iii.97). Spenser repeatedly described sword strokes "that on his shield did rattle like to haile / In a great tempest" (*F.Q.*, VI.vi.26.3-4)[33] and arrows that were "shott. . .with might and maine, / As thicke, as it had hayled" ("March," 86-87).[34]

In *The Profitable Arte of Gardening* Thomas Hill advised his farmer-readers of several tokens to protect their gardens from the ravages of hail. He suggested exhibiting the skin of a seal, a hyena, or a crocodile, or encompassing the plot with some not clearly speci-

[32] Exodus 9:22 ff. Cf. also such passages as Psalms 78:47-48; Isaiah 28:2; and Revelation 16:21. "*Grando, &c.* Per quam intelligitur illa poena damnatorum" (*Biblia Sacra. . .Nicolai Lyrani*, I.567-568).

[33] Cf. also Spenser, *F. Q.*, II.viii.35.5-6, IV.iii.25.4-5, IV.vi.16.5, and VI.v.18.3.

[34] Cf. also Spenser, *F. Q.*, II.xi.19.1, V.iv.38.9, and *Mui.*, 79-80.

fied "white vine."[35]

Pliny, with his usual enthusiasm for the inexplicable, had observed inaccurately that "haile sooner melteth by farre than snow."[36] Since hail normally falls in summer, the large temperature differential between it and the summer air would naturally melt the hail more quickly than winter temperatures thaw snow—hence Pliny's mistake. Nevertheless, the melting of hail became common in imagery to suggest transitoriness, especially because of the obvious associations with mutability through the transformation of a solid into a liquid. Coriolanus taunts a crowd of citizens with the charge that they are no more stable than a "hail-stone in the sun" (I.i.178), and Falstaff orders Pistol and Nym to "vanish like hailstones" (*Merry Wives*, I.iii.90).

4. SNOW

Snow was yet a third possible product of cloud condensation in the middle region of Air. Rain formed in above-freezing temperatures; and by some process difficult to explain, snow rather than hail developed under certain conditions when the cloud was below the freezing point. Authorities generally acknowledged that "haile is engendred of raine more hard frozen: snowe of moisture more softly

[35] P. 24.
[36] *Historie of World*, p. 29 [II.lxi].

thickned"[37]—but this is description rather than explanation. Bartholomaeus had given but slightly more illumination by suggesting:

Snow is gendred in a cold clowd, but not so colde as that, in the which haile is gendered: and that witnesseth the softnesse of snowe. For heate meddeled with clowdes letteth the partes therof.[38]

Bartholomeaus seems to mean that Heat was entirely external to the hail-engendering cloud, whereas the snow-engendering cloud enclosed Heat within itself. Therefore snow in its formation would be hindered by the adjacence of Heat, and it would be less "stronglye gathered together" than hail. But meteorologians could not resolve the paradox that "in winter snowes fall, and not haile"[39]—and winter should be expected to produce the colder clouds.

Several special attributes were commonly ascribed to snow. The generally beneficial qualities of rain water were also inherent in this similar product of cloud condensation, and Bartholomaeus had asserted that "by abiding of snowe uppon the lande, the lande is fatted."[40] Bartholomaeus had also recorded that "in the high sea snowe falleth seldome"; and noting its physiological effects, he had cautioned that drinking melted snow "maketh the members astonied, and. . .gendereth the stone in the bladder, and feedeth forth cold dropsie."[41] Nicolas Monardes, however, a "phisition of Sevill," attributed great healing powers to water cooled with snow, and he prescribed this remedy for specific illnesses on the authority of Galen and Avicenna.[42]

The characteristic of snow which seems to have impressed the Renaissance mind most greatly was its whiteness. William Fulke explained that "snowe is whyght. . .by receiving the lyghte into it, in so many small partes."[43] In figures of speech, snow was usually the standard for superlative whiteness, so that Juliet cannot conceive a more extravagant hyperbole than her love-sick assertion that Romeo "wilt lie upon the wings of night / Whiter than new snow on a raven's back" (III.ii.18-19).

[37] La Primaudaye, *French Academie*, p. 210.

[38] *De proprietatibus rerum*, fol. 163. The *locus classicus* for the differentiation between hail and snow is Plato, *Timaeus*, 59D.

[39] Pliny, *Historie of World*, p. 29 [II.lxi].

[40] *De proprietatibus rerum*, fol. 163. Cf. Isaiah 55:10.

[41] *De proprietatibus rerum*, fol. 163.

[42] *The Boke Which Treateth of the Snow* [dated 1574], appended to *Joyfull Newes out of the New-found Worlde*, trans. J. Frampton (London: E. Allde, 1596).

[43] *Goodly Gallery*, fol. 55ᵛ.

Inevitably the unstained whiteness of snow had become a symbol of chastity. "As pure as snow" was proverbial (*Hamlet*, III.i.141; *Macbeth*, IV.iii.53). Shakespeare spoke of "the white cold virgin snow" (*Tempest*, IV.i.55); and Donne, reversing the metaphor, described "the cold white snowie nunnery" (*Litanie*, 100).

In another context, snow's whiteness was employed not as a sign of chastity but of old age. Donne complains with worldly levity that you can look in vain for an honest woman "till age snow white haires on thee" ("Song" [pp. 8-9], 13). And in the final scene of *The Comedy of Errors*, when Aegeon is reconciled with all his family, he ascribes his unrecognizable appearance to the fact that "now this grained face of mine be hid / In sap-consuming winter's drizzled snow" (V.i.311-312). Frequently the associated meteor of hoar frost replaced snow in imagery representing the white hair of old-age.[44]

The thawing of snow as well as the melting of hailstones suggested the ephemeral nature of mundane things,[45] and often melting snow appeared in mutability images. When Venus pleads with Adonis to shun the boar hunt, she argues that beauty's perfections when exposed to such dangers "are on the sudden wasted, thaw'd and done, / As mountain-snow melts with the midday sun" (Shakespeare, *Venus*, 749-750). Chapman employs the simile with greater ease when he intrudes to admonish Leander that "joy graven in sence, like snow in water wasts" (*Hero*, III.35). The melting-snow image lends great dramatic effectiveness to Shakespeare's *Richard II:* late in Act IV the deposed King concentrates all the pathos of his pitiable position into the exclamation:

> O that I were a mockery king of snow,
> Standing before the sun of Bolingbroke,
> To melt myself away in water-drops!
> (IV.i.260-262)

In addition to acknowledging the transference of the Sun-king's authority to Bolingbroke and appropriately reducing Richard to little more than tears, this image suggests the rapidly approaching dissolution of the former king.

If melted snow was again frozen to ice, the result was icicles.

[44] See p. 71, below.

[45] Cf. Job 24:19: "Drought and heat consume the snow waters: so doth the grave those which have sinned."

Scientific writers, as usual following the example of Aristotle, did not discuss these common formations; but creative writers frequently mentioned them, ordinarily endowing them with the general properties of snow itself. Coriolanus reflects most of the Renaissance notions about icicles when he addresses Valeria as "the moon of Rome, chaste as the icicle / That's curdied by the frost from purest snow / And hangs on Dian's temple" (V.iii.65-67).

Crystal was another derivative of melted snow. According to the Ancients,[46] it was formed when snow, after thawing and refreezing over a period of many years, became permanently solidified. Greek κρύσταλλος signified "ice." Fulke repeated the accepted opinion that "snowe melting on the high hilles, and after frosen agayne, becommeth so hard that it is a stone, & is called *Christal*";[47] while Maplet in *The Green Forest* (1567), quoting Isidore, asserted that crystal "is nothing else then a congeled ise by continuance frosen whole yeares."[48] Donne implies this theory of crystal formation when he declares that "one cunning sleight / Shall freeze my love to christall in a night" ("To Countesse of Huntington" [p. 417], 69-70)—that is, one disdainful act by a mistress will transmute his passion to the permanent chasteness of solidified snow.

5. MIST, OR FOG[49]

Sometimes a cloud could not be sufficiently developed to produce condensation, nor was the Sun's heat sufficiently strong to dispel it. Then these vapors, "resolved & fallen & shed & spred into all the parts of the aire, breed & gender mist."[50] William Fulke more technically described the process:

[46] Cf. Pliny, *Historie of World*, Tome II, p. 604 [XXXVII.ii].

[47] *Goodly Gallery*, fol. 55ᵛ. La Primaudaye questioned this belief; see *French Academie*, p. 431.

[48] Fol. 5ᵛ. The reference to Isidore is *Etymologiae*, XVI.xiii.1.

[49] "Fog" was synonymous with "mist" in the Elizabethan and Jacobean periods. Furthermore, either of these terms was often used loosely for "vapor" or "cloud."

[50] Bartholomaeus, *De proprietatibus rerum*, fol. 163.

Mist. . .goeth down toward the earth. . .when any *vapor* is lifted up into the ayre, by the heate of the sunne, which not being strong enough to drawe it so high, that the colde maye knitte it: suffereth it after it is a lytle made thicke, to fall downe agayne.[51]

Bartholomaeus had completed the atmospheric cycle by noting that "when mist is all smitten with the beames of the Sunne, it falleth downe & turneth againe into the matter that it came of, and vanisheth. . . .And so the aire is purged."[52]

But mist and fog seem generally to have been associated with darkness and evil rather than with any function of purifying the atmosphere. Following a long tradition, Shakespeare thought that fogs and night were inseparable, and he depicted darkness as a loathsome mist formed from the condensed breath of the horses that drew Night's chariot:

> . . .now loud-howling wolves arouse the jades
> That drag the tragic melancholy night;
> Who, with their drowsy, slow and flagging wings,
> Clip dead men's graves and from their misty jaws
> Breathe foul contagious darkness in the air.[53]
> (2 *Henry VI*, IV.i.3-7)

Spenser quite literally enveloped the Deadly Sins in an atmosphere of evil: when they appear leading Lucifera's coach, "before their way / A foggy mist had covered all the land" (*F. Q.*, I.iv.36.6-7).

Bartholomaeus had listed three specific instances of fog's malignancy.[54] (1) "Sometime mist is corrupt [i.e., infectious]"—so that to curse an irreverent daughter Lear exclaims, "Infect her beauty, / You fen-suck'd fogs, drawn by the powerful sun" (II.iv.168-169). (2) "Mist is friend to theeves, and to evill doers, for it hideth their spiers and waitings"—a statement which immediately brings to mind the Witches of the heath who "hover through the fog and filthy air" (*Macbeth*, I.i.12). And (3) "Myst letteth waye faring men and pilgrimes, for in greate mistes waies be unknowen"—and

[51] *Goodly Gallery*, fol. 48. Contrast this statement with Aristotle's definition: "Mist is the residue of the condensation of air into water, and is therefore a sign of fine weather rather than of rain; for mist is as it were unproductive cloud" (*Meteorologica*, 346^{b}). Cf. also Aristotle, *De mundo*, 394^{a}; and du Bartas, *Devine Weekes*, p. 48.

[52] *De proprietatibus rerum*, fol. 163-163^{v}.

[53] Cf. Marlowe, *1 Tamb.*, 2075-2079.

[54] *De proprietatibus rerum*, fol. 163^{v}.

this is the baleful result assigned to fog by Oberon when he commands Puck to "overcast the night; / The starry welkin cover thou anon / With drooping fog as black as Acheron," so that the four lovers will hopelessly lose their respective ways in the forest (*M.N.D.*, III.ii.355-357).

6. DEW

Not only mist, but dew was confined to the lowest region of Air. This meteor occurred when the Sun's exhalative power was not sufficiently strong or was not operative for an adequate length of time to raise the vapor to an appreciable height in the atmosphere. Then, rather than being a condensation product formed when the vapor entered the cold middle region of Air, dew resulted from congelation of the vapor by the coldness of night following the Sun's setting. In terms similar to his explanation of mist, William Fulke explained the formation of dew, which "by colde of the nyghte, is condensede into water, and falleth downe in verye smalle droppes."[55] Pliny had

[55] *Goodly Gallery*, fol. 53. This explanation in general principle is correct. What actually happens is that after sunset the earth radiates heat at a more rapid rate than does the air, and a temperature differential between earth and air develops. The earth then cools the air, water vapor in the air is squeezed out, and "dew" is condensed on the earth's surface.

perceptively noted that "dewes shew not either in frost, or in hote seasons; neither when winds be up, but only after a calme and cleere night."[56]

After sunrise in the morning, of course, the warmth of the Sun evaporated the condensed moisture—a process that made dew, like snow and hail stones, an evident example of mutability. In these terms Samuel Daniel warns Delia:

> Beautie (sweet Love) is like the morning dew,
> Whose short refresh upon the tender greene:
> Cheeres for a time, but till the Sunne doth shew,
> And straight tis gone as it had never beene.
> (*Delia*, L.1-4)

And in *The Rape of Lucrece* Shakespeare apostrophizes happiness, which, he laments, is "soon decay'd and done, / As is the morning's silver-melting dew" (lines 23-24).[57]

Since dew was thought to evolve from condensation of the same vapors as did the other Watery meteors, it was frequently described as "nothing else but a weake and feeble raine."[58] Bartholomaeus said flatly, "Dewe is lyttle raine, and raine is much dew."[59] Quantity is the only distinction between dew and rain implied by old Capulet when he reproaches Juliet for her excessive weeping, supposedly over Tybalt's recent death:

> When the sun sets, the air doth drizzle dew;
> But for the sunset of my brother's son
> It rains downright.
> (III.v.127-129)

As Capulet knew, only a small quantity of dew dropped each night in proportion to the much larger amount of rain which fell at any one time. But this was to be expected, since the vapors which devel-

[56] *Historie of World*, p. 29 [II.lxi]. During a clear night, maximum radiation from the earth can take place and a large temperature differential between earth and air can develop. This temperature differential can be most easily established in the absence of wind.

[57] Cf. Hosea 6:4: "Your goodness is as a morning cloud, and as the early dew it goeth away"; and Hosea 13:3: "They [sinners] shall be as the morning cloud, and as the early dew that passeth away."

[58] Plutarch, *Naturall Questions* (in *The Morals*, trans. Holland), p. 1011 [no. 24].

[59] *De proprietatibus rerum*, fol. 161.

oped the rain cloud were ordinarily gathered over a period of many days, whereas the vapors which formed dew exhaled and condensed as a daily process.

In Holy Scriptures dew was coupled with rain as a prime source of fertility,[60] and its continued absence was considered a curse.[61] Just as rain proved beneficial to growing plants, so also "dew giveth vertue & strength to trees, hearbes, and grasse, and things that the heat of the day had dryed."[62] Dew was "refreshing" (Chapman, "Hymne to Hymen," 61), "sweet and fruitfull" (Jonson, *Vision of Delight*, 147).[63]

Also in common with the figurative use of rain was dew's frequent use as an image for tears. In Kyd's *Spanish Tragedie* Horatio, recounting his funeral rites for Andrea, recalls that "there [I] laid him downe, and dewd him with my teares" (I.iv.36); and Greene, fitting the tears:dew image into the florid style of his *Menaphon*, described the sorrowful demeanor of Sephestia, whose "teares. . . hung on her cheekes like the droppes of pearled deaw uppon the riches of *Flora*" (VI.42).

Being a formation from vapors, dew was inevitably associated with the other Watery meteors which were commonly thought to appear at sunset. Shakespeare repeatedly referred to the "dew of night" (*Lucrece*, 396);[64] and Spenser indicated the approach of nightfall by observing, "Now gan the humid vapour shed the ground / With perly deaw" (*F. Q.*, III.x.46.5-6). Just as commonly, however, dew formation was considered an early morning phenomenon. Shakespeare described "the morning's silver-melting dew" (*Lucrece*, 24),[65] and Spenser almost invariably connected the appearance of dawn with dew.[66] Quite possibly some distinction, not necessarily for-

[60] Cf. Genesis 27:28; Deuteronomy 32:2, 33:13. Dew formation in Palestine is unusually heavy, and it quite literally sustains many plants which otherwise would die in the long rainless seasons.

[61] Cf. 2 Samuel 1:21; 1 Kings 17:1; Haggai 1:10.

[62] Bartholomaeus, *De proprietatibus rerum*, fol. 161v.

[63] Of course, dews formed of vapors exhaled from infectious areas were "rotten" (*Coriolanus*, II.iii.35) and "wicked" (*Tempest*, I.ii.321).

[64] Cf. *Lucrece*, 1232; *King John*, II.i.285; *Romeo*, II.iii.6, III.v.127; *Caesar*, V.iii.64; *Cymbeline*, IV.ii.284.

[65] Cf. *Pass. Pilgrim*, 71; *L.L.L.*, IV.iii.27; *M.N.D.*, IV.i.126; *Shrew*, II.i.174; *T. Andron.*, II.iii.201; *Romeo*, I.i.138; *Hamlet*, I.iii.41.

[66] Cf. as examples from only Book I of *F. Q.*, I.ii.7.1-3, I.v.2.1-4, I.xi.33.3-4, and I.xi.51.1-3.

mal, was made between evening and morning dew; for in *The Unfortunate Traveller* Nashe, rapturously describing the Earl of Surrey's Geraldine, reports that "sweet morne and evening deaw flowes from her breath" (II.254). Because dew was associated not only with the beginning but also with the closing of day, Shakespeare without incongruity could speak of both "the morn and liquid dew of youth"[67] (*Hamlet*, I.iii.41) and "the honey-heavy dew of slumber" (*Caesar*, II.i.230).[68]

A tradition beginning in Greek lyric poetry had portrayed dew as the son or daughter of the Moon, a notion consistent with the Moon's control over all things moist. Abraham Fraunce stated: "Her [Diana's] daughter was *Herse*, that is Deaw, whom she conceaved of *Jupiter*."[69] Some meteorologians, apparently influenced by this tradition, explained dew as a product of the Moon's, rather than the Sun's, ability to draw up vapors. According to this theory, since the Moon was less powerful than the Sun, she was unable to lift her evaporations above the lowest region of the Air, so that when she set at dawn they dropped back upon the earth as dew.[70] This theory furthered the dichotomy between "dew of night" (formed from vapors exhaled by the Sun and congealed at sunset by the resultant coldness) and "the morning's silver-melting dew" (formed from vapors drawn up by the Moon and allowed to fall back to earth at dawn).

Many creative writers of the Renaissance alluded to the Moon as "the mother of moist dew" (Marston, *Malcontent*, II.iii.154). In *Midsummer-Night's Dream* Lysander confides to Helena the time at which he and Hermia plan to steal from Athens:

[67] Cf. Psalms 110:3: "Thou hast the dew of thy youth."

[68] Dew was a common symbol of sleep: cf. Shakespeare, *Richard III*, IV.i.84; and Spenser, *F. Q.*, I.i.36.3-4. This notion was a development of the Homeric conceit that sleep was a cloud descending upon the eyes of the sleeper, and so "sweete slumbring deawe" (Spenser, *Gnat*, 323) was simply condensation from this cloud.

[69] *Third Part of Countesse of Pembrokes Ivychurch*, L4^{v}.

[70] See Plutarch, *Naturall Questions* (in *The Morals*, trans. Holland), p. 1011 [no. 24]; and Bartholomaeus, *De proprietatibus rerum*, fol. 161^{v}. Cf.: "Rorem Alcyna lyricus poeta lunae atque Aeris fuisse filium dicit: teste Macrobio: quod quidem figmentum a natura sumptum est, agente quidem luna vapores terrae humidos nequentes absente sole consurgere altius frigiditate aeris & lunae alternati vertuntur in tenuem aquam: quae decidens ros estivo tempore appellatur. Hyeme vero condensati gelu pruina dicitur" (Boccaccio, *Genealogiae*, fol. 32 [IV.xvii]). The reference to Macrobius is *Saturnalia*, VII.xvi.31. "Alcyna lyricus poeta" is Alcman, who is supposedly the founder of Doric lyric poetry.

> To-morrow night, when Phoebe doth behold
> Her silver visage in the watery glass,
> Decking with liquid pearl the bladed grass.
> (I.i.209-211)

As befitted an encomium of Elizabeth, Sir Walter Raleigh deftly fused the ideas that the Moon engenders dew and that dews are regal favors, and he unctuously began, "Praisd be Dianas faire and harmles light, / Praisd be the dewes wherwith she moists the ground" (lines 1-2).[71]

Without corroboration from serious meteorologians, some imaginative writers fantastically described dew as sweat of the earth's bodily organism. With this concept in mind, Marston referred to dawn as the time when "the mounting sun's all-ripening wings / [Had] Swept the cold sweat of night from earth's dank breast" (*Malcontent*, IV.i.111-112). Chapman spoke more simply of "nights cooling sweate" ("Hymne to Hymen," 10). By a further stretch of the imagination, the idea that dew was sweat of earth's body was transferred to the human body, so that dew came to represent human sweat also. Donne in "The Comparison" praised his mistress to the detriment of his friend's unworthy wench, claiming that "as the almighty balme of th'early East, / Such are the sweat drops of my Mistris breast" (lines 3-4).

Another fanciful explanation of dew lay in the Greek legend of Memnon, the son of Aurora and Tithonus. The *Aethiopis* of the Epic Cycle had recounted how Memnon was slain by Achilles in the Trojan War; and Aurora, disconsolate over his death, still dewed the grass each morning with her tears.[72] Richard Barnfield indirectly referred to Memnon's story in "The Sheepheards Ode":

> . . .[Aurora] each morning (by cocks crewe)
> Showers downe her silver dewe,
> Whose teares falling from their spring,
> Give moisture to each living thing
> That on earth encrease and grow.
> (lines 14-18)[73]

[71] Cf. Proverbs 19:12: "[The king's] favour is as dew upon the grass."

[72] Cf. Ovid, *Metamorphoses*, XIII.576-622, and *Fasti*, III.403-404; Servius, *Commentarii in Virgilium*, Vol. I, p. 83 [gloss on *Aeneid*, I.489]; and Lactantius, *Narrationes fabularum*, pp. 873-874.

[73] *England's Helicon*, ed. Hyder E. Rollins (Harvard Univ. Press, 1935), p. 78.

In his eagerness to stress the beneficence of dew, Barnfield seems to have forgotten the innate sadness of Aurora's tears.

Accepted natural history had identified pearls (or "margaritas") as dewdrops which had been crystallized into precious gems by oysters in their shells.[74] In *Poly-Olbion* Drayton glorifies the river Irt:

> Her costly bosome strew'd with precious Orient pearle,
> Bred in her shining shels, which to the deaw doth yawne,
> Which deaw they sucking in, conceave that lusty spawne,
> Of which when they grow great, and to their fulnesse swell,
> They cast, which those at hand there gathering, dearly sell.
> (XXX.116-120)

Because of this belief, dew and pearls were inextricably linked in Renaissance thought and often were interchangeably used for poetical purposes. As descriptions of the dew-forming process, Phoebe at night is seen "decking with liquid pearl the bladed grass" (*M.N.D.*, I.i.211), and Flora in the morning "rain'st on the earth resolved pearle in showers" (*1 Tamb.*, 1923).[75] The tears:dew image could be extended so that tears in the eyes of a supplicant became "heaven-moving pearls" (Shakespeare, *King John*, II.i.169), and the sweat: dew image could be stretched to produce such an unlikely epithet as "pearly sweat" (Shakespeare, *Lucrece*, 396).

Dew was the source material not only for pearls, but also for manna[76] and mildew.[77] Technical commentators over the centuries had usually discussed manna and mildew together as products of dew formation, but they had seldom agreed upon the precise relationship between the two phenomena. As regards manna, Bartholomaeus had written that "in some country of Greece hony is gendred in

[74] See, for instance, Bartholomaeus, *De proprietatibus rerum*, fol. 161v. La Primaudaye rejected this belief; see *French Academie*, p. 429.

[75] Perhaps Marlowe was here thinking of the Memnon myth, for metrical reasons replacing Aurora with Flora as the weeping goddess.

[76] The Biblical account of how the Israelites lived on manna for forty years in the desert appears in Exodus 16:13-35. Manna was gathered before sunrise because, like dew, it melted in the sun (Exodus 16:21). If manna were kept longer than the day on which it had been collected, it spoiled (Exodus 16:20); and this characteristic facilitated its confusion with mildew. Nicholas of Lyra offered this allegorical interpretation of manna: "*Et mane, &c.* & isti panes fuerunt manna, per quam figurata fuit eucharistia" (*Biblia Sacra. . .Nicolai Lyrani*, I.634).

[77] "Mil-" = Latin *mel*, "honey."

flowres that commeth of the dew of heaven: & also Manna in some hearbs"; and he had described mildew as "dew gendred in corrupt aire. . .[which] infecteth tender flowres, and corrupteth greene corne . . .such corruption is called *Erugo* and *Rubigo*."[78] Bartholomaeus had clearly distinguished between manna ("that commeth of the dew of heaven") and mildew ("dew gendred in corrupt aire"). Few meteorologians were so explicit, however, and William Fulke reflected the common confusion over these two related meteors. He noted manna, "one kynde of the sweet dewes. . .being whyghte lyke sugar, whiche is made of thicke and clammye *vapors*," and he also described "another kind of swete dewes, that falleth in England called the meldewes, which is as sweet as hony being of such substance as hony is, drawen out of sweet herbes & flowers." But he further distinguished "a bitter kynde of dewe that falleth upon herbes, and lieth on them lyke brann or meale, namelye because it is of an earthly *exhalation*, & so remayneth, when the moyster is drawen away: this dewe kylleth herbes."[79] Fulke differentiated between manna ("made of . . .*vapors*"), mildew ("drawen out of sweet herbes & flowers"), and "a bitter kynde of dewe" ("of an earthly *exhalation*"). Quite understandably, literary allusions seldom delved into the muddled theory of these phenomena.

Bartholomaeus happily recorded several other popular beliefs about dew: (1) oysters not only formed pearls from dew, but also grew fat on it; (2) young ravens, before they became black, fed on dew; and (3) dew counteracted venom in poisonous beasts, thereby rendering them less harmful by night than by day.[80]

[78] *De proprietatibus rerum*, fol. 161ᵛ. Cf. Deuteronomy 28:22: "Percutiat te Dominus. . .aëre corrupto ac rubigine"; and 2 Chronicles 6:28: "Fames si orta fuerit in terra et pestilentia, aerugo, et aurugo. . . ." These sources undoubtedly explain Bartholomaeus' "erugo" and "rubigo," and their occurrence in "corrupt aire." The Romans worshiped a divinity named "Robigus," who had the power of blighting the cornfields; cf. Ovid, *Fasti*, IV.907 ff.; and Pliny, *Historie of World*, pp. 598, 600 [XVIII.lxviii, lxix].

[79] *Goodly Gallery*, fol. 53ᵛ.

[80] *De proprietatibus rerum*, fol. 161ᵛ.

7. FROST

Bartholomaeus had expressed the prevalent opinion that "hoare frost (as *Aristotle* sayth) is vapour frosen. . . .it vanisheth awaye by a lytle beame of the Sunne, and tourneth againe into dewe. For hoare frost is nought else but dew frosen."[81] Frost seemed to be nothing but a seasonal variation of dew—as du Bartas noted, condensed vapor formed "in *April* deaw, in *Januarie* ice."[82]

Most commonly the picture that frost brought to the Renaissance mind was the untimely blighting of tender plants by the harshness of cold. Petruchio's Kate, now the docile tamed-shrew, advises her feminine audience that a scornful glance "blots thy beauty as frosts do bite the meads" (V.ii.139). Robert Greene, wishing to advertise his *Never Too Late* (one of that perennial genre which chides the younger generation), appended this subtitle: "those particular vanities that with their frostie vapours nip the blossoms of everie ripe braine from attaining to his intended perfection" (VIII.3) When old Capulet sees Juliet apparently lifeless under the influence of Friar Laurence's potion, he carries to its logical conclusion the idea that frost hinders fruition, and he morosely observes: "Death lies on

[81] *De proprietatibus rerum*, fol. 162^v. The reference to Aristotle is *Meteorologica*, 347^a.

[82] *Devine Weekes*, p. 48.

her like an untimely frost / Upon the sweetest flower of all the field" (IV.v.28-29).

In a different context, frost was a conventional symbol of old age, usually through the visual connection between hoary hair and hoary frost. Literary expressions of this notion are numberless, but Shakespeare's plays furnish representative illustrations: the King in *2 Henry VI* refers to Salisbury's "frosty head" (V.i.167), Marcus in *Titus Andronicus* bemoans his "frosty signs and chaps of age" (V.iii.77), and old Adam in *As You Like It* philosophizes that "age is as a lusty winter, / Frosty, but kindly" (II.iii.52-53).

Frost was a useful meteor to convey an assortment of emotional reactions. Spenser's editor, "E. K.," describes the worry accompanying old age as "hoare frosts of care" ("Feb.," argument); Hotspur scorns a cowardly ally as "a frosty-spirited rogue" (*1 Henry IV*, II.iii.21); and in Heywood's *A Woman Killed with Kindness*, the luckless Susan complains of "the frost of grief" (III.i.72).[83]

[83] *English Drama, 1580-1642*, ed. C. F. Tucker Brooke and N. B. Paradise (New York, 1935), p. 306.

CHAPTER THREE

PHENOMENA OF EXHALATIONS

THIS group of meteors developed from the hot, dry exhalations drawn from the terrestrial components of the earth's surface. When mixed with moist vapors in the middle region of Air, these exhalations generated thunder and lightning. When ignited by friction of the rotating spheres or by proximity to the orb of Fire, they appeared in the highest stratum of Air as comets, the Milky Way, and certain other fiery meteors. In the lowest layer of the atmosphere they formed a large variety of fiery impressions and the winds, which in turn caused earthquakes.

1. THUNDER AND LIGHTNING

The powerful noises and terrifying flashings of this double meteor drew awful respect from every layman, and lengthy comment from every writer on meteors. No phenomenon, in fact, was more carefully and variously explained—by the meteorologian, the astrologer, and the merely superstitious. But as usual in such matters, the highest authority was assigned to the explanation derived by Aristotle from his conception of the atmospheric cycle. This theory held that thunder and lightning were formed when a hot exhalation was solidified by the Cold of a surrounding cloud.[1] It was thoroughly expounded by Simon Harward in *A Discourse of. . .Lightnings*:

First a viscous vapour joyned with a hot exhalation is lifted up to the highest part of the middle region of the aire, by vertue of the Planets: then the

[1] *Meteorologica*, 369a-369b

waterie vapour by the coldnesse both of place and of matter, is thickned into a clowd, and the exhalation (which was drawne up with it) is shut within the clowd, and driven into straights.

This hotte exhalation flying the touching of the cold clowd, doth flie into the depth of the clowd that doeth compasse it about, and courseth up and downe in the clowd, seeking some passage out.[2]

The compacted exhalation's rolling about inside the cloud accounted for thunder that only rumbled, as William Fulke suggested.[3] Harward continued to explain that when the exhalation could find no outlet from the cloud:

. . .it maketh a way by force, and beeing kindled, by the violent motion it breaketh through the clowde. If the sides of the hollowe clowd be thicke, and the exhalation drie and copious, then there is made both thunder and lightning: but if the clowd be thin, and the exhalation also rare and thin, then there is lightening without thunder.

According to this theory, lightning was the flash and thunder the accompanying noise when the ignited exhalation burst forth from the enclosing vaporous cloud.

Du Bartas accepted the Aristotelian explanation for thunder and lightning, and offered this poetical account of their generation:

. . .when a vapour moist,
As well from fresh as from salt waters hoist
In the same instant with hot-exhalations,
In th' Aierie Regions secondarie stations:
The Fierie fume, besieged with the croud
And keen-cold thicknes of that dampish cloud,
Strengthens his strength; and with redoubled volleys
Of joyned Heat, on the Cold leagher sallies.
. . . .
This Fire, desirous to breake forth againe
From's cloudie warde, cannot it selfe refraine,
But without resting, loud it groanes and grumbles,
It roules and roares, and round-round-round it rumbles,
Till having rent the lower side in sunder,
With sulph'rie flash it have shot downe his thunder.[4]

Here the power and impressiveness of the meteor, admirably de-

[2] *C3*.
[3] *Goodly Gallery*, fol. 24.
[4] *Devine Weekes*, pp. 54-55.

scribed as the result of the conflict between Heat and Cold, was further suggested through onomatopoeic effects.

Fulke cited an alternative theory, which explained thunder and lightning as the extinction of a star which has fallen into a cloud:

They [Epicureans] say, that the starres fall out of the firmament, and that by the fall of them, both thonder and lyghtning are caused: for the lightening (say they) is nothyng els but the shyning of that starre that falleth, which falling into a watrie clowde, and being quenched in it, causeth that great thonder, even as whoat yron maketh a noyce if it be cast into colde water.[5]

But Fulke rejected this explanation because "it is evident that the starres of the firmament can not fall, for God hath set them fast for ever."

Yet another theory of ancient origin maintained that lightning and thunder were merely the result of friction between clouds. As Bartholomaeus said, "Meeting & comming together of clowdes, setteth oft the ayre on fire and flame, and ingendereth lightening and thundering."[6]

There was one apparent difficulty with all these explanations: although thunder and lightning were formed simultaneously, lightning was usually seen some seconds before the sound of thunder reached the observer. Pliny had succinctly posed the problem and provided the stock answer:

The Lightning is seene before the thunder-clap is heard, although they come indeed joyntly both togither. . . .And no marveile, for the eye is quicker to see light, than the eare to heare a sound.[7]

Pliny's answer was steeped in premodern physiology, which considered sight the most perfect of the senses; and therefore the eye, being more acute, saw lightning before the ear heard thunder. Chapman in *The Revenge of Bussy d'Ambois* closely paraphrased the argument:

[5] *Goodly Gallery*, fol. 30. Cf. Lucretius, *De rerum natura*, VI.145-149; Pliny, *Historie of World*, pp. 20-21 [II.xliii]; and La Primaudaye, *French Academie*, p. 200.

[6] *De proprietatibus rerum*, fol. 160^{v}. Cf. *ibid.*, fol. 163^{v}. Cf. also Lucretius, *De rerum natura*, VI.160 ff.; Plutarch, *Opin. of Phil.*, p. 828 [III.iii]; Seneca, *Naturall Questions*, p. 787 [II.xxiii]; and Isidore, *Etymologiae*, XIII.ix.1.

[7] *Historie of World*, p. 26 [II.lv]. Cf. Lucretius, *De rerum natura*, VI.164-172.

. . .the thunder
Seems, by men's duller hearing than their sight,
To break a great time after lightning forth,
Yet both at one time tear the labouring cloud.
(V.i.9-12)

Shakespeare thought of lightnings as forerunners to thunder—they were "vaunt-couriers to oak-cleaving thunderbolts" (*Lear,* III.ii.5) and "precursors / O' the dreadful thunder-claps" (*Tempest,* I.ii. 201-202). At the opening of *King John* Shakespeare employed this observed principle in a dramatic context that effectively prepared for the invasion of France in Act II. With imperious anger King John commands the departing French ambassador:

Be thou as lightning in the eyes of France;
For ere thou canst report I will be there,
The thunder of my cannon shall be heard:
So hence! Be thou the trumpet of our wrath
And sullen presage of your own decay.
(I.i.24-28)

The ambassador, as lightning, will go before the thunder of John's artillery and will warn the French King of imminent destruction by the English army.

Meteorological authorities technically distinguished various sorts of lightnings. Fulke's classification, listing four distinct varieties, may be taken as a reliable description of the diverse major types:[8]

[1] *Fulgetrum*. . .is seen on sommer nights and eveninges, after a whote daie. . . .terrible to beholde, not hurtful to any thing. . . .

[2] *Coruscation* is a glistering of fyre, rather then fyre in deade, and a glymmerynge of lyghtning, rather then lightning it self. . . .[a] reflexion. . . .And this is often without thonder.

[3] *Fulgur* is that kynd of lightning which followeth thonder. . . .it is set on fyre, and casteth a great lyghte. . . .

[4] The moste dangerus, violent, & hurtfull, kinde of lightning is called *Fulmen*. . . .a whote *exhalation* is enclosed in a cloude. . . .bursteth foorth. . . and with wonderfull greate force stryken downe toward the earthe.

[8] *Goodly Gallery*, fol. 26-27ᵛ. For other important discussions on the classification of lightnings, see Seneca, *Naturall Questions*, p. 795 [II.xl]; Pliny, *Historie of World*, p. 25 [II.lii.]; Isidore, *Etymologiae*, XIII.viii.2-ix.2; Bartholomaeus, *De proprietatibus rerum*, fol. 164-164ᵛ; and Hill, *Contemplation of Mysteries*, fol. 52ᵛ-58.

Although in poetry the destructiveness of lightning was most often emphasized, the first two varieties, completely harmless, were sometimes mentioned. *Fulgetrum* was employed by Spenser to describe Britomart's hair, which, when released from her helmet, spread to her heels:

> Like as the shining skie in summers night,
> What time the dayes with scorching heat abound,
> Is creasted all with lines of firie light,
> That it prodigious seemes in common peoples sight.
> (*F. Q.*, IV.i.13.6-9)

Noiseless *coruscation* was cited by Donne in "The Dreame" when he tells his mistress that "as lightning, or a tapers light, / Thine eyes, and not thy noise wak'd mee" (lines 11-12). This recalls how Imogen, "like harmless lightning, throws her eye" on Posthumus (*Cymbeline*, V.v.394).

The Romans had established the differentiation between *fulgur*, the flash of lightning, and *fulmen*, the thunderbolt;[9] and many Renaissance meteorologians, following their example, believed that the swift destructiveness of *fulmen* was largely due to the coformation of what they called a "thunder-stone." While the potential lightning was still enclosed as a hot exhalation within the cloud, the Earthy components of the exhalation frequently solidified into a hard mass. Then when the exhalation rent the cloud and appeared as lightning, "a greate stoone is blowne out, with it. . .consistynge of brymstone and other metallycke substance."[10] This thunderbolt was wholly pernicious: "where he burneth, he gendreth therwith full evill stench and smoak,"[11] and it "stryketh downe steples, and hyghe buildynges of stoone."[12]

In *Ovids Banquet of Sence* Chapman adapted the theory of thunderstones for poetry dependent upon wit. From the cover of a thicket Ovid has been watching Corinna at her bath; and when he

[9] See Lewis and Short, *Latin Dictionary*, "fulgur" and "fulmen"; and Carl Darling Buck, *A Dictionary of Selected Synonyms in the Principal Indo-European Languages* (Univ. of Chicago Press, 1949), 1.55.2 and 1.57.2.

[10] Fulke, *Goodly Gallery*, fol. 27v. See also Hill, *Contemplation of Mysteries*, fol. 55v and fol. 60v-61. Note Figure 2. The Ancients identified thunderstones with belemnites, the conical fossils of shellfish found frequently along the Mediterranean coast.

[11] Bartholomaeus, *De proprietatibus rerum*, fol. 164.

[12] Fulke, *Goodly Gallery*, fol. 28.

Figure 2. Heavenly artillery with drums for thunder (p. 83), multiple suns (pp. 135 ff.), storm winds blowing from clouds (p. 118), and armies battling in the sky (p. 150). The triangular objects in the center foreground are recently fallen thunderstones (p. 76).

Looke Up and See Wonders (London: for R. Michell, 1628), title-page.

steps into her sight, Corinna demands, "What savage boldnes hardned thee to this?" (lxxvi.2). Ovid replies:

> Love (sacred Madam) love exhaling mee
> (Wrapt in his sulphure) to this clowde of his
> Made my affections his artillerie,
> Shot me at you his proper Cytadell.
> (lxxvi.5-8)

Ovid's argument is that Love drew him into the thicket ("this clowde," line 6); then, just as Cold of the cloud compacts the hot exhalation and ejects the thunderstone, so has infatuation with Corinna compelled him to break forth in an attempt to storm the citadel of her private person.

Following Pliny, Bartholomaeus had listed yet another sort of lightning: *clarum*, which "is of a wonderfull kinde"[13]—that is, it accounted for many wonders popularly ascribed to lightning. This Robin Goodfellow of the lightning family had a wide range of powers which might interrupt the affairs of men with no wider significance than a puckish reminder of private calamity. Since Seneca and Pliny, every major commentator on lightning had included a list of *clarum's* marvelous abilities. Thomas Hill's list deserves special mention only because of its conciseness:

> This burneth man inwarde, and consumeth the bodie to ashes, without harming the garments, it stayeth the yongling in the wombe, without harme to the mother, it consumeth money, the purses remayning whole, it melteth the sworde the sheath being whole, it harmeth the hande the glove not perished, and the vessell broken, it so astonisheth the wine, that for three dayes after, the wine sheddeth or runneth not forth.[14]

There were other equally prodigious abilities possessed by lightning. Batman inserted an item in Bartholomaeus' *De proprietatibus rerum* to state that "Lightening doth also melte yron, and burneth not lawne or silke."[15] Thomas Hill expressed the common beliefs that "a venymous beast striken with the lightning. . .lose[th] the poyson . . .but the lightning stryking a beast not venymous, poysoneth the

[13] *De proprietatibus rerum*, fol. 164v. Cf. Pliny, *Historie of World*, p. 25 [II. lii]; Philemon Holland properly translated *clarum* as "Bright and Cleare." Pliny had found authority for the penetrative powers of this lightning in Aristotle, *Meteorologica*, 371a; Lucretius, *De rerum natura*, VI.348 ff.; and Seneca, *Naturall Questions*, p. 791 [II.xxxi].

[14] *Contemplation of Mysteries*, fol. 56v-57.

[15] Fol. 164.

same," and that "a dead Serpent striken wyth lightning becommeth full of wormes."[16]

Lightning was thought to have immediate and violent effects on men. It was dangerous to some extent if seen only at a distance, so Fulke warned that those who "beholde the lightening, are either made blynd, or their face swelleth, or els become lepers."[17] Jonson in his Petrarchan "Celebration of Charis" describes her anger as lightning which "tooke my sight, / And my motion from me quite" (lines 25-26).

Being struck by lightning, of course, produced even more terrible results. A graphic description of its fatal effect was provided by La Primaudaye:

> Those which are stroken therewith, be they men or beasts, remaine all consumed within, as if their flesh, sinewes, and bones were altogither molten within their skin, it remayning sound & whole, as if they had no harme.[18]

From the accurate observation that a corpse killed by lightning showed no outward evidence of its death-agent, authorities had surmised that the intense heat caused death by disintegrating the internal components of the body. Bussy d'Ambois employs this idea as the basis for a simile to summarize the dissembling and secrecy that he will practise upon Monsieur: "A politician must like lightning melt / The very marrow, and not taint the skin" (*Bussy d'Ambois*, IV.ii. 188-189). And in *The Faerie Queene* when love for the noble Belphoebe overcomes Arthur's squire:

> . . .[lovesickness] as a victour proud, gan ransack fast
> His inward parts, and all his entrayles wast,
> That neither bloud in face, nor life in hart
> It left, but both did quite drye up, and blast;
> As percing levin, which the inner part
> Of every thing consumes, and calcineth by art.
> (III.v.48.4-9)

Therefore in the *Amoretti* Spenser tells his mistress, "When ye lowre, or looke on me askew, / then doe I die, as one with lightning

[16] *Contemplation of Mysteries*, fol. 61ᵛ and 63ᵛ, respectively. Most of Hill's information on lightning seems to have come from Fulke, *Goodly Gallery*, fol. 25ᵛ-31. The ultimate source of this belief about the effect of lightning on serpents, however, was Seneca, *Naturall Questions*, p. 791 [II.xxxi].

[17] *Goodly Gallery*, fol. 30ᵛ.

[18] *French Academie*, p. 206.

fyred" (vii.7-8), meaning that inwardly he is consumed even though there may be little external evidence for the fatal effect of her displeasure.

Since lightning was believed to be a deadly meteor, the superstitious depended upon many tokens to afford protection from it. Pliny had provided the initial authority for a list of "things. . .not smitten with Lightning":

Of all those things which growe out of the earth, Lightning blasteth not the Laurell tree. . .of all creatures in the sea, this [the Sea-calf, or Seal] alone is not subject to the stroke of lightning: like as of all flying foules the Aegle.[19]

Pliny had further noted that since thunderstones "nor entreth at any time above five foot deepe into the ground. . .men fearfull of lightning, suppose the deeper caves to be the surest and most safe."

In *The Profitable Arte of Gardening* Thomas Hill used fragments of folklore to augment Pliny's original list of tokens against lightning, and he suggested that the hide of a hippopotamus, an unidentifiable "white vine," an owl with outstretched wings, and a speckled toad in a new earthen pot would defend the garden from the havoc of lightning.[20] To this list of protective talismans, Edward Fenton added "the true stone called *Hiacynthe*";[21] and La Primaudaye commented that lightning "very seldome toucheth pillars" because of their "roundnes."[22]

Literary allusions were often made to these tokens providing protection from lightning. Robert Greene, for instance, noted the inviolability of the laurel tree and the eagle's feather: "He which weareth Laurell cannot be hurt with lightning, nor he that carrieth the penne of an Eagle perish with thunder"[23] (*Planetomachia*, V.75).

Plutarch had been responsible for widespread acceptance of the belief that "those who lie asleepe are not thought to be smitten with lightning."[24] Expressing this notion in *Bussy d'Ambois*, the Friar berates Montsurry when he drags Tamyra onto the stage:

[19] *Historie of World*, p. 27 [II.lvi].

[20] P. 24.

[21] *Certaine Secrete Wonders*, fol. 23ᵛ.

[22] *French Academie*, p. 203.

[23] Cf. Greene, *Menaphon*, VI.54, and *Perimedes*, VII.75.

[24] *Of Symposiaques* (in *The Morals*, trans. Holland), p. 704. La Primaudaye attempted a pseudoscientific explanation of this belief (*French Academie*, p. 202).

The stony birth of clouds will touch no laurel,
Nor any sleeper; your wife is your laurel,
And sweetest sleeper; do not touch her then.
(V.i.17-19)

Thomas Hill recorded the belief—frequently repeated, though inconsistent with the professed invulnerability of a sleeping man—that when a man or beast "is striken with the lightning, being dead hath the eyes fast shut, but striken sleeping, hath the eyes open."[25] Hill also noted the truism "that no person. . .be touched, which eyther afore shall see the lightning, or heare the thunder."[26]

The quality attributed to lightning which most impressed the Renaissance Englishman was its destructiveness, for which some slight visible evidence existed[27] and much hearsay evidence appeared in chronicles and wonder-books. The intense heat of lightning was also recognized as one of its distinctive features. La Primaudaye went so far as to say that lightning "is not onely more pearcing by reason of the quicke motion thereof, but it is also much hotter then all other fire."[28]

The swiftness of lightning was yet another characteristic that occasioned frequent comment. Bartholomaeus had observed that "the mooving of lyghtening is sodaine and unware";[29] and the phrase "swift as lightning" remains an automatic simile to the present day. In such terms Juliet expresses her fears to Romeo: their love, she says, "is too rash, too unadvised, too sudden; / Too like the lightning, which doth cease to be / Ere one can say 'It lightens'" (II.ii.118-120). And Lysander complains to Hermia that always the ill-aspect of cicumstance makes love brief:

Brief as the lightning in the collied night,
That, in a spleen, unfolds both heaven and earth,
And ere a man hath power to say 'Behold!'
The jaws of darkness do devour it up.
(*M.N.D.*, I.i.145-148)

Lightning had become the epitome of swiftness because of the evanes-

[25] *Contemplation of Mysteries*, fol. 62.
[26] *Ibid.*
[27] The best known incidents of lightning's destructive power were the burning of St. Paul's steeple in 1561 and again in 1563.
[28] *French Academie*, p. 201.
[29] *De proprietatibus rerum*, fol. 164v.

cence of its flash and because of the speed, greater than that of thunder, with which it reached the observer.

Although thunder and lightning were believed to have a common cause and coincident formation, by far the greater portion of technical commentary was concerned with lightning alone. This inequality of attention was probably due to the greater fear prompted by the ruinous force of lightning—noise by itself was thought to be relatively harmless. In fact, Thomas Hill, pursuing the cosmological function of thunder, concluded that in its "finall causes and effects" it accomplished some good:

> The ayre first by the thunder is purged, and the evill vapours consumed, yea the pestilence and other contagiousnesse often clensed and put away.[30]

In accord with this notion, Sir John Davies observed that "the *winds* and *thunders* cleanse the ayre" (*Nosce Teipsum*, "Of Humane Knowledge," p. 23). Thomas Hill continued his list of the cosmological effects of thunder:

> . . .the thunders doe often bring showres with them, through which the earth plentifully yeeldeth.
>
> . . .the almightie God thundereth in the clowdes, to the ende that men may be procured unto a due reverence and feare towardes him.

Hill noted, though, that continuous thundering is unhealthful because "the corrupt vapours, grosse and clammy, drawne up with the vapour and exhalation, corrupting the lowest region of the ayre, are shed againe, and infect the ayre."[31] And Bartholomaeus, discoursing on the malevolence of thunder, had asserted:

> Thunder with his moving. . .stirreth the braine, and feareth the wit, and distroubleth & stirreth and corumpeth wine in tuns[32]. . . .And if it come in breeding time of foules, it greeveth their egges, and maketh women that travaile of childe, ofte to have dead borne children. . .and throweth down high towers, and destroyeth high trees.[33]

The folk belief that thunder must accompany the birth of swans was expounded by Henry Howard, Earl of Northampton:

[30] *Contemplation of Mysteries*, fol. 48.

[31] *Ibid.*, fol. 49^{v}.

[32] Thomas Lupton suggested "a way to keepe wine safe from Thunder": "It is good before such Tempest or Thunder, to lay a plate of iron with salt, or flint stones upon the saide vesselles with Wine" (*A Thousand Notable Things* [London: J. Roberts for E. White, 1595], p. 3).

[33] *De proprietatibus rerum*, fol. 163^{v}-164.

It chaunceth sometimes to thunder about that time and season of the yeare when Swannes hatch theyr young: and yet no doubt it is a paradoxe of simple men to thinke, that a Swanne can not hatch without a cracke of Thunder.[34]

The whimsy that "mushrooms be engendred of thunder" can be traced to Plutarch.[35]

Thunder was used figuratively in connection with a wide variety of loud and repeated noises, so that in the Tamburlaine plays alone Marlowe spoke of "thundring cannons" (line 1382), "thundring hooves" (line 2113), and "thundring drums" (line 2484). The comparison of artillery to thunder was an especially popular image, and thunder was often described as "heaven's artillery" (Shakespeare, *Shrew*, I.ii.205).[36]

Occult associations of thunder and lightning were strong. With his penchant for the magical, Pliny had written a paragraph on "raising or calling out Lightnings by conjuration," in which he drew upon historical precedent to show "that by certaine sacrifices and prayers, Lightnings may be either compelled or easily entreated to fall upon the earth."[37] By the Renaissance, thunder and lightning had become inseparably associated with conjuration. Especially in the drama, scenes presenting characters from the world of black magic invariably were accompanied by the rumble of thunder and the fearful flash of lightning. The practice had become so common, in fact, that Jonson in the prologue to *Every Man in His Humor* upbraids the vulgar dramatic conventions of the time by assuring the audience that in his play

> Nor nimble squibbe is seene, to make afear'd
> The gentlewomen; nor roul'd bullet heard
> To say, it thunders; nor tempestuous drumme
> Rumbles, to tell you when the storme doth come.
> (Prol., 17-20)

This passage also reveals the boisterous stage effects by which thunder and lightning were achieved in the playhouses.

Thunder and lightning had special significance to the prognos-

[34] *A Defensative against the Poyson of Supposed Prophesies* (London: J. Charlewood, 1583), $T2^v$.

[35] *Of Symposiaques* (in *The Morals*, trans. Holland), p. 704.

[36] Note Figure 2.

[37] *Historie of World*, p. 26 [II.liv].

ticator as well as the magician. In Homer, lightning on the right is considered favorable,[38] and Pliny had recorded the Roman belief that "lightnings. . .on the left hand, be supposed to be luckie and prosperous."[39] Rules for weather forecasting from thunder were offered by Leonard Digges in his *Prognostication of Right Good Effect*: "Thundres in the morning signifie wynd: about noone, rayn: in the evenyng great tempest."[40] Digges continued by giving the signification of thunder on each day of the week:

> Somme wryte (theyr grounde I see not) that Sonnedayes thundre shold brynge the deathe of learned men, judges, and others: Mundayes thundre, the deathe of women: Tuesdayes thundre, plentie of grayne: Wedensdayes thundre, the deathe of harlottes, and other blodshede: Thursdayes thundre, plentie of shepe & corne: Frydayes thundre the slaughter of a great man, and other horrible murders: Saterdayes thundre a generall pestilent plage, and great deathe.

Godfridus in his *Knowledge of Things Unknowne* gave a complete account of "what the thunder signifieth in every moneth of the yeere." The events which he forecasted from thunder were similar to those predicted by Digges: for example, "thunder in *February* signifieth that same yeere many rich men shall die in great sicknesse," and "thunder in *March* signifieth that same yeere great winds, plenty of corne, and debate amongst people."[41]

In Greek religion Zeus had originated as a sky- and weather-god worshiped specifically as the controller of thunder and lightning,[42] and thus he appeared in Renaissance fiction. When Zeus suddenly arrives to untangle the last act of *Cymbeline*, the stage direction requires that he descend "in thunder and lightning, sitting upon an eagle: he throws a thunder-bolt" (V.iv.93). The thunder-

[38] See *Iliad*, II.353 and IX.236 ff.; note also Chapman, *Caesar and Pompey*, II.iv.100-102.

[39] *Historie of World*, p. 27 [II.lv]. The apparent contradiction between the Greek and Roman interpretation of lightning omens is due to the fact that the Greeks faced north to call upon the gods, while the Romans faced south.

[40] *B*ii. Also in Erra Pater, *Pronostycacion for Ever*, *B*viii-*B*viii^{v}.

[41] Pp. 18-19. Rules with regard to the meaning of thunder in each month had previously appeared in works by Bede ("De tonitruis libellus") and Leopold of Austria. Thomas Hill (*Contemplation of Mysteries*, fol. 51^{v}) cited Hermes Trismegistus as the ultimate authority for this conventional list of rules.

[42] See Sir James G. Frazer, *The Worship of Nature* (London, 1926), pp. 43-48. Because of her relation to Zeus as his consort, Hera also was assigned powers over thunder, lightning, and the weather in general; see p. 46, n. 16, above. There was extensive Teutonic mythology dealing with a thunder-god; see Jakob Grimm, *Teutonic Mythology*, trans. J. G. Stallybrass (3 vols.; London, 1880-1883), I.166-192.

bolts hurled by Zeus were visualized as triple-pronged instruments with flames, the *ignes trisulci* of Ovid (*Metamorphoses*, II.848-849). Chapman spoke of "three-wingd lightning" (*Hero*, III.304), which Spenser described as a "fierce threeforked engin" (*F. Q.*, I.viii.9.6).

The close association between Jove and lightning gives a precise meaning to a line in Marlowe's *Faustus* which might otherwise elude exact interpretation. After rejecting all other scholarly careers and choosing magic, Faustus in his opening soliloquy declares:

> . . .Emperours and Kings
> Are but obeyd in their severall provinces:
> Nor can they raise the winde, or rend the cloudes.
> (lines 85-87)

If by magic or by other means Faustus can "rend the cloudes"—that is, generate thunder and lightning—then he will be a Jove.[43] As he himself says, he will "gaine a deitie" (line 91). Later the Evil Angel encourages Faustus to pursue magic so that he might be "on earth as *Jove* is in the skie, / Lord and commaunder of these Elements" (lines 104-105).

Because the eagle was thought to be invulnerable to lightning, this bird was represented as the armor-bearer to Jove.[44] Orcanes speaks of "the princely foule that in her wings / Caries the fearfull thunderbolts of *Jove*" (*2 Tamb.*, 2425-2426); and Henry III, wishing to indicate Bussy's appointment as regal deputy, announces that

[43] Cf. "O that I were a god, to shoot forth thunder" (Shakespeare, *2 Henry VI*, IV.i.104). Cf. *Coriolanus*, V.iii.149-151. Cf. Job 38:34-35, in which producing rain and lightning is specifically cited as beyond human power. The echoes in this dialogue from *Faustus*, however, seem to refer to a classical rather than a Biblical background; and perhaps Marlowe had in mind the story of Salmoneus, as told most completely by Aeneas when coming upon him in the Underworld:

> Eke *Sulmon* there I saw, in cruell wreake of turmentes just.
> For he the flames of god, and thondring soundes would counterfeat.
> He borne with horses foure, and shaking bronds and torches great
> Through contreys all of *Greece*, and townes triumphing went about,
> And honors due to God usurping tooke of every rout.
> A frantik man, that peereles lightning clouds would thinke to skorne,
> With brasse and ronning steedes, that footed ben with hoofe of horne.
> But *Jove* almighty than, a firy dart on him down flang,
> His artes could him not helpe, nor cressets fierce wherwith he sprang.
> But hedlong he to hell in whirling storme was thrown to deepes.

(Vergil, *The .xiii. Bookes of Aeneidos*, trans. Thomas Phaer and Thomas Twyne [London: W. How for A. Veale, 1584], *K*ii [VI.585-594]). Cf. also Apollodorus, *Library*, I.ix.7; Servius, *Commentarii*, I.388; Hyginus, *Fabulae*, p. 61; and Robert Graves, *The Greek Myths* (Penguin, 2 vols.; Edinburgh, 1955), 68.a.

[44] Note Pliny, *Historie of World*, p. 27 [II.lvi] and p. 273 [X.iv]; and Cartari, *Imagines deorum*, p. 107.

he "shalt be my eagle, / And bear my thunder underneath. . .[his] wings" (*Bussy d'Ambois*, III.ii.4-5).

Greek mythology had told the story that Zeus freed the Cyclopes (Brontes, Steropes, and Arges) when they were imprisoned by their brother Cronus, and out of gratitude they manufactured the lightning and thunderbolts that Zeus used as weapons and as agents of his wrath.[45] In *The Faerie Queene* Spenser, identifying Care with this group of superhuman blacksmiths, recalled the legend of the Cyclopes:

He [Care] like a monstrous Gyant seem'd in sight,
Farre passing *Bronteus*, or *Pyracmon*[46] great,
The which in *Lipari* doe day and night
Frame thunderbolts for *Joves* avengefull threate.
(IV.v.37.1-4)

In Jonson's *Haddington Masque* the Cyclopes appear as assistants to Vulcan, using their sledges to beat out time for the dancers (lines 317 ff.).

Quite frequently thunder was distinguished as the fierce voice of Zeus and lightning the destructiveness of his anger. In *Love's Labour's Lost*, for example, Biron's amorous sonnet confesses to Rosaline, "Thy eye Jove's lightning bears, thy voice his dreadful thunder" (IV.ii.119); and in *Bussy d'Ambois*, the King's "words and looks / Are like the flashes and the bolts of Jove" (I.i.36-37). In the same vein Galatea exhibits displeasure greater than Jupiter's, and subdues Pharamond with "a tongue-bolt" (Beaumont and Fletcher, *Philaster*, II.ii.132).

In the Hebraic-Christian tradition also, Jehovah controls thunder and lightning, and in the Holy Scriptures He uses them similarly to Zeus. Spenser warned the sinner:

. . .underneath His feet are to be found
Thunder, and lightning, and tempestuous fyre,

[45] Cf. Hesiod, *Theogony*, 501-505; Apollodorus, *Library*, I.i.2 and I.ii.1. In later mythology the Cyclopes were made assistants to Vulcan at his forge, but they still had the duties of making thunder and lightning; cf. Vergil, *Aeneid*, VIII. 424 ff.; Boccaccio, *Genealogiae*, fol. 75 v [X.xvi]; and Natalis Comes, *Mythologiae*, IX.viii. As Servius had observed (*Commentarii*, Vol. I, p. 482), the names came from βροντή, "thunder"; στεροπή, "lightning"; and ἀργής, "brightness." Natalis Comes explained the Cyclopes in terms of natural science, saying that they were merely the vapors and exhalations which produce thunder and lightning: "Dixerunt enim Cyclopes esse vapores, è quibus fulmina, & fulgura, & tonitrua nascerentur ac fierent neque vero vapores illi, nisi per calorem Solis in aera possunt extenuari, qui partim è mari, partim è terra extrahuntur" (*Mythologiae*, X."De Cyclopibus").

[46] Spenser here followed the nomenclature of Vergil and Boccaccio, who replaced "Arges" by "Pyracmon." This name derived from πῦρ, "fire," and ἄκμων, "anvil."

The instruments of his avenging yre.
("Heavenly Beautie," 180-182)

Marlowe treated thunder and lightning as visible evidence of God's displeasure: in *2 Tamburlaine* Sigismond asserts, "God hath thundered vengeance from on high" (line 2923); and Tamburlaine claims to be the scourge of "a God full of revenging wrath, / From whom the thunder and the lightning breaks" (lines 4294-4295).

2. COMETS, OR BLAZING STARS

No meteor was considered more unpropitious than the comet, the manifestation of disorder in the heavens and the portent of chaotic woe on earth. The brilliance with which comets blazed across the heavens combined with their unpredictability to terrorize a population already overconscious of its sins.

Classical scientists had accounted for comets in various, conflicting ways.[47] But until the revolutionary work of Tycho Brahe, who rightly suggested that a comet was an independent celestial body following an orbit about the Sun, the explanation of comets proposed by Aristotle was generally accepted in educated circles. This point of view, which maintained that a comet was an ignited mass of exhalation at the uppermost limit of the earth's atmosphere, was aptly expressed by John Maplet:

> The Comet is thus engendred. Whereas by the force of the sun and the other starres there is elevated and drawen up on hye very much viscous matter hoate & dry, grosse and fat. . .to the highest region of the Ayre, where it being turned aboute round, wyth the motion of the ayre, and being nighe the fire is kindled and set on fyre. . .and so other exhalations styll continuing and comming on doth both nourish and encrease the burning thereof.[48]

[47] Aristotle had reviewed the opinions of many of his predecessors in the *Meteorologica*, 342^b-344^a. See also Plutarch, *Opin. of Phil.*, p. 827 [III.ii]; and Seneca, *Naturall Questions*, pp. 886-897 [VII.ii-xxii]. C. Doris Hellman provides an exhaustive review of cometary theory to 1577 (*Comet of 1577*, pp. 13-117).

[48] *Diall of Destiny*, fol. 35.

The exhalation was raised to the highest region of the Air, where it was set on fire by the friction of the rotating spheres and by proximity to the region of Fire. It was generally agreed that the exhalation producing the comet must necessarily be of great quantity because the meteor burned steadily for several days. Almost every writer on comets quoted Pliny to the effect that this meteor continued at least seven days, and sometimes as long as eighty.[49]

La Primaudaye took issue with the explanation of comets based on Aristotle, and after noting the conventional theory, boldly wrote:

Neverthelesse some learned moderne writers which have diligently observed the height, whither these vapours may mount, do thinke cleane otherwise:[50] for they affirme that comets cannot be ingendred in the region of the elements: and are not afraid to give sentence against *Aristotle*, who in truth. . .hath failed in the resolution of many particular questions.[51]

If comets were not "ingendred in the region of the elements," they could not be classified with meteors, which by definition were confined to the sublunar sphere. Following this line of argument, La Primaudaye next gave a technical discussion of just where comets did originate, ending with the judgment:

A comet is a globe placed in heaven, which being inlightned by the Sunne doth plainely appeare: and when his rayes passe farther, they shew like the fashion of a beard or of a tayle. Whereupon it appeereth, that this flaming globe may be made in the midst of the [celestial] spheres. . .or else we must say (and that seemeth true) that the heaven is full of many stars, not verie massie, which (the aire being drie and attenuated) do present themselves to our sight.[52]

Although La Primaudaye's theory of comets held more truth than Aristotle's, at that time it represented a minority opinion.

Comets were divided into several types, according to their color ("whyte, ruddye, or blewe"[53]) or according to the shape which the exhalation assumed. If the luminosity was diffused equally on all sides, the comet was said to be "haired" or "fringed"; if the lumi-

[49] *Historie of World*, p. 16 [II.xxii].

[50] La Primaudaye left these dissenting "moderne writers" unnamed, but certainly he was talking about Tycho Brahe and his followers who wrote on the comet of 1577 (Cf. p. 27, n. 22, above). Among the Ancients, Diogenes and Pythagoras reportedly suggested that comets exist above the lunar sphere (Plutarch, *Opin. of Phil.*, p. 827 [III.ii]); and Seneca at least considered this possibility (*Naturall Questions*, pp. 887 [VII.ii] and 897 [VII.xxiii]).

[51] *French Academie*, p. 213.

[52] *Ibid.*, p. 215.

[53] Fulke, *Goodly Gallery*, fol. 15.

nosity appeared to trail behind, the comet was said to be "bearded."[54]

The name "comet" itself derived from Greek and Latin words meaning "long haired." Shakespeare spoke of comets with "crystal tresses" (*1 Henry VI*, I.i.3), and Tourneur thought of them as "stars [that] were [i.e., wear] locks" (*Revenger's Tragedy*, V.iii.30). The descriptive value of the phenomenon in this original sense is well illustrated by Spenser's account of Florimell's hair streaming in the wind as her horse gallops out of the wood past Guyon and Britomart:

> . . .her faire yellow locks behind her flew,
> Loosely disperst with puffe of every blast:
> All as a blazing starre doth farre outcast
> His hearie beames, and flaming lockes dispred,
> At sight whereof the people stand aghast.
> (*F. Q.*, III.i.16.3-7)

Not only does the simile create a precise mental picture of Florimell's bright hair wavering behind her, but it suggests the wonder incited by her rare beauty.

The wonder here induced by Forimell's beauty, it must be noted, sprang not from fear of any dire events that comets supposedly foretold, but from awe because of the infrequency of their appearance. The rarity of comets was often cited as a cause for amazement, quite independent of their terrible predictions. Donne noted that "who vagrant transitory Comets sees, / Wonders, because they are rare" ("To the Countesse of Huntingdon," 5-6). Likewise the wedding guests in *Taming of the Shrew* "gaze. . . / As if they saw some wondrous monument, / Some comet" (II.ii.96-98)—not because they are frightened at Petruchio's appearance, but simply because they are transfixed by his preposterous wedding costume.

Most of the discussion about comets, however, did center on their signification. Very few men doubted that they presaged disorders of all sorts: "drougth, the pestilence, hunger, battels, the alteration of kingdomes, and common weales, and the traditions of men. Also windes, earthquakes, dearth, landflouds, and great heate to follow."[55] Drayton gave a list but slightly abridged: "Some warre, some plagues,

[54] Aristotle had distinguished two types: χομήτης and πωγωνίας (*Meteorologica*, 344[a]). Cf. Pliny, *Historie of World*, p. 15 [II.xxii]. Note Figure 3c.

[55] Hill, *Contemplation of Mysteries*, fol. 3[v]. Johann Gartze gave a catalogue of fifty comets which purportedly had presaged major historical events (*Meteorologia* [Wittenberg, 1568], fol. 36-52[v]). The importance of comets in Renaissance astrology is discussed by D. C. Allen, *The Star-Crossed Renaissance* (Duke Univ. Press, 1941), pp. 178-181.

some famine. . . / Some falls of kingdomes, or of men of might" ("Miseries of Queene Margarite," 133-134).

Elsewhere in creative literature the comet often appears as a token of one or more of these disasters. In the Argument to the "December" eclogue, "E. K." states that Spenser likens "his manhoode to the sommer, which he sayth, was consumed with greate heate and excessive drouth caused throughe a Comet or blasinge starre, by which hee meaneth love." The martial and political implications of comets are noted by Tamburlaine when he refuses mercy to Babylon because sufficient warning has been given the city:

> . . .the view of our vermillion tents,
> . . .threatned more than if the region
> Next underneath the Element of fire,
> Were full of Commets and of blazing stars,
> Whose flaming traines should reach down to the earth.
> (2 *Tamb.*, 4198-4202)

In the Renaissance, though, there was an increasing tendency to propose natural rather than supernatural explanations for these effects of comets.[56] Pertinent to such a discussion, Fulke announced his intention to "omit nothing that hath any shadowe of reason," and he proceeded to explain why comets betokened several cosmological effects:

> Drought, because a *Comet* can not be generated without great heat, & much moisture is consumed in the burning of it.
>
> Barrines, because the fatnes of the earth, is drawen up, wherof the *Comet* consisteth.
>
> Pestilence, forsomuch as this kynd of *Exhalations* corrupteth the ayre, whiche infecteth the bodies of men & beastes.[57]

Fulke continued to discuss the "civile or politike effects" of comets—that is, "warres, seditions, changes of commen wealths and the death of Princes and noble men." For these events the author gave "reasonable" explanations: comets occurred only when many hot and dry exhalations were in the air, and this condition kindled the latent heat in already choleric men; furthermore, "Princes, living more delicatly then other men, ar more subject to infection," which

[56] On the "religio-scientific problem" of comets, see Paul H. Kocher, *Science and Religion in Renaissance England* (San Marino [California], 1953), pp. 165-168, 177-180.

[57] *Goodly Gallery*, fol. 15^v-16^v. This discussion was paraphrased by Thomas Hill, *Contemplation of Mysteries*, fol. 3^v-5.

was particularly threatening during the time of comets. Then resuming the spirit of his *Antiprognosticon*, Fulke again condemned the "*Astrologians*. . .[who] ar not ashamed, to an earthly substaunce [i.e., the comet], to ascribe an heavenly influence."

La Primaudaye similarly explained away the so-called effects of comets, tersely concluding that this meteor "may be a signe & token, but not the cause" of such dire events.[58] He characteristically voiced the religious belief that comets "advertise men that they remaine not buried in their filth and sinnes, but returne to the infinite goodnes of God, who reacheth out His hand, and calleth to us through such signes." Here the appearance of a comet was tempered to a warning rather than a threat. Nevertheless, whether the comet was the cause or merely the token of impending evil, it continued to evoke terror in the minds of Renaissance Englishmen.

3. MISCELLANEOUS FIERY IMPRESSIONS

In addition to comets, numerous other meteors could be formed by the kindling of an exhalation in the highest region of Air. Whereas the comet continued for several days, however, these other fiery impressions were unstable appearances that seldom persisted for more than an hour. Each of these fiery meteors was designated by a descriptive name, so that William Fulke included paragraphs on "Burned Stoble or Sparcles of Fire," "Torches," "Dansyng or Leaping Goates," "Burnyng Candels," "Burning Beames and Round Pillers," "Burning Speares," "Shieldes, Globes or Bowles," "Lampes," and "The Pyramidall Pyller Lyke a Spire or Broched Steeple."[59] All these fiery impressions were commonly lumped together under the term "apparitions."

[58] *French Academie*, p. 215.

[59] *Goodly Gallery*, fol. 6^{v}-11. Note Figure 3. Description of these meteors goes back to Aristotle, *Meteorologica*, 341^{b}; cf. also Seneca, *Naturall Questions*, p. 758 [I.i]; Pliny, *Historie of World*, p. 15 [II.xxii]; and Bartholomaeus, *De proprietatibus rerum*, fol. 157^{v}.

Figure 3. Various phenomena of exhalations sometimes visible at night:
(a) a flying-dragon (p. 95), dancing goats (p. 93), and a pilgrim pointing to the Milky Way (pp. 106-107);
(b) a burning candle, mounting fire, sparkles, wildfire, a burning spear, and a firebrand (pp. 91-94);
(c) a burning pillar (p. 91), a flying star (p. 96), the five planets and the Sun, a long-enduring comet (p. 88), and comets "tayled," "heared," and "bearded," respectively (pp. 88-89).

Kalender of Sheepeherds (London: J. Wally, [1560?]), *M*i[v]-*M*ii.

Which particular fiery impression was formed depended upon the shape and density of the evaporation to be ignited (and undoubtedly upon the imagination of the observer). As du Bartas stated:

> According as the vapour's thicke or rare,
> Even, or un-even, long or large, round or square,
> Such are the formes it in the Aire resembles.[60]

Typical of the descriptions and explanations given for these phenomena were Fulke's paragraphs " Of Torches" and "Of Dansyng or Leaping Goates":

> Torches or fyer brandes, are thus generated: when the matter of the exhalation is long and not broad, being kyndled at one end therof, in the highest region of the ayre, it burneth lyke a torche or fyer brande, and so continueth till all the matter be burned up, and then goeth out. . . .
>
> Dansyng Goates, are caused when the exalation is divided into twoo partes, as when twoo torches be seen together, & the flame appeareth to leape or daunce from one parte to the other.[61]

Literary allusions to these fiery impressions are likely to escape notice because the reference to the meteor is easily mistaken as a reference to the object for which the meteor is named. For example, Spenser described the hideous appearance of the Dragon ravaging the land of Una's parents, and he noted that "his blazing eyes, like two bright shining shields, / Did burne with wrath, and sparkled living fyre" (*F. Q.*, I.xi.14.1-2). Here Spenser seems to have had in mind the specific fiery meteors of "burning shields" and "sparkles of fire." Similarly, Shakespeare was thinking of "torches" when he had Juliet explain away the dawn: "Yon light is not day-light," she rationalizes, but "some meteor that the sun exhales, / To be. . .a torch-bearer" for Romeo's escape to Mantua (III.v.12-14). One of the most imaginative descriptions of a fiery impression, in this case "burning spears," occurs in Tamburlaine's boast to the vanquished kings of Turkey:

> I will persist a terrour to the world,
> Making the Meteors, that like armed men
> Are seene to march upon the towers of heaven,
> Run tilting round about the firmament,
> And breake their burning Lances in the aire,
> For honor of my woondrous victories.[62]
> (2 *Tamb.*, 3875-3880)

[60] *Devine Weekes*, p. 53.
[61] *Goodly Gallery*, fol. 7v.
[62] Cf. Vergil, *Aeneid*, V.525-528.

Tamburlaine vaingloriously asserts the magnitude of his power by claiming continued control over the entire sublunary universe, even unto the highest region of Air. Earlier, in Part I, he has boasted of his prowess in a comparable image: "Our swords, our lances and our shot / Fill all the aire with fiery meteors" (lines 1495-1496).

Pliny had mentioned a great variety of fiery impressions and had related historical tragedies occurring simultaneously with their appearance.[63] Renaissance Englishmen also thought them to be unfavorable omens which portended the same evils as did a comet. Marlowe's Dido in her infatuation with Aeneas exclaims:

> Not bloudie speares appearing in the ayre,
> Presage the downfall of my Emperie,
> Nor blazing Commets threatens *Didos* death,
> It is *Æneas* frowne that ends my daies.
> (*Dido,* 1323-1326)

In *The Teares of Peace* Chapman listed many "Metors, that did ill abode":

> The skipping Gote; the Horses flaming Mane;
> Bearded, and trained Comets; Starres in wane;
> The burning sword; the Firebrand, flying Snake;
> The Lance; the Torch; the Licking fire; the Drake.[64]
> (lines 1121-1124)

Combining information from Pliny with folklore, Chapman catalogued the conventional fiery apparitions seen in the uppermost Airy region. Thomas Watson turned this list into elegiac poetry when he besought the Air to join his lamentation over the death of Sir Francis Walsingham:

> Now set thy firie *Pyramids* to viewe,
> thy divers *Idols, Candles* burning bright:
> Inflamed *Shafts, Comets* of dreadfull hewe;
> *Sparkles* that flie, and *Starres* that fall by night.
> Let all thy *Meteors,* of what ever kinde,
> with terror sort them selves in just araie:
> And worke such fear in every mortall minde,
> that all the world may waile for ones decaie.[65]

[63] *Historie of World,* pp. 15-17 [II.xxii-xxvi].

[64] That is, the "firedrake," a fiery impression of the lowest region of Air. Note the discussion of "firedrake," p. 95, below.

[65] *Poems,* p. 161.

This passage contains at least the seed of Donne's *Anatomie of the World.*

Another important group of fiery impressions occurred in the lowest rather than the highest stratum of Air. Aristotle had explained these phenomena as projections of Fiery exhalations under pressure, forced downwards when the Air was contracted by Cold.[66] Members of this group usually appeared to individual men or to particular groups and were consequently ascribed a more restricted significance than were the uppermost fiery impressions, which blazed above the whole sublunary region.

One fantastic fiery meteor of the lower Air, reported to resemble a dragon breathing fire, was called *draco volans,* in the vernacular a "flying-dragon" or "firedrake."[67] With ingenuity controlled by reason, Fulke lengthily described the cause and appearance of this phenomenon:

> When a certen quantitie of *vapors* ar gathered on a heape, being very near compact, & as it wer hard tempered together this lompe of *vapors* assending to the region of cold [i.e., middle region], is forcibly beaten backe, which violence of moving is sufficient to kindle it (although som men will have it to be caused betwene ii. cloudes a whote & a cold) then the highest part, which was climming upward, being by reason more subtil & thin, apeareth as the Dragons neck, smoking, for that it was lately in the repuls bowed or made crooked, to represent the dragons bely. The last part by the same repulse, turned upward, maketh the tayle, both apearing smaller, for that it is farther of, & also, for that the cold bindeth it. This dragon thus being caused, flyeth along in the ayre, & somtime turneth to & fro, if it meat with a cold cloud to beat it back.[68]

Fulke added that some believed this dreadful meteor to be "the Devill hym selfe," and he recounted an incident on May Day 1547 when "there was newes come to London, that the Devill the same mornynge was seene flyinge over the Temmes." But the Cambridge don assured his readers that the apparition was only a flying-dragon, "nothing els but cloudes & smoke."

Apparently "firedrake" was a common epithet for men who tended

[66] *Meteorologica,* 342ª.

[67] Note Figure 3a. No mention of such a meteor had appeared in classical authorities. Formal description of this phenomenon seems to have originated with the encyclopedists of the thirteenth century. For persistent beliefs regarding the firedrake, see John Brand and William Hazlitt, *Popular Antiquities of Great Britain* (3 vols.; London, 1870), III.356-357.

[68] *Goodly Gallery,* fol. 10.

furnaces. Sir Epicure Mammon refers to Face as Subtle's "fire-drake, / His Lungs, his *Zephyrus*, he that puffes his coales" (*Alchemist*, II.i.26-27); and in Shakespeare's *Henry VIII* a character scornfully uses the term to describe a member of the mob who "should be a brazier by his face" (V.iv.42). Dekker noted that Hell contained some few poets—"not Poets indeede, but ballad-makers"—who "have faces like fire-drakes" (*Newes from Hell*, II.99). Such red faces became ballad-makers who blew forth the hot air of ribaldry.

Many authorities noted in the lowest region of Air a fiery impression called "a flying, shooting, or falling Starre."[69] This meteor was analogous to, but distinct from, the comet or "blazing" star, which developed in the highest region of Air just beneath the sphere of Fire.[70] The "falling" star formed under the following conditions:

> When the exhalation being gathered as it were on a round heape, and yet not throughly compacted in the hyghest parte of the lowest region of the ayer, beynge kyndled, by the soden colde of the mydle region is beaten backe, and so appeareth as though a Starre should fall, or slyde from place to place.[71]

Fulke duly commented that the name of this phenomenon was obviously misleading, because "the starres of the firmament can not fall."

There was a popular belief that when a shooting star struck the earth nothing remained except a jelly, the incombustible residue of the compacted exhalation.[72] Donne stated the idea: "He that sees a starre fall, runs apace, / And findes a gellie in the place" ("Epithalamion" [pp. 135 ff.], X.1-2). Here Donne used the idea in a jest that the bride awaiting her new husband is like a fallen star—nothing of her hard, brilliant virginity remains; instead she is an acquies-

[69] Fulke, *Goodly Gallery*, fol. 7v. Note Figure 3c.

[70] See pp. 87-88, above. Actually, Aristotle had described "shooting" or "falling" stars also as meteors of the highest rather than the lowest region of the Air. He technically distinguished between them and "blazing" stars (or comets) by noting that the "shooting" star was a small burning impression which passed through and thereby ignited a larger inflammable mass of exhalation, while the comet was a "fiery principle which is neither so very strong as to cause a rapid and widespread conflagration, nor so feeble as to be quickly extinguished" (*Meteorologica*, 344a). Both Anaxagoras and Epicurus also had carefully differentiated "comets" from "falling stars" (Diogenes Laertius, *Eminent Philosophers*, II.9 and X.111-115, respectively).

[71] Fulke, *Goodly Gallery*, fol. 7v.

[72] Cf. Gower, *Confessio Amantis*, VII.334-338. See also Brand and Hazlitt, *Popular Antiquities*, III.352-353.

cent jelly. The same quip passes between two Gentlemen watching the coronation procession in Shakespeare's *Henry VIII*; the countesses "are stars indeed; / And sometimes falling ones" (IV.i.54-55).[73]

A conventional trope displayed the "falling" or "shooting" star as a symbol of rapidly declining power which finally sinks to nothingness. In *Henry VIII* Wolsey wails, "I shall fall / Like a bright exhalation in the evening, / And no man see me more" (III.ii.225-227); and "with the eyes of heavy mind" Salisbury foresees Richard II's "glory like a shooting star / Fall to the base earth from the firmament" (*Richard II*, II.iv.19-20). Since the rising exhalation was prevented from reaching even so high as the upper region of Air, Chapman saw the falling star as a parallel to the ambitious man thwarted from achieving his high designs. Then, "(like men / Raisd to high places) Exhalations fall / That would be thought Starres" (*Teares of Peace*, 1008-1010). In *Byron's Tragedy* Chapman metaphorically employed this meteor to describe the ambitious man's downfall resulting from the withdrawal of support by the Sun-king: when Byron is taken in custody from the stage, Epernon comments, "So have I discern'd / An exhalation that would be a star / Fall, when the sun forsook it" (IV.ii.291-293).[74] In both these passages Chapman pointedly makes the distinction between the genuine stars of the celestial spheres and the pseudo stars raised as exhalations from the earth.

Yet another fiery phenomenon of the lower atmosphere was *ignis fatuus*, "a kind of light, that is seen in the night season, & seemeth to goe before men, or to followe them, leading them out of their waye unto waters, & other daungerous places."[75] Its formation was simple:

> The foulishe fyre is an *Exhalation* kendled by meanes of violent moving, when by cold of the night, in the lowest region of the ayre, it is beaten downe, & then commonly, if it be light, seeketh to ascende upward, & is sent down againe, so it danseth up & downe.[76]

Fulke observed that *ignis fatuus* was most often seen "in whote and fenny countries. . .and where as is abondaunce of suche unctuus and fat matter, as about churchyardes," an assumption which accounted for its superstitious association with "soules tormented in the fyre of

[73] Cf. Donne, "An Epithalamion" [p. 127], 33-38.
[74] Cf. Chapman, *Ovids Banquet*, l.4-8.
[75] Fulke, *Goodly Gallery*, fol. 11ᵛ.
[76] *Ibid.*, fol. 11ᵛ-12.

purgatorie."[77] Fulke exposed the nonsense of this supposition, though, and solemnly announced that "foolish fyre. . .hurteth not, but only feareth foules."

In folklore *ignis fatuus* was often associated with fairies, specifically with Puck, or Robin Goodfellow. Drayton in the *Nimphidia* introduces "*Pucke*, which most men call / *Hobgoblin*":

> [He] oft out of a bush doth bolt,
> Of purpose to deceive us.
> And leading us makes us to stray,
> Long Winters nights out of the way,
> And when we stick in mire and clay,
> *Hob* doth with laughter leave us.
> (lines 291-296)

This is the same Puck who appears in *Midsummer-Night's Dream* (II.i.33-41), and the same Robin Goodfellow who allegedly published *Tarltons News out of Purgatorie*.[78] *Ignis fatuus* was also known by a wide variety of other popular names, the most frequent of which was "Will-with-a-Wisp":

> Some call him Robin Good-fellow,
> Hob goblin, or mad Crisp,
> And some againe doe tearme him oft
> By name of Will the Wispe.[79]

Other common names for this phenomenon included "Jack-with-a-Lantern," "Friar's Lantern," "Dick-a-Tuesday," "Elf-fire," "Gillian-burnt-tail," and "Sylham Lamps."[80]

In Renaissance literature many characters are led astray by this impish phenomenon. Falstaff recalls the Gadshill incident in his mock encomium to Bardoph's nose ("an everlasting bonfire-light"), and he remembers mistaking Bardolph for "an *ignis fatuus* or a ball of wildfire" (*1 Henry IV*, III.iii.44-45). Caliban fears that in reprisal for insubordination Prospero's spirits will "lead me, like a firebrand, in the dark / Out of my way" (*Tempest*, II.ii.6-7); and later Ariel leads Stephano and his drunken companions "through / Tooth'd briers, sharp furzes, pricking goss and thorns," and deposits them

[77] On the superstition that *ignes fatui* were souls that had not attained heavenly peace, see Grimm, *Teutonic Mythology*, III.916-918.

[78] (For T. G[ubbin] and T. N[ewman], 1590), title page.

[79] From a ballad reprinted with *Robin Good-fellow, His Mad Prankes and Merry Jests* [1628] (Percy Society; London, 1841), p. xviii.

[80] See Brand and Hazlitt, *Popular Antiquities*, III.346-347. *NED* also lists each of these names.

"i' the filthy-mantled pool" (IV.i.179-182). Thomas Nashe, with the double purpose of eulogizing Sir Philip Sidney and of satirizing the pamphleteers, made effective figurative use of this meteor. Because Sidney was dead:

Ignis fatuus and grosse fatty flames (such as commonly arise out of dunghilles) have tooke occasion, in the middest eclipse of his shining perfections, to wander abroade with a wispe of paper at their tailes like Hobgoblins, and leade men up and downe in a circle of absurditie a whole weeke, and never know where they are (III.330).

Nashe pleaded that his readers be not misled into foolish ways by the *ignis fatuus* of printed nonsense.

A meteor similar to *ignis fatuus* occurred at sea.[81] The Ancients had observed this phenomenon and had described it as "lights like starres which appeere otherwhiles upon ships,"[82] and as a "resemblance of lightening. . .leaping too and fro, and shifting their places as birds doe which flie from bough to bough."[83] If but one light appeared, the impression was named "Helena" and was considered "daungerous" and "unluckie"; but if two lights were seen, the impression was called "Castor and Pollux," who "bring comfort with them, and foretell a prosperous course in the voiage."[84] Thomas Watson mentioned this significance of the Dioscuri:

> *Castor* and *Pollux, Laedaes* lovelie twins,
> whose bright aspect cheers moornful Mariners,
> Shewing them selves when pleasant calme begins,
> of gladsomē newes two welcome messengers,
> Convey great comfort to the weltred minde.[85]

Jonson also referred to the constant propitiousness of Castor and Pollux: "*Castor* sits on the maine yard, / And *Pollux* too, to helpe your *hayles* [i.e., the sailors' hauls]" (*Neptune's Triumph*, 526-527).

The relationship between the two possible forms of this meteor was fully expounded by Fulke:

Helena was the occasion that Troy was destroyed, therfore the Mariners by experience tryinge that one flame of fyre apearyng alone signified tempest

[81] Today known as St. Elmo's fire, and so called by Cortes, *Arte of Navigation* (1561), fol. li^{v}. Actually, it is an electrical discharge.

[82] Ascribed to Xenophanes by Plutarch, *Opin. of Phil.*, p. 822 [II.xviii].

[83] Pliny, *Historie of World*, p. 18 [II.xxxvii]. See also Seneca, *Naturall Questions*, p. 759 [I.1].

[84] Pliny, *Historie of World*, p. 18 [II.xxxvii]. See Brand and Hazlitt, *Popular Antiquities*, III.349-351.

[85] *Poems*, p. 175.

at hand, supposed the same flame to be the goddesse *Helena,* of whom they looked for nothing but destruction. But when two lightes ar seen together, they are a token of fayre wether & good luck, the Mariners therfor beleved, that they were *Castor* and *Pollux,* whiche saylyng to seeke their syster *Helena,* beyng caried to Troye by *Paris,* were never seen after, and thought to be translated into the nomber of the Gods that gyve good successe to them that sayle.[86]

To this fanciful explanation based on legend, Fulke appended a discussion of the "natural cause why thei may thus fore shewe either tempest or calmnes." He argued that this phenomenon, which was formed of the same matter as tempests, served as an indicator of the strength and abundance of the existing exhalations. One light (Helena) affirmed that sufficient matter for a tempest had already been gathered and compacted; while two lights (Castor and Pollux) signified that raw material for the storm was not yet joined together.

One of the fullest descriptions of this meteor in creative literature occurs early in *The Tempest.* Reporting to Prospero the means by by which the shipwreck has been achieved, Ariel declares:

> I boarded the king's ship; now on the beak,
> Now in the waist, the deck, in every cabin,
> I flamed amazement: sometime I'ld divide,
> And burn in many places; on the topmast,
> The yards and bowsprit, would I flame distinctly,
> Then meet and join.[87]
>
> (I.ii.196-201)

Ariel, an Airy spirit, transmutes himself into a Fiery impression. Fear prompted by this appearance of "Helena" causes Ferdinand and the other characters to leap overboard, and to make their entrance onto Prospero's enchanted island.

An equally wondrous impression that also occurred in the lowest layer of Air was "the flame or fyre, which cleaveth to the heares of the heade, and to the heares of beastes."[88] This phenomenon was the

[86] *Goodly Gallery,* fol. 13-13^{v}. The mythology is a garbled summary of Apollodorus (*Library,* III.x.7-III.xi.2) which was often repeated; cf., for example, Natalis Comes, *Mythologiae,* VIII.ix, and Hill, *Contemplation of Mysteries,* fol. 24-24^{v}.

[87] A source for the storm in *The Tempest* has been suggested: "one of the *Colloquia* of Erasmus, called 'Naufragium'. . .in an English translation by William Burton which appeared in 1606." See John D. Rea, "A Source for the Storm in *The Tempest,*" *MP,* XVII (1919), 279-286. On page 283 of this article descriptions of "Helena" and of "Castor and Pollux" are quoted from the English text of 1606.

[88] Hill, *Contemplation of Mysteries,* fol. 27^{v}.

fiery equivalent of dew; but while dew formed from vapors, this meteor developed from "clammy *Exhalations*, scatered abroade in the ayre in small partes, which in the night by resistaunce of the colde, are kendled."[89] Shakespeare included this meteor in a slightly modified form among the many marvels preceding Caesar's death; Casca informs Cicero:

> A common slave—you know him well by sight—
> Held up his left hand, which did flame and burn
> Like twenty torches join'd, and yet his hand,
> Not sensible of fire, remain'd unscorch'd.
> (I.iii.15-18)

Later in the same speech Casca repeats the story that "men all in fire walk up and down the streets" (I.iii.25).[90] Like *ignis fatuus*, this fiery impression caused wonder, but not harm.

4. THE MILKY WAY

The Milky Way was a familiar phenomenon described by William Fulke as "a whyte circle seen in a cleare night, as it were in the

[89] Fulke, *Goodly Gallery*, fol. 14.

[90] Shakespeare found both these prodigies in Plutarch's *Life of Caesar*; see Variorum *Julius Caesar* (Philadelphia, 1913), pp. 58-59.

firmament, passing by the signes of *Sagittarius* and *Gemini*."[91] With his telescope Galileo could tell immediately that this glowing streak was the fused light of countless stars, too small and close together to be distinguished individually. But before Galileo published his discoveries in the *Sidereus nuncius* (1610), the Milky Way was variously explained as the result of several different processes. In fact, no two of the major classical meteorologians had agreed upon its cause.

The Milky Way is here considered a phenomenon of exhalation on the authority of Aristotle, who had explained it as the ignition of accumulated exhalation drawn up to the region just below the sphere of Fire, not by a single planet, but collectively by all the stars.[92] Aristotle's discussion of the Milky Way had been confused and ambiguous, however, and not surprisingly it had been oversimplified by Plutarch, who had ascribed to Aristotle a description of the phenomenon as "an inflamation of a drie exhalation; the same being great in quantitie and continued."[93] This explanation had become standardized before the Renaissance, so that (purporting to cite Aristotle's opinion) Fulke wrote that the Milky Way "is caused by a cloude or *Exhalation* drawen up by those sterres, whiche be called *Sporades*."[94] Under this interpretation the Milky Way was simply a permanent low-power comet which spread over a considerable area of the heavens. Fulke and many other Renaissance meteorologians objected to this explanation on the reasonable grounds that if the Milky Way "were of the nature of elementes, as *Exhalations* are, it would be at length consumed. But this circle never corrupteth."[95]

Aristotle's explanation of the Milky Way, however, was only one of many; and Fulke, combining information in Aristotle's *Meteorologica* and Macrobius' *Commentarius in somnium Scipionis*, cited no less than seven other differing theories:[96]

[1] *Pithagoras* is charged with a poeticall fable, as though it had been

[91] *Goodly Gallery*, fol. 38.
[92] *Meteorologica*, 345^{b}-346^{a}.
[93] *Opin. of Phil.*, p. 827 [III.i].
[94] *Goodly Gallery*, fol. 39.
[95] *Ibid.*, fol. 39^{v}.
[96] *Ibid.*, fol. 38-39^{v}. Fulke translated his two sources rather closely. Cf. Bartholomaeus, *De proprietatibus rerum*, fol. 124. It must be noted that, strictly speaking, only Aristotle's explanation of the Milky Way permitted the classification of this phenomenon as a meteor; the theories of the other authorities placed the Milky Way above the lunar sphere.

caused by reason that the sunne did once runne out of his pathway, and burned this part wherof it loketh whyte.[97]

[2] . . .*Anaxagoras* and *Democritus* sayde, that it was the light of certeine sterres, shining by them selves, of their owne light, which in the absence of the sunne, might be seen. . . .[98]

[3] *Theophrastus* a Philosopher affirmed, that it was the joyning together, or seeme, of the two halfe globes, whiche made it appeare more light in that place then in other.[99]

[4] Other sayde, it was the reflexion of the shyning light of fyre, or sterre light, as it is seen in a glasse. . . .[100]

[5] *Diodorus* affirmed, that it was heavenly fyre, condensede or made thick, into a circle, & so became visible, wheras the rest for the purenes, clearenes, and thinnes, could not be seene.[101]

[6] *Possidonius*. . .saide: it is the infusion of the heate of sterres, which therfore is in a circle, contrarie to the *Zodiake*. . . .[102]

[7] The last opinion is of them that say, it is of the nature of heaven, thycker in substaunce then other partes of heaven be, having some lykenes to the substance of the Moone, which being lightned by the same, as al the starres be, apereth whight.[103]

Fulke believed the last opinion to be the most probable, and he discounted most of the other theories by terse dogmatic statements. For instance, he rejected (2)—that the Milky Way was a unified display of innumerable small stars—by simply asserting that "this opinion is also false, for the sterres have no light of them selves."[104]

[97] Aristotle, *Meteorologica*, 345^{a}. Fulke here fused two suggestions which had been clearly differentiated by Aristotle and many other authorities: (1) the Milky Way was a former path of the Sun; and (2) the Milky Way was the result of Phaeton's disastrous attempt to drive the Sun-chariot. Cf. Plutarch, *Opin. of Phil.*, p. 826 [III.i].

[98] Aristotle, *Meteorologica*, 345^{a}. Cf. Plutarch, *Opin. of Phil.*, p. 827 [III.i]; and Macrobius, *Somnium Scipionis*, I.xv.6. Note Figure 3a.

[99] Macrobius, *Somnium Scipionis*, I.xv.4.

[100] Aristotle, *Meteorologica*, 345^{b}. Diogenes Laertius (*Eminent Philosophers*, II.9) had ascribed this theory to Anaxagoras, even though Aristotle had linked his name with (2), which differed fundamentally from it. Plutarch had attributed to Anaxagoras yet a third theory of the Milky Way: "the shadow of the earth resteth upon this part of heaven, at what time as the Sunne being underneath the earth, doth not illuminate all throughout" (*Opin. of Phil.*, p. 827 [III.i]).

[101] Macrobius, *Somnium Scipionis*, I.xv.5. Plutarch (*Opin. of Phil.*, p. 827 [III.i]) had cited Posidonius as having offered an explanation similar to this.

[102] Macrobius, *Somnium Scipionis*, I.xv.7.

[103] Plutarch (*Opin. of Phil.*, p. 826 [III.i]) had ascribed this opinion to Parmenides. It is not found in either Aristotle or Macrobius.

[104] *Goodly Gallery*, fol. 39.

Yet this was the explanation later corroborated by the discoveries of Galileo.

That Donne was familiar with Galileo's hypothesis about the Milky Way is shown in his poem "The Primrose, Being at Montgomery Castle." One drop of dew has fallen into each of the many flowers on the hill, and the dewdrops in "their infinitie / Make a terrestriall Galaxie, / As the small starres doe in the skie" (lines 5-7). Although it is conceivable that Donne had in mind the theories of Anaxagoras and Democritus, more likely the recent impact of Galileo's *Sidereus nuncius* provided the impetus for the allusion.[105]

In addition to the numerous scientific explanations, Fulke also noted four legends proposed by "the Poetes" as causes of the Milky Way:[106]

[1] . . .*Phaeton,* whiche on a tyme guided the Chariot of the sunn, & wandring out of the way, did burne the place, wherfore of *Jupiter* he was stryken downe wyth lyghtnyng.[107]

[2] . . .it is the high strete in heaven, that goeth streight to *Jupiters* pallace, and both sydes of it, the comen sorte of Gods do dwell.[108]

[3] . . .*Hebe,* one which was *Jupiters* Cupbearer, on a tyme, stombled at a starre, and shedde the wyne or mylke, that was in the cuppe, which colloured that part of heaven to this daye. . . .[109]

[105] See Marjorie Nicolson, "The 'New Astronomy' and English Literary Imagination," *SP*, XXXII (1935), p. 450 (n. 63) and p. 459. Note Figure 3a, however, in which the Milky Way was obviously conceived as a conglomeration of individual stars. This drawing antedated the *Sidereus nuncius* by over one hundred years and appeared throughout the sixteenth century. Cf. also Thomas Watson, 'ΕΚΑΤΟΜΠΑΘΙΑ, xxxi.1-4 (in *Poems*, p. 67).

[106] *Goodly Gallery*, fol. 38ᵛ.

[107] Phaeton's havoc with the Sun-chariot had been vividly related by many, including Ovid (*Metamorphoses*, II.150 ff.). For explanation of the Milky Way as the direct result of Phaeton's accident, see Aristotle, *Meteorologica*, 345ᵃ; Plutarch, *Opin. of Phil.*, p. 826 [III.i]; and Chaucer, *House of Fame*, II.936 ff.

[108] The Milky Way as the highway to Jupiter's palace had been elaborately described by Ovid (*Metamorphoses*, I.168-176).

[109] Thomas Cooper's *Thesaurus Linguae Romanae & Britannicae* (London, 1565) included this entry: "Hebe, whom Jupiter for hir excellent favour and beautie made his cuppe bearer. But on a tyme when he was at a feast in Aethyope, and Hebe bringing his cuppe in a slippery place chaunsed to fall, and disclosed further of hir neather partes, then comlinesse would have to be shewen" (*I*4). Cf. Boccaccio, *Genealogiae*, fol. 67 [IX.ii]; Thomas Watson, *Poems*, p. 128; and Fraunce, *Third Part of Countesse of Pembrokes Ivychurch*, *I*2ᵛ. In all these accounts, however, the only result of Hebe's accident was her replacement by Ganymede as Jupiter's cupbearer, and no mention is made of the Milky Way. In classical authors I have found no hint of any legend in which Hebe spills milk or wine. "E. K." in his gloss on "nectar" in the "November" eclogue (line 195) repeated the tale of Hebe's

[4] . . .*Apollo* stoode there to fight against the Giantes. . .[and] *Jupiter* made [the Milky Way] to appeare for a perpetuall memory.[110]

Another quasi-mythological account of the Milky Way could be found in both Natalis Comes' *Mythologiae* (II.iv) and Cartari's *Imagines deorum* (p. 132). According to this story, Jupiter placed the infant Hercules to nurse at the breast of Juno while she was asleep. When the goddess awoke and saw her husband's bastard son, she pushed him away. Hercules then spewed milk across the sky, where it may still be seen as the Milky Way.[111]

These mythological accounts of the Milky Way had not been prominently treated in classical writings, nor had they acquired wide circulation among Renaissance authors. Nevertheless, some of them did infrequently appear in Elizabethan and Jacobean literature. Phaeton's responsibility for this bright path across the sky, for example, was fully recounted by Spenser:

> . . .the firie-mouthed steeds, which drew
> The Sunnes bright wayne to *Phaetons* decay,
> Soone as they did the monstrous Scorpion vew,
> With ugly craples crawling in their way,
> The dreadfull sight did them so sore affray,
> That their well knowen courses they forwent,
> And leading th'ever-burning lampe astray,
> This lower world nigh all to ashes brent,
> And left their scorched path yet in the firmament.
> (*F. Q.*, V.viii.40.1-9)

Hebe's accident, which some blamed for the Milky Way, was mentioned in "E. K.'s" gloss on "nectar" in Spenser's "November" eclogue: nectar is "white like creme, whereof is a proper tale of Hebe, that spilt a cup of it, and stayned the heavens, as yet appeareth" (line 195). And Jonson in his gloss for *Hymenaei* made ref-

causing the Milky Way, but annotators of Spenser have also failed to unearth the source of the story. "E. K." concludes his gloss with the tantalizing statement that he has "already discoursed that at large in my Commentarye upon the dreames of the same Authour."

[110] In traditional accounts of the Gigantomachia, Apollo does not appear. Fulke here refers to the account of the Milky Way given by Pontano, *Meteororum liber* (in *Opera*) (Venice, 1513), fol. 132^{v}.

[111] Cf. Manilius, *Astronomicon*, I.750-754; Hyginus, *Poeticon Astronomicon*, pp. 498-499. Tintoretto's well-known treatment of this fable hangs in the National Gallery, London.

erence to the story of the infant Hercules nursing at Juno's breast (line 219).

The most popular mythological association of the Milky Way, however, was its identification as the highway to Jupiter's palace, probably because this suggestion had appeared prominently in Ovid's *Metamorphoses* (I.168-176). Marlowe alluded to this notion in two strikingly different, though eminently decorous, images: at one point tears fall from Hero's eyes like "a streame of liquid pearle, which downe her face / Made milk-white paths, wheron the gods might trace / To *Joves* high court" (I.297-299); and Tamburlaine, planning a triumphal return to his native city, announces his intention of parading though the streets of Samarkand

> . . .in my coach like *Saturnes* royal son,
> Mounted his shining chariot, gilt with fire,
> And drawen with princely Eagles through the path,
> Pav'd with bright Christall, and enchac'd with starres,
> When all the Gods stand gazing at his pomp.
> (lines 4104-4108)

The idea of riding upon the Milky Way turns Tamburlaine's thoughts heavenward, and he concludes this speech by declaring his expectation of continued power until his "soule dissevered from this flesh, / Shall mount the milk-white way" to meet its Maker (lines 4110-4111).

In Elizabethan and Jacobean writings the Milky Way was called by many names. Sometimes it was left untranslated from its direct Latin source, *via lactea.*[112] More frequently it was referred to in the Greek form "galaxia,"[113] or more simply as "the galaxy."[114] Since the Stoics, popular opinion had considered the Milky Way to be a highway to heaven: it was the locale of Scipio's dream,[115] and for Chapman it was "eternities streight milke-white waie" (*Teares of Peace*, 846). Frequently the names of actual pilgrimage routes were therefore used as synonyms for it. "The highway of Saint James,"

[112] Note Bartholomaeus, *De proprietatibus rerum*, fol. 135; and Maplet, *Diall of Destiny*, fol. 12ᵛ.

[113] Note Maplet, *Diall of Destiny*, fol. 12ᵛ; and Greene, *Never Too Late*, VIII.92.

[114] Note Donne, "The Primrose," 6, and "Sapho to Philaenis," 60.

[115] Macrobius, *Somnium Scipionis*, I.iv.4-5; note also I.xii.1-3. The conception of the Milky Way as an abode of the blessed was originally a Pythagorean idea; see Armand Delatte, *Etudes sur la Littérature Pythagoricienne* (Paris, 1915), pp. 262-263.

leading to Santiago de Compostella in Galicia, was a widespread common name for the Milky Way in England as well as in southern Europe.[116] Specifically English adaptation of this usage identified the Milky Way with "Watling Street,"[117] the famous Roman highway passing through London and St. Albans to the Firth of Forth, and with "Walsingham's Way," the route to the old shrine of Our Lady at Walsingham in Norfolk.[118]

In poetical usage the Milky Way was most frequently cited as the epitome of brilliance or whiteness. In Donne's words, it is "heavens Zone glistering" ("Going to Bed," 5). Elsewhere Donne uses "whitenesse of the *Galaxy*" to praise a lover's cheeks ("Sapho to Philaenis," 60), and Francesco in Greene's *Never Too Late* sings of "the milke-white *Galaxia* of . . .[Infida's] brow" (VIII.92).

5. WINDS

Three distinct theories of wind formation had been proposed. (1) In the *Meteorologica* Aristotle had positively defined wind as "a body of dry exhalation moving about the earth."[119] But in the course of establishing his own thesis by refuting other arguments, Aristotle had repeated (2) the theory of Hippocrates that "wind is simply a moving current of what we call air."[120] This controversy whether wind was a true meteor formed from an exhalation (essentially like Fire), or whether it was merely Air in motion, continued into

[116] See *NED*, "Watling-street," sense 2. For instances of this term in English writings, note *Kalender of Sheepeherds*, Mi^{v} (see Figure 3a); and Fulke, *Goodly Gallery*, fol. 38. For further discussion, see Edward H. Sugden, *A Topographical Dictionary to the Works of Shakespeare and His Fellow Dramatists* (Manchester Univ. Press, 1925), "James (St.)."

[117] For instances of this term in English writings, note Recorde, *Castle of Knowledge*, p. 105; and Fulke, *Goodly Gallery*, fol. 38. "Watling Street," meaning the Milky Way, had appeared in English poetry as early as Chaucer's *House of Fame* (II.939). See Grimm, *Teutonic Mythology*, I.356-357.

[118] See Sugden, *Topographical Dictionary*, "Walsingham."

[119] 361^{a}.

[120] *Ibid.*, 348^{b}.

the Renaissance. La Primaudaye proffered support to the latter opinion.[121] Bartholomaeus had also cited the Hippocratic theory on the authority of Isidore,[122] but finally had rather grudgingly accepted Aristotle's theory as more probable.[123] Furthermore, (3) Pliny had complicated the issue by suggesting that "there be certaine caves and holes which breed winds continually without end."[124]

Through an ingenious resolution of this controversy, William Fulke was able to accept all three of the prevalent opinions—or rather, to adapt each of them to explain a particular group of winds.[125] To cover the "generall wyndes, that blowe over al the earth," he employed the Aristotelian thesis:

> The wynd is an *Exhalation* whote and drie, drawne up into the aire by the power of the sunne, & by reason of the wayght therof being driven down, is laterally or sidelongs caried about the earth.

Fulke noted, however, that there were also "particular wyndes, whiche are knowen but only in som countries"; and to explain these local winds, he paraphrased Pliny's contention:

> Within the globe of the earth be wonderful great holes, caves, or dongeons, in which when ayer abondeth (as it may be diverse causes) this ayer, that cannot abide to be pinned in, findeth a little hole in or about those countries, as it weare a mouth to break out of.

And Fulke listed "yet a thyrde kynde of wynde," which "properly is no wynde but a moving of the ayre." This wind, which Fulke described as "softe gentle and coole," was the refreshing "aura" discussed by Bartholomaeus, which "slaketh and cooleth them that bee hotte: and heateth them that bee colde."[126] Thus Fulke skilfully combined the three independent and opposing theses of Aristotle, Pliny, and Hippocrates into a single system which explained all types of winds.

[121] *French Academie*, p. 196.

[122] *De proprietatibus rerum*, fol. 156v. Cf. Isidore: "Ventus est aer commotus et agitatus" (*De natura rerum*, XXXV.1, and *Etymologiae*, XIII.xi.1). Isidore's statement had been repeated verbatim by Bede (*De natura rerum*, chap. xxvi), and Rabanus Maurus (*De universo*, IX.xxv).

[123] *De proprietatibus rerum*, fol. 158.

[124] *Historie of World*, p. 21 [II.xliv].

[125] All passages from Fulke quoted in this paragraph come from *Goodly Gallery*, fol. 18-18v.

[126] *De proprietatibus rerum*, fol. 164v. Cf. Pontano, *Meteororum liber*, fol. 124v-125. "Aura" had figured prominently in Ovid's account of Cephalus and Procris, *Metamorphoses*, VII.808 ff.

Du Bartas included in his *Devine Weekes* an excellent imaginative account of the formation of winds, which he based upon the Aristotelian theory. He described the contention between the hot wind-forming exhalations and the cold middle region of Air, and he likened this conflict to the repeated attack and retreat of a force besieging a garrison:

> But scarce so soone their [the exhalations'] fuming crest hath raught,
> Or toucht the Coldnes of the middle vault,
> And felt what force their mortall enemie,
> In garrison keeps their continually:
> When downe againe, towards their Dam [Earth] they beare,
> Holpe by the waight which they have drawn from her:
> But in the instant, to their aide arives
> Another new heat, which their heart revives,
> Re-armes their hands, and having staid their flight,
> Better resolv'd, brings them againe to fight:
> Well fortified then, by these fresh supplies,
> More bravely they renew their enterprize,
> And one-while th'upper hand (with honour) getting,
> Another-while disgracefully retreating,
> Our lower Aire they tosse in sundrie sort.[127]

In the plan of the sublunary universe the winds were confined to the lower strata of the Air because of their weight and because of their combustion into other meteors if they approached the orb of Fire. As Donne noted, wind could not venture into "the upper valt of aire" ("Calme," 20), but "at th'ayres middle marble roome did finde / Such strong resistance, that it selfe it threw / Downeward againe" ("Storme," 14-16).

Primarily through the practice of mariners, winds had been designated according to the points of the compass from which they blew. But the most advantageous number of winds to be differentiated was open to question. Pliny had recommended eight,[128] while La Primaudaye used a sixteen-point compass.[129] Du Bartas noted that actually there were an infinite number of winds, although convenience suggested that for purposes of description they be grouped under the four major points of the compass.[130] Generally, however,

[127] P. 51.
[128] *Historie of World*, p. 22 [II.xlvi].
[129] *French Academie*, p. 235.
[130] *Devine Weekes*, p. 52.

twelve winds were enumerated and described: "foure of them are called *Cardinales*, chife winds, and eight *collaterals*, side windes."[131]

Although in the *Meteorologica* Aristotle had provided a wind rose clearly labeled with proper names for the winds,[132] his nomenclature had not remained authoritative. During the Renaissance, the most popular names for winds were largely taken from Roman writers.[133] Confusion was unavoidable; but irrespective of minor variations, a more or less standard set of names had evolved.[134] The North-wind was called "Boreas," or less frequently "Septentrionarius." Its collaterals were "Corus" to the west and "Aquilo" to the east. The South-wind was named "Auster," with "Notus" as its eastern and "Affricus" its western collateral. "Favonius" was the West-wind, although possibly its side-wind of "Zephyrus" to the south was better known. "Circius" was the side-wind of "Favonius" to the north. From the east blew "Subsolanus," with "Caecias" at its northern and "Eurus" or "Vulturnus" at its southern side. Needless to say, no two authorities agreed exactly on this nomenclature. Frequently one of these names was used to designate a wind different from that indicated here, or an entirely new name for a particular wind was given.[135]

Each wind had definite characteristics, attributes, and associations, so that an author wishing to use a wind for literary purposes necessarily took great care in choosing the proper one. Like most things that the Renaissance listed according to medieval classification, the winds were fitted into a neatly interlocking complex, perfectly balanced and complete within itself. The character of each cardinal wind was fundamentally defined by an identification with both an Element and its corresponding humor: Boreas with Earth and black bile, Aus-

[131] Bartholomaeus, *De proprietatibus rerum*, fol. 158[v].

[132] 363[a]. Cf. Aristotle, *Ventorum situs et cognomina*. See also D'Arcy W. Thompson, "The Greek Winds," *Classical Review*, XXXII (1918), 49-56.

[133] Especially Seneca, *Naturall Questions*, pp. 853-854 [V.xvi]; and Pliny, *Historie of World*, pp. 22-23 [II.xlvi]. See also Isidore, *Etymologiae*, XIII.xi. 2-13; Bede, *De natura rerum*, chap. xxvii; and Boccaccio, *Genealogiae*, fol. 36-36[v] [IV.liv].

[134] Note Figure 4 for a representative Renaissance wind rose.

[135] The following alternative names, most of which derived from Greek authors, were sometimes encountered:

North-winds:	Aparctias, Meses, Thracias, Etesiae, Tramontanus
East-winds:	Apeliotes, Hellespontias
South-winds:	Libs, Libonotus, Leuconotus, Phoenicias
West-winds:	Argestes, Olympias, Sciron, Orinthias, Chelidonius, Eborus

Figure 4. A wind rose distinguishing and naming the twelve winds. Note that each cardinal wind is also identified with its appropriate Element: Boreas with Earth, Zephyrus with Water, Auster with Air, and Subsolanus with Fire.

Peter Apian, *Cosmographicum* (Landshut, 1524), fol. 53.

ter with Air and blood, Eurus with Fire and yellow bile, and Favonius with Water and phlegm. Du Bartas concisely summarized this information and further extended the association of each wind to include a particular season and a stage in man's life:

> In their [the winds'] effects I finde fower Tempraments,
> Foure Times, foure Ages, and foure Elements.
> Th' *East-wind* in working, followes properly
> Fire, Choller, Summer, and soft Infancie:
> That, which dries-up wild *Affrick* with his wing,
> Resembles Aire, Bloud, Youth, and lively Spring:
> That, which blowes moistly from the *Westerne* stage,
> Like Water, Phlegme, Winter, and heavie Age:
> That, which comes shiv'ring from cold climates soly,
> Earth, withered Eld, Autumne, and Melancholy.[136]

The tetrad arrangement of the winds, the humors, the periods of man's life, the seasons, and the Elements owed much, at least indirectly, to the τετρακτύς of Pythagoras.

Some natural explanation of the associations of each wind was implicit in its geography. Ovid in the *Metamorphoses* had recounted how, after the Creation out of chaos, the four winds contended as cruelly "as though they would the world in pieces rende":

> And therefore to the morning graye, the Realme of *Nabathie*,
> To *Persis* and to other lands and countries that doe lie
> Farre underneath the Morning starre, did *Eurus* take his flight
> Likewise the setting of the Sunne, and shutting in of night
> Belong to *Zephyr*. And the blasts of blustring *Boreas* raigne,
> In *Scythia* and in other landes set under *Charles* his waine.
> And unto *Auster* doth belong the coast of all the South,
> Who beareth shoures and rotten mistes, continuall in his mouth.[137]

Since Eurus originated "underneath the Morning starre," quite logically it represented "soft Infancie," as suggested by du Bartas; and the West-wind, blowing from "the setting of the Sunne and shutting in of night," brought to mind "heavie Age." Furthermore, as Bartholomaeus had pointed out, the East-winds "be hot and drye:

[136] *Devine Weekes*, p. 52. Cf. Godfridus, *Knowledge of Things Unknowne*, pp. 91-93. In Figure 4 note that each margin is decorated to represent the proper Element for the wind blowing from that direction.

[137] Ovid, *The .xv. Bookes. . .Entytuled Metamorphosis*, trans. Arthur Golding (London: W. Seres, 1567), fol. 1^v-2 [I.61-66]. This passage of Ovid had been quoted by Seneca in the *Naturall Questions*, p. 853 [V.xvi].

hot, for they bide long under the Sunne, & drye, for the East sea is full far from us";[138] and being hot and dry, they were most like the Element of Fire and the choleric humor. Bartholomaeus had similarly explained that the "west winde is temperatly cold and moyst: colde, for the sunne abideth but a little while in the west"; and being cold and moist—the exact opposite of the hot, dry East-wind—the West-wind was most closely related to the Element of Water and the phlegmatic humor, the eternal contraries of Fire and choler. Summer, being the hot and dry season, became the distinctive season for the East-wind; and continuing the necessity for perfect contrast, the West-wind automatically became the representative of winter, the cold and moist period.

The identification of Favonius and Zephyrus with winter agreed with the climatology of Greece, where for most cities west winds blew out of the snowy mountains.[139] But a much stronger Latin tradition described the West-winds as mild, pleasant harbingers of spring and summer. Pliny had suggested: "This wind is that spirit of generation which doth breath life into all the world";[140] and Isidore, taking a tip from Pliny, had explained: "*Favonius* dicitur, propter quod *foveat* quae nascuntur."[141] Bartholomaeus had therefore dutifully noted:

> The West winde is called *Favonius*: for he nourisheth and feedeth things that be gendred, as *Isidore* sayth, for he resolveth and unbindeth winter, & bringeth forth grasse, hearbes, and floures.[142]

Someone like Thomas Tusser (who derived his meteorology, as he did his husbandry, from experience in the fields) considered the

[138] *De proprietatibus rerum*, fol. 159.

[139] Cf. Homer, *Iliad*, XXIII.200.

[140] *Historie of World*, p. 471 [XVI.xxxix]. The belief in the West-wind as a seminal factor also accounts for this bit of folklore recorded by Pliny: "In Portugall, along the river Tagus and about Lisbon, certaine it is, that when the West wind bloweth, the mares set up their tailes, and turne them full against it, and so conceive that genitall aire in steed of naturall seed; in such sort, as they become great withall, and quicken in their time, and bring foorth foles as swift as the wind, but they live not above three yeares" (*Historie of World*, p. 222 [VIII.lxvii]). Boccaccio refers to this whimsical item (*Genealogiae*, fol. 37v [IV.lxi]). In Homer's *Iliad*, Zephyrus sires the fleet horses belonging to Achilles (XVI.148-151). Cf. *Iliad*, XX.223-229, where Boreas similarly inseminates mares to produce unbelievably fast horses.

[141] *Etymologiae*, XIII.xi.8.

[142] *De proprietatibus rerum*, fol. 159. This belief ties in with the myth of Zephyrus' marriage to Flora; see pp. 125-126, below.

West-wind a requisite to agricultural productiveness: "The West [-wind] to al flowers, may not be forborne."[143]

Technical authorities insisted upon a perfect contrast between the North- and South-winds exactly analogous to the contrariety between the East- and West-winds. As Bartholomaeus had explained in geographical terms, Boreas was cold and dry because it "riseth out of watrie places, that bee froze and bounde, because they bee so farre from the circle of the Sunne";[144] and since no source of moisture could exist in a region frozen solid, the wind was formed from almost pure exhalation with a negligible quantity of moist vapor. Boreas was therefore an exceedingly dry wind and naturally tended to disperse clouds and other vapor formations.[145] Being cold and dry, Boreas resembled most closely the Element of Earth and its corollary humor, melancholy. It was also associated with the cold, dry period of autumn. Boreas' converse—Auster, Affricus, or Notus—was hot and moist, "for that he commeth toward the South, wher is more plenty of waters, & places full of vapours & of dew."[146] Because of its heat and dampness, Auster was identified with Air, a sanguine temperament, and spring. In such manner the exact counter-natures of East- and West-winds, and of North- and South-winds, were neatly fitted into the orderly macrocosm.

Bartholomaeus had emphasized the ability of the North-winds to disperse vapor phenomena and the tendency of the South-winds to bring in moist meteors:

> The North winde. . .purgeth and cleanseth raine, and driveth away clowdes and mistes, and bringeth in cleerenesse and faire wether: and againward, for the South winde is hot & moyst, it doth the contrary deedes: for it maketh the aire thicke and troubly, & breedeth darknesse.[147]

These meteorological effects of the North- and South-winds naturally had physiological results in man. Godfridus in his *Knowledge of Things Unknowne* declared that Boreas "conserveth health," whereas Auster "ingendreth pestilence and much sicknes."[148] Bartholomaeus had attributed to the South-wind the specific sicknesses of "the

[143] *Five Hundreth Pointes of Good Husbandrie* (1597), p. 26.
[144] *De proprietatibus rerum*, fol. 159ᵛ.
[145] Cf. Proverbs 25:23: "The North wind driveth away rain."
[146] *De proprietatibus rerum*, fol. 159ᵛ.
[147] *Ibid.*, fol. 158ᵛ.
[148] P. 92.

gout, the falling evill, itch, and the ague"; but also he had noted that "the Southerne winde hath many noble propertyes, for it is softe wind. . . .And giveth us raine & dew, & openeth pores of the earth, & bringeth forth hearbes, and grasse, and seeds."[149]

In creative literature, as in classical thought, the winds retained their distinctive characters. Boreas was "bitter bleake" (Spenser, *F. Q.*, I.ii.33.7), "blustering" (Spenser, "Feb.," 226), "wrathfull" (*F. Q.*, V.xi.58.7), even "tyrannous" (Shakespeare, *Cymbeline*, I.iii.36). Zephyrus was "gentle" (*Cymbeline*, IV.ii.172) and "sweet" (*F. Q.*, II.xii.33.5). Affricus and Notus from the south were "foggy" (Shakespeare, *A.Y.L.I.*, III.v.50), "dew-dropping" (*Romeo*, I.iv. 103), "brackish" (Marlowe, *Dido*, 276), and "fennie" (Chapman, *Hero*, VI.40). In literature the East-winds were encountered less frequently than the others; but when they appeared—as did Vulturnus in Jonson's *Masque of Beautie* (lines 111 ff.) and Eurus in Chapman's *Hero and Leander* (VI.35 ff.)—their association with the Sun and the resultant heat and dryness were stressed.

La Primaudaye piously saw the various winds as essential agents in God's universal plan. Winds representing every possible combination of the four Elemental qualities—hot, cold, moist, and dry—were necessary to accomplish the Divinely ordained succession of atmospheric changes:

> . . .some [winds] to gather the cloudes together, and to bring raine and snow, or haile and tempests, by meanes of the same cloudes, according as pleaseth the Creator to dispose them: other winds on the contrarie do disperse them and make the aire cleere and pleasant, bringing faire weather.[150]

Fulke was another to marvel at "the wonderfull wysdome of the eternall God" in creating the winds—not only because they altered the weather, but because they kept in motion the Air, "which were it not continually styrred. . .would soone putrefie, and. . .would be a deadly infection to all that hath breath upon the earth."[151] In Chapman's *Gentleman Usher*, Poggio expresses this notion in his encomium of brooms:

> The wind, that sweeps foul clouds out of the air,

[149] *De proprietatibus rerum*, fol. 159ᵛ.
[150] *French Academie*, pp. 217-218.
[151] *Goodly Gallery*, fol. 19.

And for you ladies makes the welkin fair,
Is but a broom.
(II.i.238-240)

The winds had been atmospheric brooms since the time of Creation. As Palingenius reported:

For when that God had deckt the world, with Starres in trym aray,
What drosse remaynde he had the winds, to clense and sweepe away.[152]

Sir John Davies also asserted that "the *winds* and *thunders* cleanse the ayre" (*Nosce Teipsum*, "Of Humane Knowledge," p. 23).

A tradition originating with the earlier Greek philosophers had established a specific relationship between wind, Elemental Air, and human breath.[153] Greek ἄνεμος was Latin *animus* and *anima.*[154] Pliny had defined "Spirit, which the Greekes and our countrimen by one name called Aire: Vitall this element is, and as it giveth life to all things, so it soone passeth through all, and is intermedled in the whole."[155] Elsewhere he had speculated whether "wind bee that spirit of Nature that engendreth all things, wandering to and fro as it were in some wombe."[156] Both Epicurus and Lucretius had identified the human soul with wind and heat particles which suffused the entire body.[157] Sir John Davies in *Nosce Teipsum* took issue with this concept and rebuffed the "light and vicious persons" who say:

Our *Soule* is but a smoake, or ayrie blast;
Which, during life, doth in our nostrils play,
And when we die, doth turne to wind at last.
("Of the Soule of Man," p. 82)

Kyd in *The Spanish Tragedie* expressed the idea more poetically: "By force of windie sighes thy spirit breathes" (III.xiii.166). Donne, holding the Platonic notion that lovers blend into unity, playfully admonishes his wife against lamenting his temporary departure: "When thou sigh'st, thou sigh'st not winde, / But sigh'st my soule away" ("Song" [pp. 18 f.], 25-26).

[152] *Zodiake of Life*, p. 112.
[153] Anaximenes seems to have been the first to formulate the theory that the world "breathes," and that Air is the *spiritus mundi.*
[154] See Buck, *Dictionary of Synonyms*, 1.72.2, 4.51.1, and 16.11.2.
[155] *Historie of World*, p. 2 [II.iv].
[156] *Ibid.*, p. 21 [II.xlv].
[157] Epicurus, "To Herodotus," I.63; and Lucretius, *De rerum natura*, III.117 ff.

All winds were thought to possess some few qualities in common. Bartholomaeus had noted that "winde is movable, and not resting."[158] This constant motion was considered an indication of wind's complete freedom from constraint: "as swift as wind" (Spenser, *F. Q.*, IV.vii.18.7) and "free as is the wind" (Shakespeare, *Coriolanus*, I.ix.89) had both become axiomatic. From freedom to inconstancy was a further development of this notion—wind was "unstable" (*F. Q.*, II.vi.23.5), "wavering" (*F. Q.*, IV.ii.5.2), "wanton" (Shakespeare, *M.N.D.*, II.i.129), "bawdy" (*Othello*, IV.ii.78), a "strumpet" (*Merchant of Venice*, II.vi.16).[159]

The invisibility of winds was often commented upon. Shakespeare spoke of the "viewless winds" (*M. for M.*, III.i.124), and Chapman observed that the wind was "not seene, but heard" (*Teares of Peace*, 503). The ideas that breath was wind and that wind was inconstant and invisible all coalesced to form the cynical commonplace that "words are but wind"[160] (*Comedy of Errors*, III.i.75).

Popular beliefs about winds were numerous. Two of them were recorded by Bartholomaeus: (1) "when the winde findeth resisting and let, then he sheweth his might the stronger"; and (2) "in the eares winde maketh whistling, whorling, and ringing. And so winde letteth and infecteth the spirite & wit of hearing."[161] La Primaudaye referred to others: "when one opposite wind ceaseth and is laid, his contrarie riseth"; and "at his [the sun's] rising & setting they [the winds] are commonly greatest."[162]

To winds was frequently ascribed the function of gathering together rain clouds: "For raging wind blows up incessant showers" (*3 Henry VI*, I.iv.145). Yet it was believed that "the raine doth maketh it [the wind] cease: whereupon this proverbe sprung up, that little raine allaieth much winde."[163] The meteorological sequence of

[158] *De proprietatibus rerum*, fol. 158.

[159] See Morris P. Tilley, *Elizabethan Proverb Lore in Lyly's Euphues and in Pettie's Petite Pallace* (New York, 1926), p. 335.

[160] Cf. Job 6:26: "Do ye imagine to reprove words. . .which are as wind?" See Tilley, *Elizabethan Proverb Lore*, p. 338; and B. J. Whiting, *Proverbs in the Earlier English Drama* (Harvard Univ. Press, 1938), pp. 8, 77, 87, 184, 194, 283.

[161] *De proprietatibus rerum*, fol. 158^{v}.

[162] *French Academie*, p. 236.

[163] *Ibid.* See also p. 54, above. Aristotle had explained why "wind as a rule occurs after rain in those places in which the rain has happened to fall, and when rain falls the wind drops" (*Meteorologica*, 360^{b}-361^{a}).

these two interrelated processes was preserved in Shakespeare's description of Collatine's emotions at Lucrece's suicide: the bereaved husband tormentedly mutters "Tarquin"; and "this windy tempest, till it blow up rain, / Held back his sorrow's tide, to make it more" (*Lucrece*, 1788-1789). Then, his store of tears having been increased by mutterings and sighs, "at last it rains, and busy winds give o'er" to tears alone (line 1790).

Visual representation of the winds on maps and charts usually pictured them as cherubs' heads puffing their cheeks and blowing though pursed lips.[164] Lear in his mind's eye sees them after this fashion when he commands, "Blow, winds, and crack your cheeks" (III.ii.1); and Shakespeare's Ajax similarly orders his trumpeter to "blow. . .till thy sphered bias cheek / Outswell the colic of puff'd Aquilon" (*Troilus*, IV.v.8-9).

In addition to the normal, general winds distinguished by the direction from which they blew, there were also fearful, prodigious winds. Such was the storm wind described by Pliny[165] and explained by Fulke as "a thycke *Exhalation* violently moved out of a cloude without inflammation or burning." Fulke observed that this storm wind "doth alwayes goe before a great soden showere, for when the cloude is broken, the water muste needes fall downe."[166]

Another freakish wind was the "whirlwind," sometimes formed alternatively to the storm wind. Following Aristotle,[167] Pliny had described the process of its generation:

> If the clift or breach [in the cloud] bee not great, so that the wind be constrained to turn round, to rol and whirle in his discent. . .it makes a whirlepuffe of ghust called *Typhon*.[168]

Or possibly, as Fulke suggested, "a whyrlewynde some tyme is caused by meanes of twoo contrary wyndes that meete together."[169] The whirlwind was commonly regarded with terror because of its ability to lift from the ground objects of considerable weight.

In some cases the exhalation forming the whirlwind became

[164] Note Figure 4.
[165] *Historie of World*, pp. 24-25 [II.xlix].
[166] *Goodly Gallery*, fol. 31-31^{v}. Cf. Aristotle, *Meteorologica*, 370^{b}.
[167] *Meteorologica*, 370^{b}-371^{a}. Cf. Plutarch, *Opin. of Phil.*, pp. 827-828 [III.iii].
[168] *Historie of World*, p. 24 [II.xlix]. On Typhon, see pp. 126 ff., below.
[169] *Goodly Gallery*, fol. 32^{v}.

sufficiently hot to catch fire. This flaming catastrophe, which often appeared as a pillar of flame, was called "prester."[170]

Pliny had discussed the menace of whirlwinds to sailors and had prescribed as a safeguard "the casting of vinegre out against it as it commeth." In his list of dangers to mariners Pliny had also mentioned the waterspout (or "hurricano"), "that cloud which draweth water to it, as it were into a long pipe."[171] Troilus underlines the ferocity of this phenomenon when he refers to "the dreadful spout / Which shipmen do the hurricano call, / Constringed in mass by the almighty sun" (V.ii.171-173).

Often the storm at sea was considered to be a sort of windy meteor. As Bartholomaeus had stated:

By his subtilnesse and violence, winde perceth and commeth into the inner partes of the sea, and reareth up great tempests and great waves in the sea, and stretcheth them, and maketh them spred into contrary countries and parts.[172]

Shakespeare depicted the rage of "the sea puff'd up with winds" (*Shrew,* I.ii.202). Because the wind was thought actually to enter the sea, many sea storms in literature stressed the resultant confusion of the Elements, literally chaos. When Red Crosse wounds the dragon terrorizing Una's parents, the monster roars like a storm:

He cryde, as raging seas are wont to rore,
When wintry storme his wrathfull wreck does threat,
The rolling billowes beat the ragged shore,
As they the earth would shoulder from her seat,
And greedie gulfe does gape, as he would eat
His neighbour element in his revenge:
Then gin the blustring brethren boldly threat,
To move the world from off his stedfast henge,
And boystrous battell make, each other to avenge.[173]
(*F. Q.,* I.xi.21.1-9)

Air and Water, being "the two moist elements" (Shakespeare, *Troilus,* I.iii.41), could most easily commingle. So also when the four winds battled for supremacy while Leander attempted to swim the Hellespont, "the seas mixt with the skie" (Chapman, *Hero,* VI.182).

[170] Pliny, *Historie of World,* p. 25 [II.l]. See also Aristotle, *Meteorologica,* 317ª; and Vergil, *Aeneid,* XII.672 ff.

[171] *Historie of World,* p. 25 [II.l]. Cf. Lucretius, *De rerum natura,* VI.426 ff.

[172] *De proprietatibus rerum,* fol. 158ᵛ.

[173] Cf. *F. Q.,* IV.ix.23.5-9, quoted p. 124, below.

As a purely philological point concerning winds, the term "flaw" should be noted. It meant "a sudden burst or squall of wind" or "a fall of rain or snow accompanied by gusty winds."[174] Shakespeare employed the term frequently: for example, in the first sense, he spoke of "gusts and foul flaws" (*Venus*, 456), and in the second, of "flaws congealed" (*2 Henry IV*, IV.iv.35). Spenser used "flaw" to describe Radigund's tempestuous charge against Artegall in the lists (*F. Q.*, V.v.6.7).

The winds had received considerable attention in classical mythology. They were said to be the sons of Aurora and Astraeus, the Titan. After Zeus' escapade with Io and the birth of their son Epaphus, Juno out of jealousy incited the Winds against Zeus. For punishment he imprisoned them in a cave, with Aeolus as their warden.[175]

Aeolus was traditionally cited as king of the Winds,[176] whom he kept locked behind brass doors.[177] The visits to Aeolia which Odysseus and Juno had made in the *Odyssey* and the *Aeneid*, respectively, were well known, and these narratives had established both Aeolus' personality and his duties.[178] As a result of his kindness in assisting Odysseus against sea storms, he was favorably regarded, particularly by sailors. They credited him with introducing the use of sails, and also with explaining portents of impending storms.[179] John Maplet in his *Diall of Destiny* offered this thumbnail biography of Aeolus:

Another son of *Jupiter* was *Aeolus*, which raygned in *Sicilia*, and was lord over the Ilands called *Aeoliae*:[180] this *Aeolus* is called the God of Winds, which is also said to have first taught & instructed the maryners & sea-

[174] *NED*, "flaw," senses 1*a* and 1*b*, respectively.

[175] Cf. Hesiod, *Theogony*, 378-380; Boccaccio, *Genealogiae*, fol. 36 [IV.liv]; Lilio Gregorio Giraldi, *De deis gentium libri* (Lyons, 1565), pp. 164-165; and Graves, *Greek Myths*, 43.h-43.5.

[176] An ancestor of this Aeolus, also named Aeolus, was the father of seven sons, the most famous of whom were Sisyphus and Salmoneus; cf. Apollodorus, *Library*, I.vii.3, and Hyginus, *Fabulae*, pp. 126-127. For the story of Salmoneus, see p. 85, n. 43, above.

[177] Cf. Vergil, *Aeneid*, I.50 ff.; Marlowe, *Dido*, 62; Shakespeare, *2 Henry VI*, III.ii.88-89, *Pericles*, III.i.2-3; and Chapman, *Eugenia*, 128.

[178] Cf. Ovid, *Metamorphoses*, XIV.223-232; Natalis Comes, *Mythologiae*, VIII.x.

[179] See Diodorus Siculus, *Library*, V.vii.7; Graves, *Greek Myths*, 43.5.

[180] The volcanic islets between Sicily and the Italian mainland now known as the Liparis; see Pliny, *Historie of World*, pp. 62-63 [III.ix].

faringe men to knowe and understand the signes & tokens of tempests ensuing, as also the disposition & nature of the winds.[181]

Aeolus was a favorite mythological character in literature, invariably appearing as controller of the Winds. Such is his role, for example, in the Wedding Masque ending Act I of Beaumont and Fletcher's *The Maids Tragedie.*

The Winds themselves had been invested with well-developed personalities and definite physical characteristics.[182] Boreas, the North-wind, was especially active. He was usually described as strong in body and harsh in disposition—as Shakespeare said, "the ruffian Boreas" (*Troilus,* I.iii.38). Because of his identification with the primeval serpent-god Ophion[183] and the Python slain by Apollo,[184] Boreas was normally portrayed with serpents' tails for his lower limbs—hence the epithet "snake-foote *Boreas*" (Chapman, *Hero,* VI.46). In Jonson's *Masque of Beautie* Boreas enters

In a robe of russet and white mixt, full, and bagg'd; his haire and beard rough, and horride; his wings gray, and full of snow, and ycicles: his mantle borne from him with wyres, and in severall puffes; his feet ending in Serpents tayles; and in his hand a leave-lesse branch, laden with ycicles.[185]

(lines 13-18)

In personality the West-wind, Favonius or Zephyrus, was the opposite of Boreas: gentle, warm, almost effeminate. Always he either scattered flowers or wore them as a fillet. In Campion's *Masque at the Marriage of the Lord Hayes* he is attired

. . .in a white loose robe of sky coloured taffatie, with a mantle of white silke, prop't with wyre, stil waving behind him as he moved; on his head hee wore a wreath of Palme deckt with Primmeroses and Violets, the hayre of his head and beard were flaxen, and his buskins white, and painted with flowers.

(64.5-9)

The East-wind, Vulturnus or Eurus, was of similar nature to Zephyrus, with the notable exceptions of being less fertile (because of his

[181] Fol. 53.
[182] Note Figure 5.
[183] Graves, *Greek Myths,* 1.a, 2; 48.1.
[184] *Ibid.,* 36.1.
[185] See Cartari, *Imagines deorum,* p. 177; and Gilbert, *Symbolic Persons,* pp. 59-61.

dryness) and having a dark complexion (because of his origin in Ethiopia). He was usually crowned with a bright shining Sun, since both he and the Sun rose in the East. For the *Masque of Beautie* Jonson clothed him

. . .in a blue-coloured robe and mantle, pufft as the former [Boreas], but somewhat sweeter; his face blacke, and on his head a red *Sunne*, shewing he came from the *East*: his wings of severall colours; his buskins white, and wrought with gold.[186]

(lines 111-115)

The South-wind, Notus or Affricus or Auster, possessed all the characteristics associated with excessive moisture, and normally he flew wrapped in clouds. When he appeared in Ovid's *Metamorphoses* (as translated by Golding):

His beard hung full of hideous stormes, all dankish was his head,
With water streaming downe his haire that on his shoulders shead.
His ugly forehead wrinkled was with foggie mistes full thicke,
And on his fethers and his breast a stilling dew did sticke.[187]

Boreas and Notus were depicted as old and bearded, while Zephyrus and Vulturnus were much younger men. All four were winged. By nature they were contentious among themselves; and following Homer (*Odyssey,* X.1 ff.) and Vergil (*Aeneid,* I.50 ff.), most Renaissance writers pictured them as eager for a scrap. In *The Faerie Queene* four knights (Druon, Claribell, Blandamour, and Paridell) battle as the Winds:

[186] See Cartari, *Imagines deorum,* p. 177; and Gilbert, *Symbolic Persons,* pp. 254-255.

[187] Fol. 5 [I.264 ff.]. This passage was also translated in Bartholomaeus, *De proprietatibus rerum,* fol. 167^{v}.

Figure 5. Notus (upper left), bearded, with dank hair, wrapped in clouds;
Boreas (upper right), bearded and snake-footed, carrying off Orithyia among leafless trees;
Zephyrus (lower left), crowned with flowers, caressing Flora in a field of flowers;
Vulturnus (lower right), surmounted by a shining Sun, with Aethiopian facial features and hair.

Vincenzo Cartari, *Le imagini de i dei degli antichi* (Venice, 1571), p. 263.

...breaking forth with rude unruliment,
From all foure parts of heaven [the Winds] doe rage full sore,
And tosse the deepes, and teare the firmament,
And all the world confound with wide uprore,
As if in stead thereof they *Chaos* would restore.
(IV.ix.23.5-9)

In Chapman's *Hero and Leander* all four Winds "pretended to the windie monarchie" when Leander swam to Hero (VI.181), and the resultant storm at sea ended with the lovers' drowning.

Classical mythology included several legends involving these personifications of the winds. One story told of Boreas' love for the boy Hyacinthus, who was also sought by Apollo. In fact, Hyacinthus preferred Apollo to the Wind-god. So one day while Apollo and Hyacinthus were playing games, Boreas in a fit of jealousy killed the boy by blowing a discus against his head.[188] When Apollo's tears hit the ground after the death of Hyacinthus, they turned into the well-known flower.[189]

Another legend which showed Boreas' ill nature recounted his courtship of the nymph Orithyia.[190] Unsuccessful in playing the gentle lover, he finally resorted to brute strength and carried her off. Jonson gave a précis of the fable in a gloss on his *Masque of Beautie*: Orithyia, he pedantically informed the reader, was "the daughter of *Erectheus*, King of *Athens*, whome *Boreas* ravish'd away, into *Thrace*, as she was playing with other virgins by the floud *Ilissus*: or (as some will) by the fountaine *Cephisus*" (line 101). Donne's "Elegy XVI" contains a reference to this myth: not even her great beauty, he tells his mistress, could "tame wilde Boreas harshnesse"—Boreas who "in peeces shivered / Faire Orithea, whom he swore he lov'd" (lines 21-23). Orithyia must also be the unnamed "ravisht love" of Boreas mentioned by Chapman in *Hero and Leander* (VI.47), and later Boreas' "Atthaeas" (derived from "Attic") in the same poem (VI.191).

After this rape by Boreas, Orithyia bore two daughters, Cleopatra

[188] Cf. Servius, *Commentarii* (gloss on *Eclogue* iii.63), Vol. II, p. 116; Boccaccio, *Genealogiae*, fol. 37 [IV.lviii]. In some accounts the jealous Wind-god is Zephyrus rather than Boreas; cf. Philostratus, *Imagines*, I.xxiv, and Lucian, *Dialogues of Gods*, xiv.

[189] Cf. Ovid, *Metamorphoses*, X.162 ff.; see also Spenser, *F. Q.*, III.vi.45.3.

[190] Cf. Plato, *Phaedrus*, 229B-C; Apollodorus, *Library*, III.xv.1-2; Ovid, *Metamorphoses*, VI.682 ff.; and Natalis Comes, *Mythologiae*, VIII.xi.

and Chione, and twin sons, Calais and Zetes. The sons, called the Boreadae after their father, figured prominently among the Argonauts, especially in the episode of Phineus and the Harpies.[191] Phineus, a soothsayer blinded because he revealed the secrets of the gods, was tormented by Harpies, who snatched away his food whenever he prepared to eat. Calais and Zetes chased the Harpies from Phineus' house and would have killed them, had not a divine voice intervened. Thomas Watson adapted this story for a strained conceit in the Italianate mode:

> The *Harpye* birdes, that did in such despight
> Greive and annoy old *Phineus* so sore,
> Where chas'd away by *Calais* in flight
> And by his brother *Zeth* for evermore;
> Who follow'd them, untill they hard on hye
> A voyce, that said, *Ye Twinnes no further fly.*
> *Phineus* I am, that so tormented was;
> My *Laura* here I may an *Harpye* name;
> My thoughtes and lustes bee sonnes to *Boreas,*
> Which never ceast in following my *Dame,*
> Till heav'nly *Grace* said unto me at last,
> Leave fond *Delightes,* and say thy love is past.[192]

In a head-piece to this poem, Watson somewhat officiously cited his sources: "the *Argonauticks* of Apollonius, and Valerius Flaccus."

Like Boreas, Zephyrus had also chosen a wife; but in his marriage to Flora (or Chloris), Zephyrus was considered the prototype of the tender husband.[193] "E. K." related their story in his gloss on the "April" eclogue: "Zephyrus the Westerne wind being in love with her, and coveting her to wyfe, gave her for a dowrie, the chiefedome and soveraigntye of al flowers and greene herbes, growing on earth" (line 122). Jonson used the fable, greatly prettified, as the basis for the masque *Chloridia.* Echoes of this happily consummated love are heard in Jonson's *Entertainment at Highgate,* where reference is made to "that gentle winde, *Favonius,* whose subtile spirit, in the breathing forth, *Flora* makes into flowers" (lines 70-72). Else-

[191] Cf. Apollonius Rhodius, *Argonautica,* I.211-223, II.178-300; Apollodorus, *Library,* I.ix.21; Valerius Flaccus, *Argonautica,* I.468-469, IV.424-528; Hyginus, *Fabulae,* p. 10 [xix]; and Boccaccio, *Genealogiae,* fol. 37-37^{v} [IV.lix].

[192] *Poems,* p. 133.

[193] Cf. Ovid, *Fasti,* V.201 ff.; Boccaccio, *Genealogiae,* fol. 37^{v} [IV.lxi]; and Cartari, *Imagines deorum,* pp. 178-179.

where Zephryus is more simply identified as "the Father of the flowers" (Jonson, *Fortunate Isles*, 467), and as the wind "that doth in flowres rejoyce" (Chapman, *Hero*, VI.45).

The Ancients had told fearsome tales about Typhon (usually confused with Typhoeus[194]), a spiteful monster begotten by Tartarus upon Earth.[195] He in turn was the father of "boisterous winds which blow damply" (Hesiod, *Theogony*, 869)—that is, of storm winds, especially those over the ocean. Hesiod had specifically stated, however, that he was not related to the "god-sent" winds, such as Notus, Boreas, and Zephyrus. By Echidna, Typhon sired a legion of monstrous malefactors that included the hounds Orthus and Cerberus, the Lernaean Hydra, and the Chimaera (*Theogony*, 306 ff.). Valerius Flaccus charged him with fathering also the Harpies.[196] Hyginus had augmented the list of Typhon and Echidna's offspring by adding the Gorgon, Scylla, the Sphinx, and the dragons guarding the Golden Fleece and the golden apples of the Hesperides.[197]

Typhon, re-enacting the capital crime of the Titans and Giants, challenged the sovereignty of Zeus, who after a pitched and precarious battle finally overcame him with a thunderbolt (*Theogony*, 836 ff.). As punishment, Zeus buried him in Tartarus beneath Mt. Aetna,[198] so that he was often grouped with Vulcan and the Cyclopes. Later classical poets had related how Typhon at one time chased the Olympian gods into Egypt, where to escape his fury they transformed themselves into animals;[199] and Plutarch had identified Typhon as the embodiment of anticultural forces that ended the utopian reign of Isis and Osiris in Egypt.[200]

Typhon was generally depicted as a demi-reptilian giant breathing fire. He was blamed for hurricanes and cyclones[201]—in fact,

[194] See William Smith, ed., *Dictionary of Greek and Roman Biography and Mythology* (3 vols.; London, 1844-1849), III."Typhon." Typhon is also an analogue to Vergil's Enceladus; see *Aeneid*, III.578 ff.

[195] See Hesiod, *Theogony*, 820 ff.; Apollodorus, *Library*, I.vi.3; Hyginus, *Fabulae*, p. 263; Boccaccio, *Genealogiae*, fol. 33 [IV.xxii]; and Natalis Comes, *Mythologiae*, VI.xxii.

[196] *Argonautica*, IV.428.

[197] *Fabulae*, pp. 2 [prologue] and 35 [cli].

[198] Cf. Vergil, *Georgics*, I.277 ff.; Boccaccio, *loc. cit.*

[199] Cf. Ovid, *Metamorphoses*, V.321-331; Apollodorus, *loc. cit.*

[200] *Of Isis and Osiris* (in *The Morals*, trans. Holland), pp. 1286 ff.; cf. Natalis Comes, *loc. cit.*

[201] Plutarch and Pliny had made the specific identification; see *Opin. of Phil.*, p. 828 [III.iii], and *Historie of World*, p. 24 [II.xlix] (quoted p. 118, above).

the spelling of "typhoon," although the word was originally a borrowing from Oriental languages, has apparently been influenced by "Typhon."[202] And he was often cited as the cause of earthquakes and volcanoes.[203] Actually, much of his legendary history is merely etiological mythology to explain Mt. Aetna and the frequent earthquakes of the region around it.

Renaissance literature is liberally sprinkled with allusions to "roaring Typhon" (Shakespeare, *Troilus,* I.iii.160). Abraham Fraunce in *The Third Part of the Countesse of Pembrokes Ivychurch* gave this summary of the rich tradition surrounding him:

> By *Typhoeus, Sabinus*[204] understandeth the burning and flaming exhalations, cause of that fire in *Aetna*: which clustred together, and wanting free passage, shake the earth, τύφωμαι is, to smoke. See *Virgil* .3. [578 ff.] *Aeneid*[205] and *Ovid* .5.[346 ff.] *Metam.* It seemeth, that the violent fury of the windes is here also shadoed by *Typhoeus*: for his hands reach from East to West, and his head to heaven, agreeing with the nature of the severall windes blowing in every coast of heaven. His body is covered with feathers, noting the swiftnes of the windes: about his legs are crawling adders, so the windes are oftentimes pestilent and hurtfull, his eyes are red as fire, and he breathes flames out of his mouth; for the windes are made of hoate and dry vapors.[206]

Spenser was thoroughly familiar with the legends about Typhon. He made direct references to Typhon's descent from Earth (*F. Q.*, III.vii.47.8), to his uprising against the gods (III.vii.47.3-6, VII. vi. 15.6-8), to his punishment (VII.vi.29.6), and to his ability to shake the world with "tempestuous rage" (VI.vi.11.8-9). Spenser recalled that the "two headed dogge" Orthus was "begotten by great *Typhaon,* / And foule *Echidna*" (V.x.10.6-8); and he made this despicable couple the parents also of the Blatant Beast (VI.vi.11.1-9, 12.1-2). Through incest with his mother, Earth, Typhon became the

[202] See *NED,* "Typhon" and "typhoon."

[203] Cf. Ovid, *Metamorphoses,* V.346 ff.; Boccaccio, *loc. cit.*

[204] Sabinus was the assumed name of George Schüler (1508-1560), a German dilettante whose interpretation of Ovid was first published as Wittenberg in 1555. Fraunce is referring to Sabinus' gloss on *Metamorphoses,* V.346 ff., where he also notes; "Poëtæ fingunt Gigantem Typhoëa reluctantem & conantem dimovere montes, esse causam terræmotus" (*Fabularum Ovidii interpretatio. . .Georgio Sabino* [Cambridge, 1584], p. 194).

[205] In this passage Vergil relates the story of Enceladus; but Fraunce assumes that Typhon and Enceladus were identical.

[206] Fol. 22. After the references to Vergil and Ovid, the remainder of this passage was cribbed from Natalis Comes, *Mythologiae,* VI.xxii.

father of the still more despicable twins, Ollyphant and Argante (III.vii.47.6-9, 48.1-4). Generally speaking, Typhon was the prototype of the monstrous evil-doer, and the prolific sire of malevolent progeny.

6. EARTHQUAKES

Although today a discussion of earthquakes belongs to the science of seismology rather than meteorology, in the Renaissance they were considered meteors because of their direct relation with wind. It was generally agreed that earthquakes were the natural results of vapors and exhalations compressed within subterranean caverns. As they struggled for escape, these evaporations disturbed the earth's surface.

Arthur Golding in *A Discourse upon the Earthquake* provided a technical explanation of the phenomenon:

> Earthquakes are sayde to be gendred by winds gotten into the bowels of the earth, or by vapors bredde and enclosed within the hollowe caves of the earth, where by their stryving and struggling of themselves to get oute, or being [ex-]haled outwards by the heat and operation of the Sun, they shake the earth for want of sufficient vent to issue out at.[207]

Pliny had suggested that the struggle between earth and exhalation resulting in earthquakes was analogous to the struggle of cloud and exhalation resulting in lightning. The fissures in the earth caused by the earthquake were comparable to "the clift whereout the lightening breaketh, when the spirit enclosed within struggleth and stirreth to goe forth at libertie."[208] Not the least terror invoked by earthquakes was the possibility that stagnant infectious airs, imprisoned in subterranean caves, might be released by this rending

[207] *B1*^{v}. Cf. Aristotle, *Meteorologica*, 365^{b}-366^{a}; and Seneca, *Naturall Questions*, pp. 876-877 [VI.xxiv-xxv].

[208] *Historie of World*, p. 37 [II.lxxxi]. This comparison between lightning and earthquakes may also be found in Spenser, *F. Q.*, I.viii.8 and 9; and Dekker, *Strange Horse-Race*, p. 346.

of the earth's surface. Then pestilence would almost certainly follow.[209]

In *1 Henry IV* Hotspur wishes to present a reasonable explanation of earthquakes to refute Glendower's superstitious declaration that at his birth various meteors, including fiery impressions and earthquakes, proclaimed his greatness. To counter Glendower's vaunts, Hotspur retorts that regardless of Glendower's birth the same phenomena would have appeared:

> Diseased nature oftentimes breaks forth
> In strange eruptions; oft the teeming earth
> Is with a kind of colic pinch'd and vex'd
> By the imprisoning of unruly wind
> Within her womb; which, for enlargement striving,
> Shakes the old beldam earth and topples down
> Steeples and moss-grown towers. At your birth
> Our grandam earth, having this distemperature,
> In passion shook.
>
> (III.i.27-35)

Shakespeare not only put into Hotspur's mouth the accepted explanation of earthquakes, but in this passage he reflected most of the beliefs about earthquakes prevalent in the Renaissance.

First, the dramatic context of the passage demonstrates the popular view that earthquakes were omens connected with the supernatural and Divine. In this instance Glendower interprets the earthquake at his nativity as indication of his superiority to ordinary men (III.i.41 ff.) and of his innate proficiency in the occult arts (III.i.47 ff.). But generally earthquakes were considered as portents predicting widespread miseries similar to those presaged by comets. Thomas Hill in *The Contemplation of Mysteries* gravely stated that the signification of earthquakes was "verie sad & heavie. . .as of battels, land-floodes, mutation of emperies, the dearth of victuals, &c."[210] In this vein Lennox, recounting the disorders of the night during which Macbeth murdered the King, reports several evil omens: destructive winds, pitiable sounds in the air, hootings of an owl—and to climax his list of awful signs, he fearfully concludes, "Some say the earth / Was feverous and did shake" (II.iii.65-66). This association of the earthquake with impending evil derived from the idea

[209] See Seneca, *Naturall Questions*, p. 879 [VI.xxviii].
[210] Fol. 72^{v}.

that the anomaly reflected a disruption in the ordered plan of Nature. As Hotspur so aptly phrases the attitude, it was a "distemperature" of "our grandam earth."

When the earth was considered a living organism, as (following Plato) was common in the Renaissance, an earthquake was expressed in terms of "a conflict and force of some sore windes pent up and. . . denied of their free course within the entrailes or body of the earth."[211] To complete the analogy, earthquakes became "fevers and maladies of the earth"[212]—or as Hotspur suggests, "a kind of colic." Much of this meaning is explicit also in his use of "distemperature," which specifically denotes bodily derangement. Donne made interesting use of this analogy in *An Anatomie of the World*: he stated that the world, distressed at Elizabeth Drury's death, in a "great earthquake languished" (line 11); and continuing in terms of bodily sickness, he later referred to "this great consumption [which] to a fever turn'd, / And so the world had fits" (lines 19-20).

The conception of the earthquake as a derangement of earth's body was easily correlated with the prevalent belief that violent emotion was a similar derangement of the human body. Hotspur refers to this correlation when he states that the earth, suffering the earthquake, "in passion shook," where "passion" is given its precise meaning as the emotion accompanying pain. Hotspur thus inverts the analogy, and maintaining a consistency with the remainder of the passage, attributes to earth a human reaction. More frequently, however, the correlation was used in the direction opposite to that employed by Hotspur, so that the earthquake became the basis of similes to express intense human feelings of various sorts. For example, Tamyra sees the development of her uncontrollable infatuation with Bussy d'Ambois as a relentless earthquake, and she describes it in the purest technical language:

> . . .as when a fume,
> Hot, dry, and gross, within the womb of earth
> Or in her superficies begot,
> When extreme cold hath struck it to her heart,
> The more it is compress'd, the more it rageth;
> Exceeds his prison's strength that should contain it,
> And then it tosseth temples in the air,

[211] Maplet, *Diall of Destiny*, fol. 70. Cf. Aristotle, *Meteorologica*, 366b.
[212] La Primaudaye, *French Academie*, p. 258.

All bars made engines to his insolent fury;
So, of a sudden, my licentious fancy
Riots within me.

(*Bussy d'Ambois*, II.ii.34-43)[213]

Chapman, writing in a flamboyant manner, wished to show the inexorable fury of the *grand amour* between his hero and heroine. At the other end of the scale, the earthquake:love simile was used by Spenser: when Britomart is softly suffering the pangs of love-sickness, her nurse perceives her breast "to pant and quake, / As it an earthquake were" (*F. Q.*, III.ii.42.8-9).

The earthquake was employed to convey many emotions besides love. When Shakespeare's Venus sees the wounded Adonis, she displays mixed feelings of woe, horror, and wilful disbelief:

...[she] quakes;
As when the wind, imprison'd in the ground,
Struggling for passage, earth's foundation shakes,
Which with cold terror doth men's minds confound.

(lines 1045-1048)

In *The UnfortunateTraveller* Jack Wilton for some time masquerades as his master, the Earl of Surrey; and when the real Earl unexpectedly enters the scene, Nashe depicts Wilton's surprise and fear as "a trembling earthquake or shaking feaver" (II.268). Probably the earthquake could be most graphically employed in the description of fury. When Paridell meets Britomart in single combat before Malbecco's gates:

He forth issew'd; like as a boistrous wind,
Which in th'earthes hollow caves hath long bin hid,
And shut up fast within her prisons blind,
Makes the huge element against her kind
To move, and tremble as it were agast,
Untill that it an issew forth may find;
Then forth it breakes, and with his furious blast
Confounds both land and seas, and skyes doth overcast.

(*F. Q.*, III.ix.15.2-9)

The blind rage of Paridell, his strength, and the violence of the ensuing encounter are all admirably expressed through this simile of subterranean winds.

[213] This passage, which appeared in the 1641 text but not in the 1607 quarto, is here quoted from *English Drama, 1580-1642*, ed. Brooke and Paradise, p. 336.

The violence and destructiveness of earthquakes were the characteristics constantly emphasized by Renaissance writers. Hotspur includes, contrary to his purpose of being rational rather than fearful, the irrelevant information that an earthquake "topples down / Steeples and moss-grown towers"; and Tamyra notes the rage of the explosion that "tosseth temples in the air." Mention of an earthquake invariably brought visions of tottering towers and crumbling cities.

Several kinds of earthquake were specified besides that which merely shook the earth. Fulke, and other authorities,[214] listed at least four distinct varieties:

> [1] . . .when the earth is shaken laterally, to one syde. . . .
> [2] . . .when the earth with great violence is lifted up. . .and by and by synketh downe agayne. . . .
> [3] . . .[when] a gapinge, rendyng, or cleaving. . .[appeareth in] the earth, when the earth synketh downe, and swalloweth up cities. . . .
> [4] . . .when greate mountaynes ar cast up out of the earth, or els when some part of the lande synketh downe, and in steade thereof aryse ryvers, lakes, or fyers, breakyng out with smoke and ashes [i.e., volcanoes].[215]

Probably but few fiction writers were consciously aware of these distinctions between the various sorts of earthquakes, but nonetheless an author usually differentiated between the quake that only trembled and one that gaped. And Shakespeare, at least, knew that "mountains may be removed with earthquakes" (*A.Y.L.I.*, III.ii.195-196).

Certain portents were believed to precede an earthquake, just as they supposedly warned the populace before other calamities. Arthur Golding, closely following an established tradition,[216] gave a complete list of the "signes and tokens" commonly thought to appear before the disaster:

> . . .a tempestuous working and raging of the sea, the wether being fair, temperate, and unwindie: calmnesse of the aire matched with great colde: dimnesse of the Sunne for certaine dayes afore: long and thinne

[214] Cf. La Primaudaye, *French Academie*, p. 256; and Hill, *Contemplation of Mysteries*, fol. 66-68. These descriptions of various sorts of earthquakes were based on Seneca, *Naturall Questions*, pp. 875-876 [VI.xxi-xxiii], and Pliny, *Historie of World*, pp. 37-39 [II.lxxxii, lxxxiv, and lxxxvii].

[215] *Goodly Gallery*, fol. 20-21.

[216] Cf. Aristotle, *Meteorologica*, 367ᵃ-368ᵃ; Pliny, *Historie of World*, p. 38 [II.lxxxiii]; Digges, *Prognostication of Right Good Effect*, Di; Fulke, *Goodly Gallery*, fol. 22-23ᵛ; Hill, *Contemplation of Mysteries*, fol. 74ᵛ-75ᵛ; and *Perpetuall and Naturall Prognostications*, B6ᵛ-B7.

strakes of cloudes appearing after the setting of the Sun, the weather being otherwise cleere: the troubledness of water even in the deepest welles, yeelding moreover an infected and stinking savour: and lastly, greate and terrible sounds in the earth, like the noise of gronings or thunderings, as wel afore as after the quaking.[217]

The wide variety of these signs suggests the large number of natural phenomena with which the earthquake was thought to be connected.

Writings of the period contain many references to the earthquake and solar eclipse at Calvary.[218] Christ's crucifixion made God's "owne Lieutenant Nature shrinke, / It made his footstoole crack, and the Sunne winke" (Donne, "Goodfriday, 1613," 19-20). There were also some few earthquakes which Elizabethans knew by firsthand experience or by eyewitness report:

12 March 1571	6:00 P. M.	Hereford[219]
26 February 1574	5-6:00 P. M.	York, Worcester, Bristol, Hereford, Gloucester
6 April 1580	6:00 P. M.	throughout England
1 May 1580	12:00 P. M.	County of Kent
24 December 1601		London[220]

In addition to these earthquakes in England, there were many others on the Continent during this period.

Classical mythology had associated earthquakes with various gods, including Typhon[221] and Hephaestus. In the *Odyssey* the usual epithet for Poseidon is ἐνοσίχθων, "the earthshaker."[222] Ovid, perhaps following a passage in Homer (*Iliad*, I.528-530) or Vergil (*Aeneid*, X.115), had related a fearful incident when Jupiter "terrificam capitis concussit terque quaterque / Caesariem; cum qua terram, mare, sidera movit" (*Metamorphoses*, I.179-180). And so

[217] *Discourse upon Earthquake*, Bii-Bii^v.

[218] See Matthew 27:45-51.

[219] William Camden, *Annales. . .regnante Elizabetha* (London: G. Stansby for S. Waterson, 1615), p. 195.

[220] From Robert Mallet, *Catalogue of Earthquakes from 1606 B. C. to 1755* (Report of the 22nd Meeting of the British Association for the Advancement of Science; London, 1853), p. 61. For writings in English about the earthquake of 6 April 1580, see pp. 24-26, above.

[221] See p. 127, above.

[222] See Cartari, *Imagines deorum*, p. 174.

a tradition grew that Jupiter caused earthquakes by shaking his hair. In Marlowe's *Dido*, Jupiter swears by "this earth threatning haire, / That shaken thrise, makes Natures buildings quake" (lines 10-11); and Nashe in *The Unfortunate Traveller* reports that "*Jupiter* is said with the shaking of his haire to make heaven & earth to quake" (II.217).

CHAPTER FOUR

PHENOMENA OF REFLECTION

IN addition to the meteors formed from vapors and exhalations, there was a third group of meteors which may be classified as phenomena of reflection. Members of this group were merely reflections of the Sun, Moon, or other stars from cloud formations; as Plutarch had noted, they "have no more but a bare apparence, without any reall subsistence."[1] Because the reflection could come from any one of several celestial bodies, and because the reflecting cloud could be of various shapes and in various positions relative to the celestial body, numerous sorts of reflection phenomena were distinguished.

1. MULTIPLE SUNS AND MULTIPLE MOONS

The most alarming phenomenon of reflection was the wondrous spectacle of two or possibly three suns seen simultaneously.[2] The similar occurrence of multiple moons was also believed to be within the realm of possibility. Following classical example, Thomas Hill called the meteor of double suns "Parelius";[3] and he explained that this phenom-

[1] *Opin. of Phil.*, p. 828 [III.v].

[2] Historical accounts of such phenomena in England were frequent. For an unusually complete report and a review of previous examples, see John Everard, *Somewhat: Written by Occasion of Three Sunnes Seene at Tregnie in Cornewall* (London: [for T. Walkeley], 1622).

[3] From Greek παρά, "beside," and ἥλιος, "Sun." Aristotle had used the term παρήλιοι (*Meteorologica*, 372[b]); cf. Aratus, *Phaenomena*, 881. For discussion of this term, see Seneca, *Naturall Questions*, p. 770 [I.xi].

enon was caused "when a clowde of the one side of the Sunne, shall be placed eyther of the East, or West, especially equall, and a like thicke, which as a Glasse receaveth and expresseth the ymage or fygure of the sunne."[4] Similarly Hill explained the anomaly of double moons, which he called "Paraselinai." If reflections came from two clouds, one each side of the Sun or Moon, then three of the celestial bodies seemed visible.

These explanations, which derived from Aristotle[5] and Pliny,[6] were also cited by William Fulke, who added a careful distinction between multiple suns and other phenomena of reflection. The reflecting cloud, Fulke stated, did not appear beneath the Sun, "for then it wolde make the circles called crownes or garlonds, it is not opposit to the sunn, for then wold it make the rainbow, but it is sayd to be on the side [of the Sun]."[7] Du Bartas' poetical explanation was equally technical and precise:

> . . .if the cloud side-long sit,
> And not beneath, or justly opposite
> To Sunne or Moone: then either of them formes
> With strong aspect double or treble formes
> Upon the same. The vulgar's then affright
> To see at once three Chariots of the Light,
> And in the welkin on Nights gloomie throne,
> To see at once more shining Moones then one.[8]

Du Bartas stressed the fear that this anomaly caused among the populace. Spenser considered the awe occasioned by double suns to be an effective comparison for the amazement of Marinell when he sees the false Florimell beside the true:

> As when two sunnes appeare in the azure skye,
> Mounted in *Phoebus* charet fierie bright,
> Both darting forth faire beames to each mans eye,
> And both adorn'd with lampes of flaming light,
> All that behold so strange prodigious sight,
> Not knowing natures worke, nor what to weene,
> Are rapt with wonder, and with rare affright.
> So stood Sir *Marinell*, when he had seene
> The semblant of this false by his faire beauties Queene.
> (*F. Q.*, V.iii.19.1-9)

[4] *Contemplation of Mysteries*, fol. 40^{v}.
[5] *Meteorologica*, 377^{a}-378^{a}.
[6] *Historie of World*, pp. 17-18 [II.xxxi].
[7] *Goodly Gallery*, fol. 41^{v}-42.
[8] *Devine Weekes*, p. 57.

More usually, multiple suns were interpreted as prophecies of political strife. As Fulke concluded from his reading of chronicles and wonder-books, "they have often tymes been noted to have portended the contention of Princes for kingdomes."[9]

In *3 Henry VI*, civil war is accompanied by the appearance of multiple suns. Edward and Richard, sons of the Duke of York, meet with their armies on a plain, and they discuss their father's valor and his fortunes in the current battle. Then to call attention to the general state of the sky, Richard describes the beauty of the approaching dawn:

> See how the morning opes her golden gates,
> And takes her farewell of the glorious sun!
> How well resembles it the prime of youth,
> Trimm'd like a younker prancing to his love!
> (II.i.21-24)

Edward interrupts with a startled "Dazzle mine eyes, or do I see three suns?";[10] and Richard follows with an amplified account of the meteor:

> Three glorious suns, each one a perfect sun;
> Not separated with the racking clouds,
> But sever'd in a pale clear-shining sky.
> See, see! they join, embrace, and seem to kiss,
> As if they vow'd some league inviolable:
> Now are they but one lamp, one light, one sun.
> In this the heaven figures some event.
> (II.i.26-32)

The princes first interpret this omen as favorable; but a messenger soon enters with news of the Duke of York's death (II.i.43), and the rest of the play deals with civil war.[11]

[9] *Goodly Gallery*, fol. 42^{v}.

[10] Multiple suns "are most often seen. . .about the rysing or going downe of the sunn, seldome at noone tyme. . .because the heat will soon dissolve them" (Fulke, *Goodly Gallery*, fol. 42). Cf. Aristotle, *Meteorologica*, 377^{b}.

[11] Holinshed had likewise recorded the appearance of "three sunnes. . .[which] suddenlie joined altogither in one" (*Chronicle*, III.660). As a gloss on the passage, cf.:

"There were three Sunnes seene at *Rome* [c. 41 B.C.] which by little and little did all grow into one bodie. It was answered by the Colledge of *Southsayers*, that it portended the uniting of the three parts of the world, (which then were only knowen) *Asia*, *Africke*, and *Europe* into one empire . . . .

"Notwithstanding, even at that time, there were some that on the other side did stiffely maintaine, that these *three Sunnes* could not presage any good unto the

The appearance of multiple moons could be used in a similar context, as Shakespeare showed in *King John.* When Hubert enters to report on his mission of murdering Prince Arthur, the rightful heir to the throne, he declares:

> . . .five moons were seen to-night;
> Four fixed, and the fifth did whirl about
> The other four in wondrous motion.
> . . .Old men and beldams in the streets
> Do prophesy upon it dangerously.
> (IV.ii.182-186)

In his desire to convince the King that the murder has been done, Hubert describes a wildly fantastic prodigy.[12] Significantly, the reported death of the lawful ruler is accompained by a report of multiple moons, and the remaining action of the play does recount "the contention of Princes for kingdomes."

2. SOLAR AND LUNAR HALOS

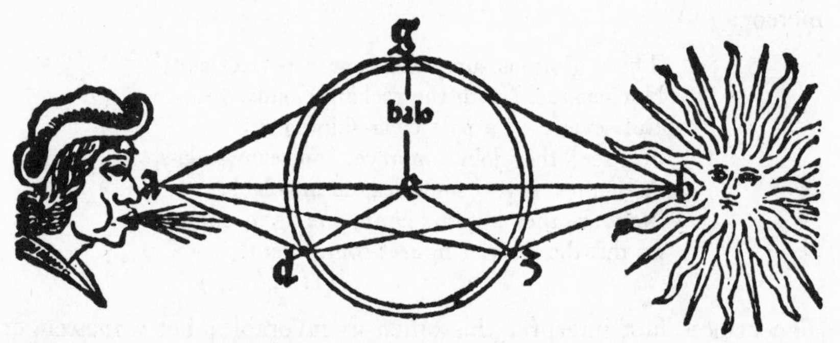

The formation of this meteor differed from the formation of multiple suns and moons only in the position of the reflecting—or in this case, the refracting—cloud. In the phenomenon of halos the cloud formation was directly beneath, rather than beside, the celestial body supplying the beams of light. William Fulke competently described and explained the meteor:

Romane Empire; but rather a division and distraction of that Imperiall power, as indeed it proved true; for the yeare following began the *Triumvirate* of *Lepidus, Caesar,* and *Antonie* [with the ensuing civil wars and murders]" (Everard, *Three Sunnes. . .in Cornewall,* pp. 7-8).

[12] Shakespeare found this prodigy of five moons in his source for *King John: The Troublesome Raigne of John, King of England, Part I* (xiii.130 ff.), reprinted in the Variorum *King John* (Philadelphia, 1919).

> The Circle called *Halon* is a garland of diverse collours that is seen about the Sunne, the Moone, or any other sterre. . . .
>
> The matter wherin it is made, is a cloude of equall thicknes, or thinnes, comming directly under the body of the Sunn, the Moone, or other sterres, into whiche the lyght of the heavenly body is receyved, and so appeareth rounde, because the sterre is rounde.[13]

Fulke also observed that "this circle is oftener seen about the Moone, then about the Sunne, because the heate of the Sunne draweth the *vapors* to hyghe, where it can not be made," owing to the dissipative effect of solar heat.

This meteor was commonly alluded to as a "crown" or a "garland," names literally translated from the Latin *corona*. In these terms Spenser flatteringly described the appearance of Cynthia at court in *Colin Clouts Come Home Againe*: first he likened her to "a crowne of lillies" (line 337), and shortly after to "faire *Phebes* garlond shining new, / In which all pure perfection one may see" (lines 342-343).

A variation of the solar halo occurred when the beams of the Sun shone through a refracting cloud of unequal density. Rays of the Sun seemed to pierce the cloud, and in Fulke's words to "slope downward, or divers collors."[14] Fulke continued by noting that "the common people cal it the descending of the holy ghost, or our Ladies *Assumption*, because these things are painted after suche a sort," and he recorded several other popular names for the meteor: "roddes, wandes, coardes of tents. . .staves and lytle pyllers." Spenser used this phenomenon as the basis for a simile to describe Britomart's hair, which when unbound falls to her heels:

> . . .like sunny beames,
> That in a cloud their light did long time stay,
> Their vapour vaded, shew their golden gleames,
> And through the persant aire shoote forth their azure streames.
> (*F. Q.*, III.ix.20.6-9)[15]

In *The Unfortunate Traveller* Nashe employed the same image in listing the beauties of Geraldine; he declared that "her bright brow drives the Sunne to cloudes beneath, / Hir haires reflex with red strakes paints the skies" (II.254).

[13] *Goodly Gallery*, fol. 34. Cf. Aristotle, *Meteorologica*, 371^b; and Seneca, *Naturall Questions*, p. 760 [I.ii].
[14] *Goodly Gallery*, fol. 40.
[15] Spenser found this image in Ovid, *Metamorphoses*, XIV.768-769.

3. RAINBOWS

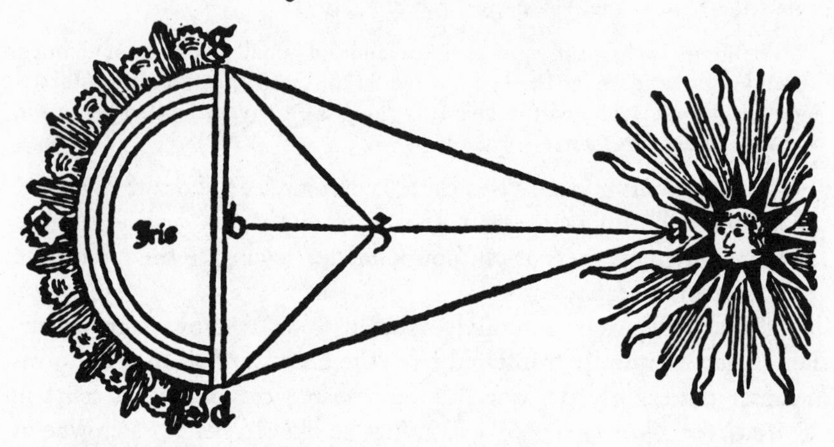

With negligible disagreement between authorities, the rainbow was thought to be a reflection of sunbeams by a cloud not beside nor beneath, but opposite the Sun:

The manner of the generation of the raynbowe is suche, there is opposit againste the sunne, a thycke watrye cloude, whiche is alreadye resolved into dewye droppes of rayne. . . .Wherfore upon such a cloude, the sunne beames strykynge, as uppon a smoothe glasse, doe expresse the image of the sunne unperfectly, for the great distance.[16]

As another distinction from the halo, which formed a complete ring, the shape of the rainbow was confined to "halfe a Circle" or less.[17] From *coelestis arcus* it was commonly known as "the arch."

Aristotle had recorded instances of lunar rainbows,[18] but many subsequent authorities openly disputed the occurrence of such phenomena.[19] The appearance of multiple rainbows—the second and third being the reflection of the original—had also been noted.[20]

[16] Fulke, *Goodly Gallery*, fol. 36-36ᵛ. Cf. Aristotle, *Meteorologica*, 371ᵇ and *passim;* Plutarch, *Opin. of Phil.*, p. 828 [III.v]; Seneca, *Naturall Questions*, pp. 762-768 [I.iii-vi]; and Vergil, *Aeneid*, V.88-89.

[17] Fulke, *Goodly Gallery*, fol. 36.

[18] *Meteorologica*, 372ᵃ. Joseph Hall composed a poem on the "nightly Rainbowe" (line 1) which had been reported over London just before Prince Henry's death in 1612 (*Poems*, p. 149).

[19] For example, Pliny, *Historie of World*, p. 28 [II.lx], and La Primaudaye, *French Academie*, p. 224.

[20] First in Aristotle, *Meteorologica*, 371ᵇ and 375ᵃ-375ᵇ; then repeated, among others, by Fulke, *Goodly Gallery*, fol. 37; Hill, *Contemplation of Mysteries*, fol. 31-32ᵛ; and Maplet, *Diall of Destiny*, fol. 34-34ᵛ. For an eyewitness report of multiple rainbows, see Everard, *Three Sunnes. . .in Cornewall*, pp. 12-13.

In classical mythology the rainbow had been identified with Iris, a minor goddess given duties as a messenger, usually serving Juno.[21] The rainbow that man saw in the sky appeared when Iris, dressed in her many-colored robe, carried out some mission. In Ovid's *Metamorphoses* she leaves Olympus on an earthward journey:

> Dame *Iris* takes her pall wherein a thousand colours were
> And bowwing lyke a stringed bow upon the clowdy sphere,
> Immediately descended.[22]

In Prospero's masque for the two lovers in *The Tempest,* a character representing Iris announces her identity as Juno's "watery arch and messenger" (IV.i.71). Then the goddess Ceres salutes her in a perfect Renaissance vignette of Iris:

> Hail, many-colour'd messenger, that ne'er
> Dost disobey the wife of Jupiter;
> Who with thy saffron wings upon my flowers
> Diffusest honey-drops, refreshing showers,[23]
> And with each end of thy blue bow dost crown
> My bosky acres and my unshrubb'd down,
> Rich scarf to my proud earth.
> (IV.i.76-82)

Iris also figures in three entertainments by Jonson: (1) *Kings Entertainment, in Passing to His Coronation,* in which she appears as the daughter and herald of Electra (lines 708 ff.),[24] but does not speak;

[21] Cf. Vergil, *Aeneid,* IV.693 ff.; and Cartari, *Imagines deorum,* p. 122. See H. J. Rose, *A Handbook of Greek Mythology* (London, 1928), pp. 27-28. In Plato's *Cratylus,* Socrates explains: "Iris. . .seems to have got her name from εἴρειν, because she is a messenger" (408B).

[22] Trans. Arthur Golding, fol. 144v [XI.589-591].

[23] Cf.:

> "Dame *Rainbow* down therfore with safron wings of dropping shoures,
> Whose face a thousand sundry hewes against the sunne devoures,
> From heaven descending came."

(Vergil, *Aeneidos,* trans. Phaer and Twyne, Giv [IV.700-702])

[24] For this genealogy Jonson himself referred to Aristotle, *Meteorologica,* III.2. The text of the *Meteorologica* does not discuss the mythological aspects of the rainbow, but probably the edition that Jonson used was supplemented by a commentary which supplied this information on Iris' parentage. By tradition the father of Iris was Thaumas ("Wonder"); cf. Plutarch, *Opin. of Phil.,* p. 828 [III.v]; Vergil, *Aeneid,* IX.2-5; Ovid, *Metamorphoses,* XI.647; Hyginus, *Fabulae,* p. 2 [prologue]; Natalis Comes, *Mythologiae,* VIII.xx; Palingenius, *Zodiake of Life,* p. 164; Spenser, *F. Q.,* V.iii.25.1 ff.; and Fraunce, *Third Part of Countesse of Pembrokes Ivychurch,* fol. 16. Natalis Comes correlated the genealogical mythus of Iris with the natural causes of the rainbow: "Iridem Thaumantis & Electrae filiam fuisse tradiderunt, quia Thaumas sit Ponti filius. Electra vero Coeli sive Solis. . . .Iridem dixerunt antiqui nasci è filia Oceani & Sole, quia sine pluvia non fit, aut sine Sole intra nubes" (*Mythologiae,* VIII.xx, and X."De Iride").

(2) *Hymenaei*, in which again silent, she attends Juno; and (3) *Chloridia*, in which she reports to Juno "the truth of what is done below" (line 256).[25]

In some instances the rainbow was considered to be not Iris herself, but only the path by which she descended from Olympus to the mundane residence of men.[26] Then by extrapolation the rainbow also became an earthward path for other deities, so that in Chapman's completion of *Hero and Leander* the goddess Ceremony comes down the beams of a rainbow to chide the overimpulsive suitor (III.109 ff.).

The natural cause of the rainbow's many colors was explained as a "mixture of the clouds, of the aire, and of the fire, which are found there togither."[27] Expanding this argument, Bartholomaeus had quoted Bede:

> [The rainbow] taketh coulour of the foure Elementes. . . .of fire he taketh redde coulour in the overmost part, and of earth greene in the neathermost, & of the aire manner of browne coulour, and of water somedeale bliew in the middle.[28]

Pliny had offered a similar explanation,[29] while Aristotle's discussion on the colors of the rainbow had provided a basis for the science of optics.[30]

Because of the complete range of tints in the rainbow, this meteor was commonly cited to express the multicolored. In *Merry Wives of Windsor* Falstaff snaps at Mistress Quickly: "What tellest thou me of black and blue? I was beaten myself into all the colours of the the rainbow" (IV.v.117-118); and in *The Winter's Tale* Autolycus is reported to sell "ribbons of all the colours i' the rainbow" (IV.iv. 205-206). Such a gaudy display inevitably suggested the epithet "gay rainbow" (Chapman, *Revenge of Bussy*, III.i.54), and this in turn led to inferences of ostentation and arrogance. When Peele in *The Arraignment of Paris* described the flowering fields prepared to welcome the goddesses contending for the golden apple, he noted that

[25] See Gilbert, *Symbolic Persons*, p. 143.

[26] Cf. Vergil, *Aeneid*, V.606 ff.; Ovid, *Metamorphoses*, XI.629 ff.; and Isidore, *Etymologiae*, XIII.x.1. The belief that the rainbow was a heavenly bridge for the deities was supported by folklore, specifically as expressed in the Edda; cf. Grimm, *Teutonic Mythology*, II.731-732.

[27] La Primaudaye, *French Academie*, p. 224.

[28] *De proprietatibus rerum*, fol. 161. The reference to Bede is *De natura rerum*, chap. xxxi; cf. Isidore, *De natura rerum*, XXXI.2.

[29] *Historie of World*, p. 28 [II.lx].

[30] *Meteorologica*, 374^b-377^a. Cf. p. 14, n. 19, above.

"not Iris, in her pride and bravery, / Adorns her arch with such variety" (I.i.49-50). And in an image extended yet one step further, Shakespeare recounted Ulysses' anger at Achilles sulking in his tent and Ulysses' plan to "make him fall / His crest that prouder than blue Iris bends" (*Troilus*, I.iii.379-380).

According to Plutarch, a poetical tradition maintained that the rainbow, "having a bulles head, drinketh up the rivers."[31] This unusual idea accounts for Chapman's observation that imperfect rainbows look "like a buls necke shortned" (*Eugenia*, 59), and for Spenser's simile that a bullock's "hornes bene as broade, as Rainebows bent" ("Feb.," 73).

The significance of the rainbow for the weather prognosticator was debatable, as La Primaudaye noted:

> Astrologians. . .argue upon the divers predictions of this bowe, as presaging sometimes raine, sometimes faire weather, sometimes winde. . . .Yet *Plinie* saith, that it is often seene, when it doth not prognosticate any thing.[32]

Leonard Digges offered the following rule to prognosticate the influence of the rainbow on weather: "The rayne bowe appering, if it be fayr, it betokeneth fowle weather: if fowle, loke for fair weather. The grener, the moare raine: redder, wynde."[33] The majority opinion, however, seems to have regarded the rainbow as a sign of rain—indeed, many meteorologians claimed that it gathered together the rain clouds. Therefore to Shakespeare the rainbow was the "distemper'd messenger of wet" (*All's Well*, I.iii.157), and to Jonson "raine- / Resolving *Iris*" (*Vision of Delight*, 154-155).

The rainbow was generally welcomed as a beneficial sign because it accompained rain, and consequently it "quickeneth and bespringeth the neather thinges, and maketh them plenteous."[34] In this connection Greene portrayed Flora, who "proude in pompe of all her flowers / Sat bright and gay, / And gloried in the deaw of *Iris* showers" (VIII.207). Moreover, on Scriptural authority "the Rainebow betokeneth peace and accord betweene God and the world, &. . .bringeth to minde that Gods dome by water is passed."[35] George

[31] *Opin. of Phil.*, p. 828 [III.v]. Cf. Angelo Poliziano, *Rusticus* (in *Le Selve e la Strega*, ed. Isidoro del Lungo [Florence, 1925]), lines 497-499.

[32] *French Academie*, p. 224. The reference to Pliny is *Historie of World*, p. 28 [II.lix]; cf. *ibid.*, p. 612 [XVIII.lxxx].

[33] *Prognostication of Right Good Effect*, Bii.

[34] Bartholomaeus, *De proprietatibus rerum*, fol. 161.

[35] *Ibid.* The reference is to Genesis 9:11-17. *Biblia Sacra. . .Nicolai Lyrani* commented at length on the religious interpretation of the rainbow: ". . .coelestis arcus, per quem significatur Christus, in quo est forte lignum & chorda mollis, per

Gascoigne voiced this belief in his metrical prayer, "Gascoigne's Good Morrow":

> The Rainbowe bending in the skye,
> Bedeckte with sundrye hewes,
> Is like the seate of God on hye,
> And seemes to tell these newes:
> That as thereby he promised,
> To drowne the world no more,
> So by the bloud which Christ hath shead,
> He will our helth restore.
>
> (lines 41-48)

Several authorities had confirmed the quasi-religious tradition that for forty years before Judgment Day the rainbow would be incapable of forming, a condition "that shall be token of drieng & of default of Elements."[36]

"Water-gall," "wind-gall," and "weather-gall" were terms in common usage to designate imperfectly formed rainbows.[37] Seneca had mentioned the formation of these reflections which "appeare for the most part neere unto the sunne in a moyst cloud, that beginneth but to spread."[38] Shakespeare spoke of them simply as "blue circles" (*Lucrece*, 1587). Chapman more fully described their appearance:

> Nor could he [the Sun] paint so faire,
> Heavens bow in dewie vapors, but he left
> The greater part unform'd; the circle cleft,
> And like a buls necke shortned; no hews seene,
> But onely one, and that was watrish greene.
>
> (*Eugenia*, 56-60)

The formation of such phenomena was regarded as a certain portent of rain—they "foretell new storms to those already spent" (*Lucrece*, 1589).

---

quae significatur virtus divinitatis, & fragilitas humanitatis, & sicut in arca chorda mollis flectit lignum, sic in passione humanitatis flexus fuit rigor justitiae & severitatis. Qui vero fide pera [*sic*] & devotione respiciunt hunc arcum, securi sunt a diluvio vitiorum" (I.167-168). In his commentary on this passage of Genesis, Gervase Babington provided a similar "allegorie of the Rainbow": "The *Rainbowe* is taken as a figure of Christ, and therefore wee [are] thereby taught, that when either the darke blacknesse of uglye sinne, or the thicke cloudes of greefe and adversitie, doe threaten unto us any fearefull overthrowe, wee should clap our eyes streight upon our Rainebowe Christ Jesus" (*Notes upon Genesis*, fol. 37^{v}). Cf. also Rabanus Maurus, *De universo*, IX.xx.

[36] Bartholomaeus, *De proprietatibus rerum*, fol. 161. This tradition was especially strong in medieval Germany; see Grimm, *Teutonic Mythology*, II.733-734.

[37] *NED*, "water-gall," sense 2.

[38] *Naturall Questions*, p. 770 [I.ix]. Cf. also Plutarch, *Opin. of Phil.*, p. 829 [III.vi].

CHAPTER FIVE

PSEUDO METEORS AND RELATED NATURAL PHENOMENA

METEORS were interrelated in various ways with many other natural phenomena. Perhaps some meteors and what for convenience may be called pseudo meteors were both formed from the same natural influences; perhaps both appeared, or were believed most commonly to appear, only in conjunction with one another; or possibly the pseudo meteor presaged certain events which the true meteor likewise foretold.

1. ECLIPSES

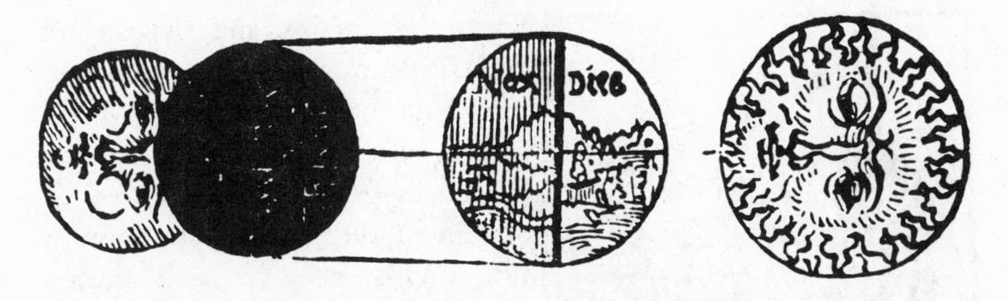

In the Renaissance the true cause of eclipses was generally known, and technical discussions explaining the mechanics of how one celestial body obscured the Sun's light from another were easily available in such popular textbooks of astronomy as Sacrobosco's *De sphaera* and Robert Recorde's *Castle of Knowledge*.

Eclipses were usually considered along with meteorological anomalies as portents of imminent calamity. In *King Lear*, for example, Gloucester gravely declares that "these late eclipses in the sun and moon portend no good" (I.ii.112-113), and he gives a concise statement of the unnatural events foretold by them:

. . .love cools, friendship falls off, brothers divide: in cities, mutinies; in countries, discord; in palaces, treason; and the bond cracked 'twixt son and father.

(I.ii.115-118)

Since these were the same dire occurrences predicted by meteorological omens of evil, eclipses were frequently included in a list of such omens. In *Hamlet,* for instance, Horatio declares that shortly before the assassination of Julius Caesar there appeared:

> . . .stars with trains of fire and dews of blood,
> Disasters in the sun; and the moist star
> Upon whose influence Neptune's empire stands
> Was sick almost to doomsday with eclipse.
>
> (I.i.117-120)

Here an eclipse of the Moon is considered as ominous as shooting stars, dews of blood, and unfavorable aspects of the Sun.

2. SPRINGS

Springs, fountains, and rivers were rightly seen as necessary phases in the continuous atmospheric cycle of evaporation and distillation described by Aristotle.[1] In the words of Pliny, "waters ascend up, and turn into clouds; they congeale. . .and downe they hasten headlong into brookes and land flouds."[2]

Hot baths and medicinal springs were considered special sorts of wells or fountains rising from veins of brimstone.[3] Floods were interpreted as temporary abnormalities in the natural scheme: Northumberland, planning rebellion against King Henry IV, exclaims, "Let not Nature's hand / Keep the wild flood confined! let order die!" (*2 Henry IV*, I.i.153-154).

[1] *Meteorologica*, 347[a] and 349[b].
[2] *Historie of World*, p. 29 [II.lxiii].
[3] See Fulke, *Goodly Gallery*, fol. 57[v].

3. TIDES

The phenomenon of tides was surrounded with an aura of half-truths. But although their exact nature was not known, even common knowledge correctly assigned their control to the Moon, "the moist star / Upon whose influence Neptune's empire stands" (*Hamlet,* I.i.118-119). Because the Moon was believed to govern all Watery things, including many meteors, the tides were often associated with the science of meteorology. In *A Goodly Gallery*, for instance, William Fulke deals with them in the traditional place, at the conclusion of his section on "moiste and watry impressions" (fol. 61ᵛ).

4. METALS

Metals were commonly classified as "earthly Meteores," as in William Fulke's *Goodly Gallery*.[4] This classification went back to Book

[4] Fol. 62 ff.

III of Aristotle's *Meteorologica*, which closed with a discussion of metals and minerals.[5] Aristotle described two sorts of evaporations imprisoned within the earth, which were the counterparts of the vaporous and the smoky evaporations which formed meteors in the region of Air. These earth-confined evaporations, likewise vaporous or smoky, formed respectively metals and "fossilia" (i.e., stones). Moist evaporations condensed into metals, which were malleable and meltable because of inherent moist characteristics. "Fossilia" developed from dry evaporations and therefore could not be melted. All this esoteric discussion of metals is elaborated in *The Alchemist* by Subtle, who wishes to counter the cynical Surly and to impress the credulous Sir Epicure Mammon (II.iii.145 ff.).

5. CHASMS IN THE SKY

This phenomenon had been mentioned by Aristotle in connection with his discussion of fiery impressions.[6] It had the appearance of gapings or chinks in the firmament, and resulted from the combustion of a loosely collected exhalation among clouds in the higher levels of the Air. The contrast of light against the darkness gave the illusion of chasms in the heavens, which revealed "the mightie burning of some place,"[7] presumably the sphere of Fire. Chapman accurately described these conditions in *Hero and Leander*:

> . . .streames of fire,
> As when the rarefied ayre[8] is driven
> In flashing streames, and opes the darkned heaven.
> (IV.241-243)

[5] See D. E. Eichholz, "Aristotle's Theory of the Formation of Metals and Minerals," *Classical Quarterly*, XLIII (1949), 141-146.

[6] *Meteorologica*, 342ᵃ-342ᵇ.

[7] Hill, *Contemplation of Mysteries*, fol. 28ᵛ. Cf. Seneca, *Naturall Questions*, p. 772 [I.xiv].

[8] Elemental Air when "rarefied" became Fire; cf. "Ayre too much rarefied breakes forth in fire" (Chapman, *Ovids Banquet*, lxxxix.8).

Like most phenomena of exhalations in the upper Airy region, "chasms" filled the beholder with great terror. Thomas Hill noted that the appearance of gaping in the sky "pronounceth drye tempestes to follow,"[9] and he cited Pliny to the effect that the chasms "be foreshewers of mightie perils. . .as be battels, seditions and infinite like calamities."[10]

6. VOLCANOES

The phenomenon of volcanoes was well known in Renaissance England, although no such marvel appeared in England itself. Many encyclopedias and wonder-books contained information on volcanoes, usually with specific reference to Mt. Aetna. Bartholomaeus' comment on Mt. Aetna was typical: "*Aetna* is an hill in the lande or Ile of *Cecile*, and out of that hill breaketh fire with brimstone, as it were in hell."[11] Spenser's description of an eruption of Aetna has all the conventional details:

> . . .burning *Aetna* from his boyling stew
> Doth belch out flames, and rockes in peeces broke,
> And ragged ribs of mountaines molten new,
> Enwrapt in coleblacke clouds and filthy smoke,
> That all the land with stench, and heaven with horror choke.[12]
> (*F. Q.*, I.xi.44.5-9)

Following Aristotle,[13] the Renaissance believed that some relationship existed between volcanoes and earthquakes. Fulke reported:

> Where earthquakes have been, great aboundaunce of smoke, flame, & ashes is cast out, when the aboundaunce of brymstone that is under the grounde, through violent motion, is set on fyre, & breaketh forth.[14]

[9] *Contemplation of Mysteries*, fol. 28^{v}.
[10] *Ibid.*, fol. 30.
[11] *De proprietatibus rerum*, fol. 204^{v}. See also Sugden, *Topographical Dictionary*, "Aetna."
[12] Cf. Vergil, *Aeneid*, III.571-577.
[13] *Meteorologica*, 366^{b}-367^{a}.
[14] *Goodly Gallery*, fol. 23.

Sixteenth-century meteorologians did not know the exact connection between these two phenomena—nor, indeed, is the relationship fully understood today.

According to late classical mythology, volcanoes were the underground forges where Vulcan and his assistants, the Cyclopes, made metal ornaments and arms for the gods, including thunderbolts for Zeus.[15] Parallel mythology attributes volcanoes to Typhon, a malevolent Giant whom Zeus had imprisoned beneath Mt. Aetna.[16]

7. APPARITIONS IN THE SKY

In addition to fiery impressions which suggested various animate and inanimate forms,[17] many writers reported the occurrence of other strange and wonderful apparitions in the heavens. Fulke recounted the appearance of castles, cities, battles, monsters, and assorted religious symbols.[18] Shakespeare's Antony recalls having seen in the sky

> A tower'd citadel, a pendent rock,
> A forked mountain, or blue promontory
> With trees upon't, that nod unto the world.
> (*Antony*, IV.xiv.4-6)

Antony suggests that these apparitions are various cloud forms, and perhaps today these phenomena would be called mirages. For the most part, however, they were figments of superstitious imaginations or products of pens attempting to impress an overcredulous populace. Pliny reported incidents involving not only apparitions, but also wondrous sounds from above— "the rustling of Armour and sound of Trumpets heard from Heaven."[19]

[15] Cf. Vergil, *Aeneid*, VIII.418 ff.; and Fraunce, *Third Part of Countesse of Pembrokes Ivychurch*, F2.
[16] See pp. 126 ff., above.
[17] See pp. 91 ff., above.
[18] *Goodly Gallery*, fol. 45-45^{v}.
[19] *Historie of World*, p. 28 [II.lviii].

PART III

METEOROLOGICAL IMAGERY IN THE MAJOR CREATIVE WRITERS

CHAPTER ONE

EDMUND SPENSER

WITHOUT a doubt, Spenser revolutionized English poetry. In 1579 *The Shepheardes Calender* conclusively proved to every sensitive ear that classical and Continental models were superior to the unpolished works loyal to the native English tradition. Theocritus, Vergil, Mantuan, Marot—these were clearly the authors to imitate. And Spenser's talent lay largely in imitating. His poetic office, as he saw it, was to prepare English works comparable to the earlier accounts of great men in action. His poetry was to provide an exemplary code of conduct for his English contemporaries. With this in mind, Spenser chose at the beginning of his career to progress like Vergil from pastoral eclogues to a twelve-book epic. Therefore, while he may be considered radical in his renunciation of England's literary heritage,[1] he was conservative in his conformity to the larger tradition of European literature.

Spenser's conservatism in poetical matters is manifest in his imagery based on weather phenomena. He made frequent use of information about meteors; but his poetry concerned with them, especially when examined alone, is disappointingly trite and unimaginative. His meteorological imagery is seldom more than adequate and never more than pretty. It is not distinguished by boldness, novelty, acuteness, subtlety, nor variety. Spenser merely drew from the imagistic equipment which he found ready in the poetic toolbox. He did not develop new tools, nor did he manipulate the old ones for the fashioning of new poetic ornament. He handled the traditional equipment with self-assurance admirable in an Englishman, proving thereby that the English language could successfully

[1] Of course Spenser did turn to account the household stuff which he found in England. But his methods of developing poetry from this raw material were derived from non-English models. When Spenser larded his work with Chaucerisms, he was following the example of Vergil's Homeric echoes; and when he incorporated epic materials indigenous to Albion, he was doing only what every great epic poet had done. While his matter is often English, his manner seldom is.

render the accepted poetic genres. But in his imagery derived from meteorology, he never sought to snatch a grace beyond the reach of art.

Spenser shows little familiarity with scientific explanations for atmospheric phenomena. Technical terms which Marlowe and Shakespeare used freely do not appear in his poems. He knew—at least superficially, as did every man in the street—that lightning was ejected from the interior of clouds, that earthquakes resulted from wind enclosed within subterranean caverns, that the rainbow was merely the Sun's reflection. But his technical knowledge seems to have ended here. Moreover, he paid but scant attention to the great stock of magical lore and wondrous meteors; and except for casual references to the general beneficence of dew and rain, he ignored the Biblical associations of atmospheric processes. He did not draw upon personal observation (perhaps the most conspicuously absent of all) and create imagery of natural description. With very few exceptions, in fact, his meteorological imagery is patently literary: for imagistic needs he depended upon the most ordinary of the poetic conventions, and in his narrative verse he consistently employed the language of classical mythology to describe even the most usual meteorological occurrences.

If we analyze his references to the phenomenon of snow, we observe at once Spenser's dependence upon poetic convention. To the Renaissance Englishman, snow was a meteor with physical strangeness and metaphysical suggestiveness, adaptable for a wide variety of striking images. But Spenser's allusions to it are covered by two of the commonest conventions: snow as the superlative of whiteness, and as a symbol of purity. In his poetry Spenser makes forty-nine references to snow, and by far the largest number note only its whiteness:

. . .a snowie Swan of heavenly hiew (*Time*, 590)
. . .a Bull as white as driven snowe (*Vanitie*, 16)
. . .a lowly Asse more white then snow (*F. Q.*, I.i.4.2)
. . .her snowy Palfrey. . . (*F. Q.*, I.iii.8.8)
. . .beard as white as snow (*F. Q.*, I.viii.30.2)
. . .snowy lockes. . . (*F. Q.*, I.x.48.2)
. . .her snowy brest. . . (*F. Q.*, II.i.11.7)
. . .her snowy brest. . . (*F. Q.*, II.iii.29.6)

. . .their snowy limbes. . . (*F. Q.*, II.xii.64.6)
Her snowy brest. . . (*F. Q.*, II.xii.78.1)
. . .her snow-white smocke. . . (*F. Q.*, III.i.63.7)
. . .a Palfrey. . .more white then snow (*F. Q.*, III.v.5.6)
. . .a snowy Swan (*F. Q.*, III.xi.32.1)
. . .snowy neckd *Doris*. . . (*F. Q.*, IV.xi. 49.9)
. . .her brode snowy brests (*F. Q.*, IV.xi.51.5)
. . .her snowy brest (*F. Q.*, VI.i.17.7)
. . .snowy brests. . . (*F. Q.*, VI.viii.40.9)
. . .her snowy brest (*F. Q.*, VI.xii.15.2)
her snowy browes. . . (*Amor.*, lxiv.7)
Her snowie necke. . . (*Epith.*, 177)
. . .her snowy bosome. . . (*H. L.*, 289)
The snow which doth the top of *Pindus* strew,
Did never whiter shew [than the swans] (*Proth.*, 40-41)
Their snowie Foreheads. . . (*Proth.*, 86)

Under this convention we must also list allusions to the "snowy" false Florimell, since the Witch of Book III molded her body from snow to obtain the necessary fairness, which was then tinted with "vermily" (III.viii.6.1-9):

. . .a snowy Lady (*F. Q.*, III.viii.Arg.1)
. . .her snowy skin (*F. Q.*, III.viii.24.9)
The snowy *Florimell*. . . (*F. Q.*, IV.ii.4.7)
. . .that snowy *Florimell* (*F. Q.*, IV.iv.8.1)
. . .that snowy Mayd (*F. Q.*, IV.v.26.1)
. . .that same snowy maid (*F. Q.*, IV.ix.24.2)
. . .the snowy maide (*F. Q.*, IV.ix.28.7)
. . .snowy Dame (*F. Q.*, V.iii.10.4)
. . .snowy *Florimele* (*F. Q.*, V.iii.17.1)
. . .that snowy mayd (*F. Q.*, V.iii.18.7)
. . .that snowy one (*F. Q.*, V.iii.24.1)
Her snowy substance. . . (*F. Q.*, V.iii.24.7)

On other occasions Spenser intensified the whiteness-of-snow convention by juxtaposing a brilliant color for contrast:

His snowy front curled with golden heares.
(*F. Q.*, II.viii.5.5)

The bashfull bloud her snowy cheekes did dye.
(*F. Q.*, II.ix.41.4)

. . .the snowy substaunce [ivory] sprent
With vermell.
(*F. Q.*, II.xii.45.5-6)

. . .the gore,
Which staines his snowy skin with hatefull hew.
(*F. Q.*, III.i.38.5-6)

. . .[Tears] like two Orient pearles, did purely shyne
Upon her snowy cheeke.
(*F. Q.*, III.vii.9.3-4)

. . .[Blood] dyde in sanguine red her skin all snowy cleene.
(*F. Q.*,III.xii.20.9)

Unwares it [a knife] strooke into her snowie chest,
That little drops empurpled her faire brest.
(*F. Q.*, III.xii.33.4-5)

How the red roses flush up in her cheekes,
And the pure snow with goodly vermill stayne.
(*Epith.*, 226-227)

But such contrasts between white and some vivid color were also poetical commonplaces, and nothing in these passages is novel.

Spenser's other references to snow follow the convention about its purity. He speaks of "pure snow" (*Epith.*, 227) and "purest snow" (*F. Q.*, III.viii.6.2); and the water of a personified stream, we are told, "is chast and pure, as purest snow" (*F. Q.*, II.ii.9.7). But the pureness of snow did not come to Spenser's mind nearly so often as its whiteness.

Only four of Spenser's references to snow do not follow one of these two poetic conventions, and these other references are certainly ordinary enough. In the February eclogue, "heaped snowe" (line 233) is one of the several hardships of winter which beset the Briar after the Oak has fallen. In the Mutabilitie Cantos, "rayne, hayle, and snowe" are listed as "bitter storms" which harass the region of Air (*F. Q.*, VII.vii.23.5-7). In *The Faerie Queene* we read that love for Belphoebe wastes the life of Arthur's squire just as the bright sun melts "the snow congealed" (III.v.49.5-6), an image that Spenser cribbed from Ovid (*Metamorphoses*, III.488-490). And in one instance Spenser alludes to "fluttring arrowes, thicke as flakes of snow" (*F. Q.*, II.xi.18.2). Here, of course, Spenser adapted the convention of hail as a simile for arrows,[2] inserting "snow" probably because he needed the rhyme.

We can see from this analysis of his snow imagery how closely Spenser adhered to the time-tested recipes of the poetic profession. His images based on snow are undeniably dull and unvaried. The beauty of snow, the mystery of its origin, its ephemeral nature, its coldness—all this wealth of connotation failed to stir Spenser's imagination. His imagistic use of the meteor is limited to the tradition inherited from classical and Continental poets.

We also find Spenser relying upon many poetic conventions other than those dealing with snow. A closely associated image was the figurative use of frost to indicate old age, usually through the visual similarity between hoarfrost and gray hair. In *The Faerie Queene*, for example, Contemplation is personified as an old man:

> With snowy lockes adowne his shoulders shed,
> As hoarie frost with spangles doth attire
> The mossy braunches of an Oke halfe ded.[3]
> (I.x.48.2-4)

To dew, the warm-weather counterpart of frost, Spenser applied the conventional adjectives: "pearly" (*F. Q.*, III.x.46.6, IV.v.45.5), "silver" (*Bellay*, 151; *F. Q.*, I.i.39.8, II.xii.61.7; *Colin Clout*, 507), "sweete slumbring" (*Gnat*, 323; *F. Q.*, I.i.36.4), "precious" (*F. Q.*, III.vi.43.8), "holy water" (*F. Q.*, I.xi.36.2, III.xii.13.6; "Feb.," 210), "celestiall" (*H. H. L.*, 46). These epithets fittingly reflect the religious conception of dew and rain as superior agents of Divine good.[4] Spenser likewise overworked the cliché of tears described as rain[5] or dew drops.[6]

Another poetic commonplace that attracted Spenser was the representation of adversity as bad weather. He was particularly fond

[2] See p. 57, above.

[3] For other instances where frost represents old age, see *F. Q.*, I.xii.12.2, II.i.7.3, II.iv.4.5, III.viii.30.3; "Jan.," 31-34; "Feb.," 31, 43-44; "Dec.," 135; *Colin Clout*, 248-250.

[4] Cf. *F. Q.*, I.xi.48.1-5, I.xii.6.7-8, IV.viii.20.8-9, IV.viii.33.3-5, V.xii.13.1-6; "Nov.," 31-32; "Dec.," 111; *Epith.*, 416; *H. B.*, 27; *H. H. L.*, 44-47.

[5] *F. Q.*, I.iii.6.8-9, III.v.34.3; "Jan.," 35, 41; "April," 5-8; "Nov.," 131; *Tears*, 109, 476-478; *Gnat*, ded.3; *Daph.*, 376; *Amor.*, xviii.3.

[6] *F. Q.*, I.xii.16.9, III.v.34.3, IV.vii.35.5, VI.xii.8.4; "Dec.," 112; *Astrophel*, 191-192, 204.

of the phrase "storme of fortune."[7] Spenser also followed the convention that fierce or unpleasant emotions are inner tempests. Hate is "the stormie wind / Of malice" (*F. Q.*, II.vi.8.8-9), "the storme of your despight" (*F. Q.*, II.viii.27.5), or "stormy enmitie" (*F. Q.*, III.viii.21.7). Anger is "the tempest of his wrathfulnesse" (*F. Q.*, II.xii.83.4), "the tempest of his yre" (*F. Q.*, V.xi.58.8), "angers tempest" (*F. Q.*, VI.i.36.9), "tempestuous rage" (*F. Q.*, VI.vi.11.8), or "the dreadfull tempest of her wrath" (*Amor.*, xxxviii.7). Grief is "storming paine" (*F. Q.*, I.vii.38.5), "tempestuous griefe" (*F. Q.*, III.iv.8.1), "the stormie passion of his troubled brest" (*Daph.*, 192), or "cloudy grief" (*Amor.*, xxxiv.12). Uncontrollable love is "the tempest of that stormie passion" (*Tears*, 380) or "the storme that passion did begin" (*Amor.*, viii.11).

One poetic convention adapted by Spenser may be traced to the works of Homer, where a solicitous god or goddess often saves a protegé from an enemy by enveloping him in a protective cloud.[8] The *Iliad* is the obvious model for Duessa's speech to the Red Crosse Knight when Sans-joy is miraculously rescued from single combat:

> . . .lo th'infernall powres
> Covering your foe with cloud of deadly night,
> Have borne him hence to *Plutoes* baleful bowres.
> (*F. Q.*, I.v.14.6-8)

The action exactly parallels Paris' rescue by Aphrodite from the victorious arms of Menelaus (*Iliad*, III.369 ff.); and Spenser continues this passage with a Homero-Vergilian visit to the underworld.

From Homer also came the traditional trope that death is a cloud covering the victim. So Spenser speaks of a "cloud of death" (*F. Q.*, I.iii.39.8, VI.xi.21.5), or death appears as a "cloud of night" (*F. Q.*, V.xi.14.8; *Daph.*, 305). Sleep was an imitation of death,[9] so it could be similarly represented as a cloud covering the eyes of the sleeper.[10]

A poetic convention especially favored by Spenser was the com-

[7] He used it in *Petrarch*, 84; *F. Q.*, V.v.38.3, VI.ix.31.5, VI.xii.10.4. For other instances where tempests represent misfortune, see *F. Q.*, I.vii.25.1, I.vii.28.7, II.vii.14.1-2, V.iii.1.1-4, V.vii.35.9, VI.ix.19.3-5, VI.x.38.9.

[8] As examples, see *Iliad*, III.380-382, V.344-346.

[9] Hesiod (*Theogony*, 758 ff.) had stated that Death and Sleep were the twin sons of Night. Cf. Homer, *Iliad*, XIV.231, XVI.672, 682.

[10] Cf. *Gnat*, 321-323; *F. Q.*, I.i.36.1-4, II.viii.24.7-9, III.vi.10.8, IV.viii.34.3-4, V.vii.26.7-8. For the physiological explanation of sleep as a vapor, see Ruth L. Anderson, *Elizabethan Psychology and Shakespeare's Plays* (Univ. of Iowa Humanistic Studies; Iowa City, 1927), pp. 49-50.

parison between hail and arrows or sword strokes. The usual phrase was "strokes as thicke as showre of hayle" (*F. Q.*, IV.vi.16.5).[11] Thunder could express a similar notion: "He hewd, and lasht, and foyned, and thundred blowes" (*F. Q.*, II.v.9.1).[12] In a somewhat comparable manner, but with emphasis on sound, thunder could describe bursts of artillery[13] and the beating of horses' hoofs.[14] And finally, thunder could be a hyperbolic comparison for any loud noise.[15]

Spenser's conventional images go beyond this. For instance, he knew the commonplaces about wind: movement can be "as swift as wind" (*F. Q.*, IV.vii.18.7);[16] "the wind [is] unstable, and doth never stay" (*F. Q.*, II.vi.23.5);[17] and "words bene wynd, and wasten soone in vayne" ("Oct.," 36).[18] But we have seen the sort of standardized tropes repeatedly employed by Spenser, and also the extent to which he depended upon poetic convention for meteorological imagery. Most of these conventions are at the lowest level of imagery; they are ready-made, and therefore emasculated, similes and metaphors. They were the accepted poetic idiom of the day. They function, in fact, as poetic diction rather than as imagery.

Poetic conventions account for a major portion of the references that Spenser made to weather phenomena. The other body of meteorological notions from which he drew most often had survived in classical mythology. Yet here again we find that Spenser limited

[11] See p. 57, above.

[12] Cf. also *F. Q.*, I.v.7.4-5, I.vi.43.1-2, II.ii.20.5-9, II.viii.41.1-3, IV.iii.15.1-8, V.ii.21.6-8, V.iii.8.8-9, V.v.19.2, V.x.35.1, V.xii.17.6.

[13] Cf. *F. Q.*, IV.ii.16.8, V.x.34.6-8.

[14] Cf. *F. Q.*, II.iii.11.4, III.viii.15.3-5, III.x.33.6.

[15] Cf. *F. Q.*, II.iii.7.3, II.iii.45.6-7, II.x.73.9, VI.v.19.8; *Vanitie*, 67; *Amor.*, lxxxv.13.

[16] Cf. also *F. Q.*, III.x.55.1-2, IV.vii.30.1-2, IV.viii.7.5-7, V.vi.7.8.

[17] Cf. also *F. Q.*, IV.ii.5.1-2, VII.vii.22.5-8; "Dec.," 126. In *Mother Hubberds Tale* an honorable courtier will not "be carried with the common winde / Of Courts inconstant mutabilitie" (lines 722-723). Here Spenser is making a fresh metaphor from the commonplace; but this instance is unique. Perhaps Spenser felt somewhat liberated from tradition because he was writing satire in the native English vein rather than pastoral. Significantly, references to meteors in *Mother Hubberds Tale*, as compared to *The Shepheardes Calender* and *The Faerie Queene*, are all but absent, occurring only in lines 340 and 1236. References to meteors in Spenser's other early satiric piece, *Muiopotmos*, are similarly scarce, and in fact are limited to three mythological allusions (lines 79-80, 92-93, 419-420). We may infer that Spenser intentionally loaded his pastoral works with meteorological imagery because such imagery was a traditional part of the pastoral apparatus; but in the *Muiopotmos* and *Mother Hubberds Tale*, primarily inspired by native English wit, he felt that such imagery was out of place.

[18] Cf. also *F. Q.*, IV.v.27.7, IV.viii.26.1-5, VI.vi.42.9; *Colin Clout*, 715-718.

himself to the common poetic idiom. The Olympian deity most frequently mentioned by Spenser is naturally Jove; and since Jove originated as a weather-god, he properly appears with his attributes of thunder and lightning. Spenser repeated "thundring *Jove*," the orthodox epithet, five times.[19]

Spenser also placed the other gods and goddesses at their habitual weather tasks. At one point Juno is called the mistress of the Airy region (*F. Q.*, VII.vii.26.6); and at another, the Cyclopes are described at their underground forge: "in *Lipari*. . .day and night / [They] Frame thunderbolts for *Joves* avengefull threate" (*F. Q.*, IV.v.37.3-4). Aeolus is correctly cited as warden of the contentious Winds,[20] but twice he is incorrectly depicted as a Wind himself.[21] Of the true Winds, only Zephyrus and Boreas are called by name. The former is graced by the approved adjectives: "myld" (*F. Q.*, II.v.29.8), "sweet" (II.xii.33.5), and "sweete breathing" (*Proth.*, 2); while Boreas is fearfully but conventionally decried as "blustring" ("Feb.," 226), "bitter bleake" (*F. Q.*, I.ii.33.7), and "wrathfull" (*F. Q.*, V.xi.58.7). There are two allusions to Iris,[22] and once she is given the esoteric title, "the daughter of *Thaumantes*" (*F. Q.*, V.iii. 25.1).[23] On two occasions Spenser talks about Phaeton's tragedy and its visible result in the Milky Way (*F. Q.*, I.iv.9.1-9, V.viii.40.1-9). But these are, at best, the most customary allusions to the Greek weather-gods.

Although Spenser's range of meteorological mythology was relatively narrow, he nonetheless called upon it often. In *The Faerie Queene* he drew most extensively from this body of meteorological notions to set a scene: to indicate the time of day and the state of the weather, and secondarily to create a mood. He was never subtle about any of this, nor did he attempt to disguise his direct imitation of previous epic poets.

Spenser was especially fond of describing daybreak, when the vapors condensed by the cold of night are dispersed by heat of the Sun. Many episodes of *The Faerie Queene* are started in this fashion. But Spenser never depicts dawn by technical or even by natural de-

[19] *F. Q.*, I.iv.11.5, I.v.42.9, II.vi.10.7, III.xi.30.1, V.vii.10.5.
[20] *F. Q.*, III.viii.21.6-7, IV.ix.23.1-4; *Mui.*, 419-420.
[21] *F. Q.*, I.vii.9.2-5, III.vi.44.9.
[22] *F. Q.*, III.xi.47.8-9; *Mui.*, 92-93.
[23] On the parentage of Iris, see p. 141, n. 24, above.

scription. Classical mythology not only provides the terms, but insistently delineates the pagan picture: Aurora leaves the bed of Tithonus to precede Phoebus, who begins his daily journey in the Sun-chariot and dispels the gloomy dampness generated by Night. A prototype of this mythological account of dawn was translated by Spenser in *Virgils Gnat*:

> The fiery Sun was mounted now on hight
> Up to the heavenly towers, and shot each where
> Out of his golden Charet glistering light;
> And fayre *Aurora* with her rosie heare,
> The hatefull darknes now had put to flight,
> When as the shepheard seeing day appeare,
> His little Goats gan drive out of their stalls.
> (lines 65-71)

When the passages describing sunrise in *The Faerie Queene* are gathered together, we can see that poetic presentation of dawn had become almost a formula to Spenser; and although in some instances, for metrical reasons perhaps, the entire mythology of the event is not detailed, nevertheless in all instances the entire formula is implied:

> . . .*Phoebus* fiery carre
> In hast was climbing up the Easterne hill,
> Full envious that night so long his roome did fill.
> (I.ii.1.7-9)

> Now when the rosy-fingred Morning faire,
> Weary of aged *Tithones* saffron bed,
> Had spred her purple robe through deawy aire,
> And the high hils *Titan* discovered,
> The royal virgin [Una] shooke off drowsy-hed.
> (I.ii.7.1-5)

> At last the golden Orientall gate
> Of greatest heaven gan to open faire,
> And *Phoebus* fresh, as bridegrome to his mate,
> Came dauncing forth, shaking his deawie haire:
> And hurld his glistring beames through gloomy aire.
> Which when the wakeful Elfe perceiv'd, streight way
> He started up.
> (I.v.2.1-7)

> The morrow next gan early to appeare,
> That *Titan* rose to runne his daily race;

But early ere the morrow next gan reare
Out of the sea faire *Titans* deawy face,
Up rose the gentle virgin.

(I.xi.33.1-5)

The joyous day gan early to appeare,
And faire *Aurora* from the deawy bed
Of aged *Tithone* gan her selfe to reare,
With rosie cheekes, for shame as blushing red;
Her golden lockes for haste were loosely shed
About her eares, when *Una* her did marke
Clymbe to her charet, all with flowers spred,
From heaven high to chase the chearelesse darke;
With merry note her loud salutes the mounting larke.

Then freshly up arose the doughtie knight.

(I.xi.51.1-9, 52.1)

Scarsely had *Phoebus* in the glooming East
Yet harnessed his firie-footed teeme,
Ne reard above the earth his flaming creast,
When the last deadly smoke aloft did steeme.

(I.xii.2.1-4)

Soone as the morrow faire with purples beames
Disperst the shadowes of the mistie night,
And *Titan* playing on the eastern streames,
Gan cleare the deawy ayre with springing light,
Sir *Guyon* mindfull of his vow yplight,
Uprose from drowsie couch.

(II.iii.1.1-6)

Early before the Morne with cremosin ray,
The windowes of bright heaven opened had,
Through which into the world the dawning day
Might looke, that maketh every creature glad,
Uprose Sir *Guyon*.

(II.xi.3.1-5)

Earely the morrow next, before that day
His joyous face did to the world reveale,
They both uprose.

(III.ii.48.1-3)

And earely, ere the morrow did upreare
His deawy head out of the *Ocean* maine,
He up arose.

(III.iv.61.3-5)

The morow next, so soone as *Phoebus* Lamp
Bewrayed had the world with early light,
And fresh *Aurora* had the shady damp
Out of the goodly heaven amoved quight,
Faire *Britomart* and that same *Faerie* knight
Uprose.

(III.x.1.1-6)

Early before the heavens fairest light
Out of the ruddy East was fully reard,
The heardes out of their foldes were loosed quight.

(III.x.52.6-8)

The morow next so soone as *Titan* shone,
They both uprose.

(IV.i.16.5-6)

So soone as heavens window shewed light,
These warlike Champions all in armour shine,
Assembled were in field.

(IV.iii.3.7-9)

And now the day out of the Ocean mayne
Began to peepe above this earthly masse,
With pearly dew sprinkling the morning grasse:
Then up he rose.

(IV.v.45.3-6)

So soone as day forth dawning from the East,
Nights humid curtaine from the heavens withdrew,
[Artegall and Radigund prepared to fight].

(V.v.1.1-2)

The morrow next, so soone as dawning houre
Discovered had the light to living eye,
She [Britomart] forth yssew'd out of her loathed bowre.

(V.vi.35.1-3)

The morrow next, so soone as dawning light
Bad doe away the dampe of drouzie sleepe,
The warlike Amazon out of her bowre did peepe.

(V.vii.26.7-9)

The morrow next appear'd, with purple hayre
Yet dropping fresh out of the *Indian* fount,
And bringing light into the heavens fayre,
When he [Prince Arthur] was readie to his steede to mount.

(V.x.16.5-8)

The morrow next, that was the dismall day,
Appointed for *Irenas* death before,
So soone as it did to the world display
His chearefull face, and light to men restore,

. . . .

Then up she rose.

(V.xii.11.1-4, 12.1)

The morrow next, before the lampe of light
Above the earth upreard his flaming head,
The Dwarfe, which bore that message to her knight,
Brought aunswere backe.

(VI.i.31.1-4)

Earely, so soone as *Titans* beames forth brust
Through the thicke clouds, in which they steeped lay
All night in darkenesse, duld with yron rust,
Calidore rising up as fresh as day,
Gan freshly him addresse unto his former way.

(VI.iii.13.5-9)

The morrow next, so soone as joyous day
Did shew it selfe in sunny beames bedight,

. . . .

[Serena] Uprear'd her head to see that chearefull sight.

(VI.iii.45.1-2, 5)

Spenser could have found this mythological account of dawn in any number of classical and Renaissance poets. But Homer is enough, since all of Spenser's descriptions of sunrise are merely ornamented reworkings of four basic passages from the *Iliad*:

As soon as early Dawn appeared, the rosy fingered (I.477).

The sun was now just striking on the fields, as he rose from softly-gliding, deep-flowing Oceanus, and climbed the heavens (VII.421-423).

Now Dawn rose from her couch from beside lordly Tithonus, to bring light to immortals and to mortal men (XI.1-2).

Now Dawn the saffron-robed arose from the streams of Oceanus to bring light to immortals and to mortal men (XIX.1-2).

The picture of sunrise was enriched for Spenser by intervening poets—for instance, by Ovid's long description of Phoebus' chariot and the preparations for his daily journey (*Metamorphoses*, II.107-121). But Spenser almost certainly was working with Homer in mind, because he alone of all epic poets habitually used references to dawn as an introduction to a new episode in his narrative, and only Homer employed a formula to announce the arrival of a new day.[24]

The dependence upon mythology to express the natural process of daybreak is characteristic of Spenser's style. Poetic tradition, rather than any demand for naturalism, dictated the terms of the description. Spenser employed the same technique to indicate the arrival of night with its attendant dampness. Eight of the twelve eclogues in *The Shepheardes Calender* end with similar references to approaching darkness:

> By that [time], the welked *Phoebus* gan availe,
> His weary waine, and nowe the frosty *Night*
> Her mantle black through heaven gan overhaile.
> Which seene, the pensife boy halfe in despight
> Arose, and homeward drove his sonned sheepe.
> ("Jan.," 73-77)

Passages depicting nightfall in *The Faerie Queene* also follow this pattern.[25] The disappearance of Phoebus and his Sun-chariot into the western sea is merely a final phase of the mythology of sunrise; and Aurora, who preceded Phoebus at dawn, is now replaced by Night, who follows behind and covers the sky with her black cloak.

Spenser's habit of depicting weather processes through classical myth extends to meteors other than the moisture changes at sunrise and nightfall. Lightning rarely occurs unless Jove himself hurls "the fierce threeforked engin" (*F. Q.*, I.viii.9.6), and the wind is blown by mild Zephyrus or blustering Boreas. The action of *The Faerie Queene* is in fact begun by such a mythological meteor; immediately after the entrance of Una and Red Crosse, they are forced to seek cover from a shower produced by Jove for his paramour, the earth (I.i.6.4-8), and thereby they chance upon Errour's den. In the next canto the interlude of Fradubio and Fraelissa is begun when Duessa and the Knight stop under the trees to escape the oppressive

[24] No less than twenty-two times Homer repeated the line

ἦμος δ' ἠριγένεια φάνη ῥοδοδάκτυλος Ἠώς

(*Iliad*, I.477; XXIV.788; *Odyssey*, II.1; III.404, 491; IV.306, 431, 576; V.228; VIII.1; IX.152, 170, 307, 437, 560; X.187; XII.8, 316; XIII.18; XV.189; XVII.1; XIX.428).

[25] Cf. *F. Q.*, I.iv.44.1-3; I.v.44.7-9; I.xi.31.1-5; I.xi.49.5-9; II.ix.10.1-3; III.ii.28.1-4; III.iv.51.5-9; III.viii.51.3-6; III.x.45.9, 46.5-7; III.xii.1.1-5; V.vii.8.6-8; VI.iii.29.1-2, 7; VI.ix.13.1-3.

noonday heat, which is attributed to the fierce riding of Phoebus in his Sun-chariot:

> For golden *Phoebus* now ymounted hie,
> From fiery wheeles of his faire chariot
> Hurled his beame so scorching cruell hot,
> That living creature mote it not abide.
> (I.ii.29.3-6)

Such pretentious passages, patterned after Tasso's ornate pastoralism, recur throughout Spenser's work. The scene of the *Prothalamion* is set by a breeze that tempers the sun's heat—or rather, Zephyrus moderates the heat of Phoebus' rays:

> Calme was the day, and through the trembling ayre,
> Sweete breathing *Zephyrus* did softly play
> A gentle spirit, that lightly did delay
> Hot *Titans* beames, which then did glyster fayre.
> (lines 1-4)

These examples of mythological meteorology would not be particularly significant if there were comparable passages describing meteors in naturalistic terms. But such passages of natural description are indeed rare in Spenser. Only when describing a tempest does he lay aside the mythology, and often even in these passages mythology is sublimated into personification:

> And the faire welkin fowly overcast,
> Gan blowen up a bitter stormy blast,
> With shoure and hayle so horrible and dred.
> (*F. Q.*, III.ix.11.4-6)

> With that, an hideous storme of winde arose,
> With dreadfull thunder and lightning atwixt,
> And an earth-quake, as if it streight would lose
> The worlds foundations from his centre fixt;
> A direfull stench of smoke and sulphure mixt
> Ensewd.
> (*F. Q.*, III.xii.2.1-6)[26]

Meteors presented in this naturalistic manner have a physical frame of reference. They recall to the reader's mind his own sense experience of the physical world. Their effect is therefore different from

[26] For other passages presenting tempests in primarily naturalistic terms, see *F. Q.*, II.vii.1.1-5, II.viii.48.1-7, III.iv.13.1-6, IV.i.45.5-9, IV.iv.47.1-9, IV.ix.33.4-9. Note that all of these passages are in fully developed Homeric similes. Many of the *Amoretti* are based on the conceit that the mistress' displeasure is a cloud which overcasts the Sun and brings on tempest; cf., for examples, xxxiv, xl, xlvi, lxiii.

the effect of meteors depicted through mythology, where literary tradition provides the only frame of reference.

Until now we have considered Spenser's presentation of meteors with little regard to his poetical intent, except in so far as any description is useful in setting a scene. But for what poetical purposes did Spenser use meteorological information? What sort of similes and metaphors and allegories did he create from this set of beliefs?

We have already noted Spenser's extensive use of short standardized tropes based on meteorology, and their primary effect as poetic diction rather than as full-bodied images. Spenser did not expect these conventions to give his work imagistic dimensions—that is, sensuous vividness or intellectual clarity. He repeated them because he was consciously attempting to be literary. They were in the poetic tradition, and he was writing poetry. They created a satisfying bond between educated poet and educated reader.

Today we tend to discount the effectiveness of such self-conscious signs of sophistication on the very grounds for their existence: they were conventional. And in *The Faerie Queene,* we find the most striking imagery, apart from the larger framework of allegory, to be the extended similes. Frequently Spenser halts the action to allow the full development of a comparison, much in the manner of Homer, Vergil, Ariosto, and Tasso. No less than seventy stanzas of *The Faerie Queene* begin with an "as" or "like" which introduces such an Homeric simile, and many more occur elsewhere than at the beginning of stanzas. Spenser drew from many fields for these extended comparisons: ships and navigation, beasts and birds, geography, Greek legend. But meteorology, as often as any other body of beliefs, supplied the material. In fact, nowhere does Spenser display meteorological information with greater effect.

Quite often these similes are neatly packaged in a single stanza of *The Faerie Queene,* as when Orgoglio's club misses Prince Arthur and strikes into the earth:

> As when almightie *Jove* in wrathfull mood,
> To wreake the guilt of mortall sins is bent,
> Hurles forth his thundring dart with deadly food,
> Enrold in flames, and smouldring dreriment,
> Through riven cloudes and molten firmament;
> The fierce threeforked engin making way,
> Both loftie towres and highest trees hath rent,

And all that might his angrie passage stay,
And shooting in the earth, casts up a mount of clay.
(*F. Q.*, I.viii.9.1-9)

When the simile fills an entire stanza, as in this case, it tends to become parenthetical to the main movement of the narrative. It is not integral, but appears as external elaboration. Even in cases where the simile does not coincide with a stanza unit, it usually seems extravagantly decorative and often contains completely extraneous elements. For example, when the beautiful Florimell dashes out of the thicket and passes Sir Guyon and Britomart:

. . .her faire yellow locks behind her flew,
Loosely disperst with puffe of every blast:
All as a blazing starre doth farre outcast
His hearie beames, and flaming lockes dispred,
At sight whereof the people stand aghast:
But the sage wisard telles, as he has red,
That it importunes death and dolefull drerihed.
(*F. Q.*, III.i.16.3-9)

The image is apt, especially since (as Spenser reminds us, if we have forgotten our Latin) the comet has "hearie beames, and flaming lockes." This is good physical description, and the fifth line emphasizes the wonder of Florimell's beauty. But what functional value have the last two lines, which recall the prognosticative significance of comets? This is not an attempt at epic forecast because, although plenty of "dolefull drerihed" is in store for Florimell, she ends not in "death" but happily wedded to Marinell. So the conclusion must be either that Spenser was unfortunately carried away with the excitement of the simile, or else that he wrote these two lines merely to fill out his stanza. Either conclusion points to the externality, and rules against the essentiality, of the image.

Spenser exhibits his widest range of meteorological knowledge in such similes. Previous epic poets had elaborated their comparisons at great length; and with these models reassuringly before him, Spenser seems to have felt a greater than usual freedom in developing such figures. As a result, he here ventured to present meteors in ways which he otherwise avoided. Many of his Homeric similes are still nothing but meteorological mythology:

[Britomart blushes]
As faire *Aurora* rising hastily,

Doth by her blushing tell, that she did lye
All night in old *Tithonus* frosen bed,
Whereof she seemes ashamed inwardly.
(*F. Q.*, III.iii.20.4-7)

[The Souldan's horses run away with him]
As when the firie-mouthed steeds, which drew
The Sunnes bright wayne to *Phaetons* decay,
Soone as they did the monstrous Scorpion vew,
With ugly craples crawling in their way,
The dreadfull sight did them so sore affray,
That their well knowen courses they forwent,
And leading th'ever-burning lampe astray,
This lower world nigh all to ashes brent,
And left their scorched path yet in the firmament.
(*F. Q.*, V.viii.40.1-9)

Others begin with meteorological mythology but evolve into natural description, so that the net effect is a visual image rather than a classical allusion:

As when faire *Cynthia*, in darkesome night,
Is in a noyous cloud enveloped,
Where she may find the substaunce thin and light,
Breakes forth her silver beames, and her bright hed
Discovers to the world discomfited;
Of the poore traveller, that went astray,
With thousand blessings she is heried;
Such was the beautie and the shining ray,
With which faire *Britomart* gave light unto the day.
(*F. Q.*, III.i.43.1-9)

As when the daughter of *Thaumantes* faire,
Hath in a watry cloud displayed wide
Her goodly bow, which paints the liquid ayre;
That all men wonder at her colours pride;
All suddenly, ere one can looke aside,
The glorious picture vanisheth away,
Ne any token doth thereof abide:
So did this Ladies [false Florimell's] goodly forme decay,
And into nothing goe, ere one could it bewray.
(*F. Q.*, V.iii.25.1-9)

Another sort depends primarily upon natural description, and includes the only passages in which Spenser seems to have drawn from his own observation of atmospheric phenomena:

As when a windy tempest bloweth hye,
That nothing may withstand his stormy stowre,
The cloudes, as things affrayd, before him flye;
But all so soone as his outrageous powre
Is layd, they fiercely then begin to shoure,
And as in scorne of his spent stormy spight,
Now all attonce their malice forth do poure;
So did Prince *Arthur* beare himselfe in fight.
(*F. Q.*, II.viii.48.1-8)

[Britomart restores the prize to the Knights of Maydenhead]
Like as in sommers day when raging heat
Doth burne the earth, and boyled rivers drie,
That all brute beasts forst to refraine fro meat,
Doe hunt for shade, where shrowded they may lie,
And missing it, faine from themselves to flie;
All travellers tormented are with paine:
A watry cloud doth overcast the skie,
And poureth forth a sudden shoure of raine,
That all the wretched world recomforteth againe.
(*F. Q.*, IV.iv.47.1-9)

These examples are sufficient to show the kind of meteorology that Spenser adapted for Homeric similes. Although such images perhaps seem daring, they are daring only in well-tried ways. They provide no considerable insight nor a fresh point of view. And they make such clamor for themselves that they tend to divert our attention from the main movement of the narrative. The trope then seems to exist for its own sake, not to elucidate the major action.

In one remarkable instance Spenser embodies in a meteor one phase of his allegorical intent. In Book I of *The Faerie Queene* Orgoglio is clearly an earthquake, as his parentage discloses:

The greatest Earth his uncouth mother was,
And blustring *Aeolus* his boasted sire,
Who with his breath, which through the world doth pas,
Her hollow womb did secretly inspire,
And fild her hidden caves with stormie yre,
That she conceiv'd.
(I.vii.9.1-6)

Orgoglio, Spenser pointedly tells us, has been generated by a boisterous Wind blowing through subterranean caves. Moreover, his entrance is heralded by "a dreadfull sownd":

> Which through the wood loud bellowing, did rebownd,
> That all the earth for terrour seemd to shake,
> And trees did tremble.
>
> (I.vii.7.5-7)

And when he walks, "the ground eke groned under him for dreed" (I.vii.8.6). A personified earthquake is particularly fitting as an embodiment of pride, since this meteor is the interaction between wind (words) and earth (gross desires). As noted at the end of his genealogy, Orgoglio is "puft up with emptie wind," the heritage from Aeolus, his father, and "fild with sinfull crime," his birthright from the earth, his mother (I.vii.9.9).

From this examination of Spenser's meteorological imagery, two major points emerge: (1) Spenser constantly repeated the short meteorological similes and metaphors which poetic convention had standardized, and (2) for his description of weather phenomena he relied much more heavily upon mythology than upon technical knowledge or personal observation. These two points coalesce into a final comment that Spenser preferred to follow the poetic traditions dealing with meteors rather than to attempt new techniques which would describe atmospheric processes with greater sensuous immediacy or would adapt meteors for more intellectually exciting imagery. His meteorological images draw their meaning from our literary experience, and have little relation to our experience of the physical everyday world. Spenser employed meteorological imagery only to make his work more "poetic," to recall the rich literary tradition and to display accepted ornament. It is seldom essential to meaning, nor even integral—it rarely carries the burden. This strictly literary meteorology gives Spenser's poetry a precious, hothouse atmosphere, so that even *The Shepheardes Calender* and *The Faerie Queene* never really get outdoors.

We must conclude that Spenser's individual images drawn from meteorology fail to evoke any profound response. The genius from which he drew his power rested in the more comprehensive ability to blazon forth great truths by means of characters and symbols in action. The suggestion that Orgoglio is a personified earthquake illustrates the basic method by which Spenser stated his poetic meaning, a method larger in scope than single images. His greatness derives from the virtuosity and veracity of his allegory.

CHAPTER TWO

CHRISTOPHER MARLOWE

MARLOWE used fewer images based on meteors than did Spenser, and yet Marlowe's meteorological imagery is much more memorable. It has the qualities of freshness and vividness which Spenser's imagery largely lacks. It adds richness without seeming artificial. It adds forcefulness without seeming forced. It is bold in the way that Marlowe's intellect itself was bold. Marlowe's *inventio*, at least so far as imagery is concerned, was considerably more virile than Spenser's.

Marlowe repeated some of the poetic conventions involving meteors, but much less frequently than Spenser and with much less servility. The only convention that Marlowe used a number of times was the comparison of thunder to artillery, horses' hoofs, or drums.[1] But whatever the convention, Marlowe gave it a new twist, usually by the addition of rejuvenating elements. For instance, Tamburlaine declares that Zenocrate is "fairer than whitest snow on Scythian hils" (*1 Tamb.*, 285). Here Marlowe cites the traditional whiter-than-snow hyperbole, but he refurbishes it by adding a bit of exotic geography. In *Hero and Leander* he repeats the cliché that Fame "is swifter than the wind." But he immediately appends touches of mythology and technical theory to modify this conventional wind: "whose tardie plumes / Are reeking water and dull earthlie fumes" (II.115-116). From mythology Marlowe calls up the picture of a winged Wind-god; and his feathers are dripping the vapors and exhalations which technical theory believed the Sun to draw up from the earth. So this commonplace about the swiftness of wind is infused with new vitality.

Marlowe could wreak the same transformation on trite ideas from mythology. For example, he did not slavishly reiterate the poetic formulas for sunrise and sunset. He began with the traditional pic-

[1] Cf. *1 Tamb.*, 616-619, 1382, 2113; *2 Tamb.*, 2484, 2864, 3406, 3686; *Faustus*, 631; *Edward II*, 930-931.

ture of Aurora and Phoebus; but from this raw material, he constructed entirely fresh and individual images:

> Now had the morne espy'de her lovers steeds,
> Wherat she starts, puts on her purple weeds,
> And red for anger that he stayd so long,
> All headlong throwes her selfe the clouds among.
> (*Hero*, II.87-90)

In *1 Tamburlaine* Bajazeth prays for the arrival of Night in her chariot, but the traditional picture is embellished with lively details:

> O highest Lamp of everliving *Jove*,
> Accursed day infected with my griefs,
> Hide now thy stained face in endles night,
> And shut the windowes of the lightsome heavens.
> Let ugly darknesse with her rusty coach
> Engyrt with tempests wrapt in pitchy clouds,
> Smother the earth with never fading mistes:
> And let her horses from their nostrels breathe
> Rebellious winds and dreadfull thunderclaps.
> (lines 2071-2079)

The vigor of Marlowe's presentation of dawn and nightfall makes Spenser's handling of these events seem puerile and merely pretty. Marlowe has added novel details and he has contrived uncommon wording to rework the stereotypes into fresh images which combine the dignity of tradition with the vitality of innovation.

Marlowe's meteorological images also reveal considerable technical knowledge. This scientific theory is never obtrusive, however, and it is always skilfully subdued to the poetical intent of the image. The fundamental principle that the Sun and stars exhale evaporations from the earth explains this curse on Tamburlaine:

> Make heaven to frowne and every fixed starre
> To sucke up poison from the moorish fens,
> And poure it in this glorious Tyrants throat.
> (lines 1449-1451)

The theory of earthquakes, expressed as a battle between "windy exhalations" in subterranean hollows, underlies this forecast about the invincibility of Tamburlaine's army:

> . . . their waight shall make the mountains quake,
> Even as when windy exhalations,
> Fighting for passage, tilt within the earth.
> (lines 245-247)

Tamburlaine recounts his capture of Bajazeth in terms of the technical belief that lightning results from the conflict between a compacted exhalation and an enclosing cloud:

> . . .I took this Turke:
> As when a fiery exhalation
> Wrapt in the bowels of a freezing cloude,
> Fighting for passage, make[s] the Welkin cracke,
> And casts a flash of lightning to the earth.
> (lines 1486-1490)

Upon the same technical theory of lightning and thunder Faustus builds a prayer for salvation:

> You starres that raignd at my nativitie,
> Whose influence hath alotted death and hel,
> Now draw up Faustus like a foggy mist,
> Into the intrailes of yon labring cloude,
> That when you vomite foorth into the ayre,
> My limbes may issue from your smoaky mouthes,
> So that my soule may but ascend to heaven.
> (lines 1443-1449)

Faustus begs the planets to exhale him upward into a cloud. There his gross Earthly parts would be compacted into a thunderstone and rejected, thus purifying his soul for admission into heaven.

Although as a general rule Marlowe did not use many meteorological images, in the Tamburlaine plays meteors assume an unusual prominence. The first prologue assures the audience: "You shall heare the Scythian *Tamburlaine* / Threatning the world with high astounding tearms" (lines 4-5); and in carrying out this promise, Marlowe draws upon the full repertory of wondrous meteors. Usually these atmospheric anomalies are described by Tamburlaine himself in boasts about his control over the entire sublunary world, even up to the highest region of Air. Tamburlaine delivers a lengthy example of such a boast when he steps upon Bajazeth as a footstool to his throne:

> Now cleare the triple region of the aire,
> And let the majestie of heaven beholde
> Their Scourge and Terrour treade on Emperours.
> Smile Stars that raign'd at my nativity:
> And dim the brightnesse of their neighbor Lamps,
> Disdaine to borrow light of *Cynthia*,

For I the chiefest Lamp of all the earth,
First rising in the East with milde aspect,
But fixed now in the Meridian line,
Will send up fire to your turning Spheares,
And cause the Sun to borrowe light of you.
My sword stroke fire from his coat of steele,
Even in *Bythinia,* when I took this Turke:
As when a fiery exhalation
Wrapt in the bowels of a freezing cloude,
Fighting for passage, make[s] the Welkin cracke,
And casts a flash of lightning to the earth.
But ere I martch to wealthy *Persea,*
Or leave *Damascus* and th'Egyptian fields,
As was the fame of *Clymenes* brain-sicke sonne,
That almost brent the Axeltree of heaven,
So shall our swords, our lances and our shot
Fill all the aire with fiery meteors.
Then when the Sky shal waxe as red as blood,
It shall be said, I made it red my selfe,
To make me think of nought but blood and war.
(lines 1474-1499)

This is Tamburlaine at his bombastic best. His tirade is enhanced by the exotic geography, the obscured classical allusion to Phaeton, the uncommon technical phrases—but most of all by visual images of terrible meteors: Tamburlaine himself appearing in the East brighter than the Sun, showing first a "milde aspect," but now growing red and therefore threatening storms; the simile describing Tamburlaine's encounter with Bajazeth as the battle between cloud and fiery exhalation, resulting in destructive lightning; the vaunting claim that his weapons and artillery will fill the air like fiery meteors, presaging bloodshed and war.

These boasts in terms of wondrous meteors continue throughout both plays and epitomize more than any other imagery the high-reaching claims of Tamburlaine. Early in the first play he declares to his assembled officers:

Our quivering lances shaking in the aire,
And bullets like *Joves* dreadfull thunderbolts,
Enrolde in flames and fiery smoldering mistes,
Shall threat the Gods more than Cyclopian warres.
(lines 616-619)

In the final act of the first play, Tamburlaine observes that the portentous anomaly of bloody rain has resulted from his successes, an anomaly which foredooms the world (lines 2239-2244). When Zenocrate dies, Tamburlaine orders forth a lengthy catalogue of dreadful portents (lines 3191-3204); and after taking the city of Babylon, he compares the significance of his vermillion tents to the dire significance of comets (lines 4198-4202).

Even Tamburlaine's enemies think of him in terms of terrible meteors. When Agydas' treachery has been exposed, the fury of Tamburlaine shows in his eyes, which "shine as Comets, menacing revenge" (line 1059); and Agydas, interpreting these tokens of disaster, prepares for his own death like a seaman preparing for a tempest (lines 1061-1071). Orcanes, preparing to meet Tamburlaine in battle, declares that "with the thunder of his martial tooles / [He] Makes Earthquakes in the hearts of men and heaven" (lines 2864-2865). And the defeated King of Jerusalem ineffectually rants before his conqueror:

> Thy victories are growne so violent,
> That shortly heaven, fild with the meteors
> Of blood and fire thy tyrannies have made,
> Will poure down blood and fire on thy head:
> Whose scalding drops wil pierce thy seething braines,
> And with our bloods, revenge our bloods on thee.
> (lines 3814-3819)

But Tamburlaine is unperturbed, and replies by repeating his boast of continued sway over the entire sublunary universe:

> I will with engines, never exercisde,
> Conquer, sacke, and utterly consume
> Your cities and your golden pallaces,
> And with the flames that beat against the clowdes
> Incense the heavens, and make the starres to melt,
> As if they were the teares of *Mahomet*
> For hot consumption of his countries pride:
> And til by vision, or by speach I heare
> Immortall *Jove* say, Cease my *Tamburlaine*,
> I will persist a terrour to the world,
> Making the Meteors, that like armed men
> Are seene to march upon the towers of heaven,
> Run tilting round about the firmament,

And breake their burning lances in the aire,
For honor of my woondrous victories.
(lines 3866-3880)

Finally, Tamburlaine compares his triumphal entry into Samarkand with the mythological account of Jupiter riding along the Milky Way to his palace:[2]

Then in my coach like *Saturnes* royal son,
Mounted his shining chariot, gilt with fire,
And drawen with princely Eagles through the path,
Pav'd with bright christall, and enchac'd with starres,
When all the Gods stand gazing at his pomp.
So will I ride through *Samarcanda* streets,
Until my soule dissevered from this flesh,
Shall mount the milk-white way and meet him there.
(lines 4104-4111)

As thoughts of death encroach, the Milky Way becomes the highway to heaven, and the gaudy picture of pagan pomp quickly transforms itself to Christian sentiment.

In the Tamburlaine plays the imagery based on marvelous meteors is largely visual, and its simple purpose is to generate awe in the audience. The imagery presents the greatest possible magnificence and terror in the natural processes of the Airy region. By continued association, it transfers these attributes to Tamburlaine, who, taking a lesson from Faustus' Evil Angel, attempts to be "on earth as *Jove* is in the skie, / Lord and commaunder of these Elements" (*Faustus,* 104-105). This *modus operandi* is overwhelmingly effective in Tamburlaine, where excess is the rule. Marlowe abided by decorum, however, and marvelous meteors are all but absent in his other work.

Marlowe's meteorological imagery is most notable, then, for its forcefulness. Inevitably he echoed some of the poetic conventions, but always he transmuted the commonplace into a freshly provocative image. Marlowe knew his Vergil and Ovid, but he also knew his Pliny; and he saw in classical meteorology not just a storehouse of mythological allusions, but a source for almost unlimited imaginative wonder. He ventured to adapt esoteric technical information for imagistic purposes, and he cleverly transferred to Tamburlaine the

[2] See p. 104, above.

excitement of marvelous meteors found in chronicles and wonder-books.

Marlowe recoiled from the banal and reveled in the extraordinary. His poetry flaunts unusual words and combinations of words. Often the denotations are incongruous and preclude a precise statement of his meaning, as when Tamburlaine mourns beside the sick-bed of Zenocrate:

> Blacke is the beauty of the brightest day,
> The golden balle of heavens eternal fire,
> That danc'd with glorie on the silver waves:
> Now wants the fewell that enflamde his beames
> And all with faintnesse and for foule disgrace,
> He bindes his temples with a frowning cloude,
> Ready to darken earth with endlesse night.
> (lines 2969-2975)

The words are used promiscuously and the metaphors are mixed. But the phrases sound well together, and they merge into a vigorous general idea with highlighted details and an infinitude of shadowy implications. Perhaps this is the basic technique of romantic poetry.

CHAPTER THREE

BEN JONSON

LIKE Marlowe, Jonson was primarily a playwright. Jonson's most enduring works, his plays and masques, were prepared for the stage. When we turn from Marlowe to Jonson, however, the flamboyance of the earlier dramatist accentuates the classical restraint of James's laureate. Marlowe's boldness at first makes the carefulness of Jonson seem pallid. But Jonson's carefulness is not the old-fashioned conservatism of Spenser; it is instead a new attention to order and organization taught by Horace. Jonson possessed the potential power of Marlowe, but kept it tightly in check.

Jonson exhibited firsthand knowledge of many of the pseudo sciences that flourished in Elizabethan London. He continually parodied the hokus-pokus of astrologers,[1] and he displayed considerable learning in Renaissance metallurgy[2] and physiology.[3] Jonson was also well informed about the accepted theories of meteorology, as he clearly shows in his description of the stage mechanism for the masque *Hymenaei*.[4] Circumscribed by the sphere of Fire, Juno presides over the atmospheric system of Aristotelian meteorology—the three regions of Air with the meteors appropriate to each.

But Jonson seldom drew upon the esoteric details of meteorology. Perhaps his overdeveloped sense of decorum prevented his frequent use of such unusual information. In any event, meteorological imagery is not often found in Jonson. He repeated some few of the poetical conventions: there are showers of tears,[5] noises

[1] Note, as examples, Sordido's dependence upon almanacs in *E.M.O.H.H.;* Subtle's gulling of Dapper and Drugger in *Alchemist;* Meercraft, "the projector," in *Devil Is an Ass;* and Almanac in *Staple of News.*

[2] The most obvious instance is *Alchemist,* II.iii.142 ff.

[3] For Jonson's most memorable take-off on quack doctors, see *Volpone,* II.ii.33 ff.

[4] Quoted p. 45, above.

[5] *Cynthias Revels,* I.ii.69 ff.; *Sejanus,* II.226-229; *Sad Shepherd,* I.iii.52-55, I.v.38-39.

as loud as thunder,[6] storms of displeasure[7] or misfortune,[8] and comparisons with the whiteness of snow[9] and the swiftness of lightning.[10] But even these do not occur as prominently in his work as in most literature of the period.

The only meteors that stand out conspicuously in Jonson's writings are the weather gods and goddesses that appear in his masques. Jonson was fully aware of the pictorial impressiveness of the inhabitants of Olympus, and many of them ornamented his court entertainments. The postperformance description of *Hymenaei*, in which Juno reigns as mistress of the weather, is typical of the ostentatious effect for which he strove.

The meteorological deity most often seen in Jonson's court productions was Zephyrus (or Favonius), usually in connection with his marriage to Chloris (or Flora), goddess of flowers. Jonson's last masque at court, *Chloridia*, was fundamentally a glorification of Zephyrus' association with Chloris. In *The Entertainment at Highgate* Zephyrus and Flora, accompanied by Aurora, entered to sing for the King and Queen visiting the gardens of Sir William Cornwallis on May-morning (lines 68 ff.). In *The Vision of Delight*, midway through the masque "the whole scene changed to the Bower of *Zephyrus*" (lines 126 ff.); and although it is midwinter (the entertainment was given at Christmas), the presence of the King brings about a mock spring of flowers (lines 142-148). Throughout Jonson's poems and masques there are references to "the soft West-wind" (*Sad Shepherd*, I.i.7), "the Father of the flowers" (*Fortunate Isles*, 467).[11]

[6] "Ode" [*Under-wood*, p. 239], 7-9; "To the King" [*Under-wood*, p. 249], 1-4; *Volpone*, IV.iv.21; *Catiline*, I.406, IV.464-465; *Magnetic Lady*, I.vi.17; *Kings Entertainment*, 282-284; *Panegyre*, 152-154; *Entertainment at Highgate*, 29-30; *Gypsies Metamorphos'd*, 730-732.

[7] "Elegie" [*Under-wood*, p. 191], 13-14; *Volpone*, V.iii.39; *Catiline*, III.585-587; *Sad Shepherd*, I.vii.2; *Prince Henries Barriers*, 113-117; *Lovers Made Men*, 46, 60.

[8] "On William Lord Burleigh" [*Under-wood*, p. 185], 9-10; *Case Is Altered*, III.iv.29-33; *E.M.O.H.H.*, IV.vi.138; *Volpone*, III.iv.39 ff.; *Bartholomew Fair*, V.ii.5-6; *Sad Shepherd*, III.v.4.

[9] "Her Triumph" [*Under-wood*, p. 134], 23-24; "Her man described. . . ." [*Under-wood*, p. 141], 18; "Ode" [Ungathered Verse, p. 367], 40; *Volpone*, I.v. 110-111; *Devil Is an Ass*, II.iv.106-107; *Staple of News*, IV.ii.70-71.

[10] "To the King" [*Under-wood*, p. 249], 1-4; *E.M.I.H.H.*, IV.vii.13-14; *E.M.O.H.H.*, IV.viii.24; *Catiline*, I.304.

[11] Cf. "His Discourse with *Cupid*" [*Under-wood*, p. 137], 27-28; "Elegie" [*Under-wood*, p. 191], 58; "The Mind" [*Under-wood*, p. 277], 66-68; *Enter-*

Although Jonson exploited the mythological meteorology that he derived from the Greeks and Romans, his poetic imagery based on meteors is not imitative of the classics in either design or effect. Unlike Spenser, who outrightly cribbed numerous poetic devices from Homer and Vergil, Jonson has almost no meteorological imagery that can be traced directly to these poets. It is true that in his marginal glosses he often refers to a specific author of antiquity, but normally this is little more than a pretentious display of erudition. The allusion could not be pinpointed without the pedantic footnote supplied by Jonson.

This passage from *Catiline*, in which Lentulus calls attention to the foreboding state of the morning sky, illustrates the way in which Jonson reworked classical materials:

> It is, me thinks, a morning full of fate!
> It riseth slowly, as her sollen carre
> Had all the weights of sleepe and death hung at it!
> Shee is not rosy-finger'd, but swolne black!
> Her face is like a water, turn'd to bloud,
> And her sick head is bound about with clouds,
> As if shee threatned night, ere noone of day!
> (I.191-197)

The basic image is the traditional picture of Aurora advancing in her chariot. Jonson actually repeats "rosy-finger'd," Homer's usual epithet; and "the weights of sleep and death" which retard her car are a vague echo from Hesiod, who had contended that Sleep and Death were the twin offspring of Night (*Theogony*, 758 ff.). Jonson's image, however, is a re-creation of the classical Aurora rather than an imitation of ancient sources. Jonson does not call her by name, and in consequence the personification is not emphasized. The image is left ambivalent. Morning appears to the audience as a natural phenomenon as well as a goddess, and therefore the presentation need not be entirely mythological, but may contain touches of natural description. Moreover, in his re-created picture Jonson includes a weather sign: "Her face is like a water, turn'd to bloud" is Jonson's circumlocution for the commonplace that a red morning foretells a stormy day.[12] In summary, this passage has unmistakable

---

tainment at Highgate, 70-74, 124-125; *Vision of Delight*, 151-152, 184, 226-227; *Fortunate Isles*, 502-503.

[12] See p. 220 below.

classical antecedents; but Jonson has made additions of natural description and commonplace belief so that the resultant image differs greatly from its classical origins. Under Jonson's firm hand the disparate materials have combined to form an eye catching, but not gaudy, image—an image which perfectly fulfils Jonson's purpose of presaging the evil and violence shortly to break out in *Catiline*.

By his dedication to classical restraint, Jonson subdued the exuberance that characterized the earlier Elizabethans. He rejected Spenser's naïve earnestness and Marlowe's poetic fervor, and chose instead the rigid tenets of *ars poetica Horatiana*. Jonson reasoned through each literary problem. In his guarded use of poetic imagery, in the carefulness by which he makes the imagery completely subservient to his immediate intention, Jonson is most clearly a precursor of the Augustan Age.

CHAPTER FOUR

GEORGE CHAPMAN

CHAPMAN is perhaps the most complex author of his age. He was a genius dedicated to literature, but a genius who produced no original work that commands a place in the first rank. This failure to create poetry with permanent vitality is difficult to reconcile with his exceptional talent and intellect.

Chapman's greatest asset was a sensitivity to words comparable to Marlowe's, and he retained much of the energetic forcefulness that enlivens the best Elizabethan poetry. His lines often lack direction and clarity, however; and without this sweetness and light, his intellectual vigor expends itself futilely. Chapman's inattention to form, in both his poems and plays, is no doubt the major defect that accounts for his failure to please succeeding generations. His most readable works are the translations of Homer and Hesiod, where the form was already provided and he needed to supply only words. Chapman lacked the ability to order his materials into well-organized entities—but throughout his works, even in the dullest of his plays, there are isolated passages of surprising beauty and power.

Chapman of all his contemporaries brought into his poetry the purest meteorological theory. His inquiring mind ranged through many fields of learning; and though he fancied himself pre-eminently a classical scholar, his knowledge of the natural sciences was extensive. The suspicion of his activities in such a group as the School of Night, even if not substantiated, at least indicates a direction toward which his interests tended. And the fact is indisputable that during the 1590's he dedicated important poems to Matthew Roydon, the mathematician, and Thomas Harriot, the astronomer.

Turning from external to internal evidence, we can see in Chapman's poetry ample proof that he drew inspiration from the science of meteorology. Everywhere there are esoteric terms: "meteor," "vapor," "fumes," "exhalation," "impressions," "air's middle region." Chapman was careful to give these terms their technical meaning; and as to be expected, they occur in passages based squarely on meteorological theory. Underlying the opening lines of the *Hymnus in Noctem*, for example, is the fundamental principle of Aristotelian meteorology: the earth exhales two sorts of evaporations, one moist (which Chapman identifies with sighs) and another burning (which he associates with grief). The poet addresses Night:

> Great Goddesse to whose throne in Cynthian fires,
> This earthlie Alter endlesse fumes exspires,
> . . .in fumes of sighes and fires of griefe.
> (lines 1-3)

For the uninformed reader who might miss the scientific basis for these lines, Chapman obligingly provided a gloss, complete with reference to a time-honored authority:

> He cals these Cynthian fiers of Cynthius or the Sunne. In whose beames the fumes and vapors of the earth are exhald. The earth being as an aulter, and those fumes as sacrificing smokes, because they seeme pleasing to her in resembling her. That the earth is cald an aulter, *Aratus* in *Astronimicis* [408 ff.] testifies in these verses [a quotation follows].

The entire moisture cycle of Renaissance meteorology is expounded in a passage from *Byron's Tragedy,* which, when taken out of context, has all the didacticism of Vergil's *Georgics* or du Bartas' *Devine Weekes*:

> The clouds, observing their aerial natures,
> Are borne aloft, and then, to moisture [c]hang'd,
> Fall to the earth; where being made thick and cold,
> They lose both all their heat and levity;
> Yet then again recovering heat and lightness,
> Again they are advanc'd, and by the sun
> Made fresh and glorious.
> (V.iii.42-48)

The clouds rise as Airy vapors, hot and moist, but potentially like Water, cold and moist. Reaching the cold middle region of Air, they condense to Water and fall as rain to the ground. There, losing their heat and lightness (i.e., their Airy qualities), they are transmuted into Earth, cold and dry. At this point the heat of the Sun exhales fresh vapors, and so the cycle continues. This explanation of cloud formation is exact according to Renaissance theory, and only

Byron's exegesis and personal application of this parable-like lesson in meteorology gives the passage poetic meaning:

> . . .and since clouds are rapt
> With these uncertainties, now up, now down,
> Am I to flit so with his [the King's] smile or frown?
> (V.iii.48-50)

Byron's conclusion remains true to the original image: the King is still the Sun who exhales or neglects the evaporations by his smile or his frown.

A mistress as well as a king could be the Sun that drew up evaporations. Corinna assumes this imagistic role when Ovid partakes of the first course in his *Banquet of Sence* by hearing her sing:

> And like a fiery exhalation
> [He] Followd the sun, he wisht might never set.
> (xiii.5-6)

Chapman elaborates this image in the third course of the *Banquet*, when Ovid first looks upon Corinna:

> He blusht, lookt pale, and like a fevour shooke,
> And as a burning vapor being exhalde
> Promist by *Phoebus* eye to be a star,
> Heavens walles denying to be further scalde
> The force dissolves that drewe it up so far:
> And then it lightens gainst his death and fals,
> So *Ovids* powre, this powrefull sight appals.
> (l.3-9)

Chapman glossed this passage with a marginal note calling attention to the scientific theory behind the image, and to the venerable poets of antiquity who also used *stellae cadentes* in similes:

> This simile expresseth the cause and substance of those exhalations which vulgarly are called falling starres: so *Homer* and *Virgill* calls them, *Stellas cadentes*, *Homer* comparing the descent of *Pallas* among the Troyans to a falling Starre.

Chapman has here translated scientific theory into a pretty simile by the elementary trick of referring to the Sun as "*Phoebus* eye" and to the region of Air as "heavens walles." There are also hints of the Ovidian notion that love is a war and the mistress a fortress to be taken. But basically the image is still technical; and we may suppose that Corinna's disdainful hostility is sufficient to chill Ovid in his metaphorical state as a hot exhalation, thus sending him dejectedly back to his place of origin in melancholy earth.

The exhalation:man image appears elsewhere in a political context. In *Teares of Peace* Chapman muses upon the uncertainty of fortune and decides to withdraw from "the hot glades of Ambition," because he has observed:

> . . .how (like men
> Raisd to high places) Exhalations fall
> That would be thought Starres.
> (lines 1008-1010)

Here the exhalation falls because it lacks the celestial nature of the true star, so that when the Sun withdraws support, the earthly meteor drops. Epernon repeats the same idea as an epitaph for Byron when he is taken in custody from the stage:

> Farewell for ever! So have I discern'd
> An exhalation that would be a star
> Fall, when the sun forsook it, in a sink.
> (*Byron's Tragedy*, IV.ii.291-293)

The aspiring courtier is again an exhalation drawn up by a Sun-king, and he plummets like a falling star when the Sun-king changes his smile of favor to a frown of disapproval.

In many other instances the technical preciseness of Chapman's meteorological imagery gives evidence of his close familiarity with scientific theory. In *Bussy d'Ambois* Tamyra describes her sudden passion for Bussy as a violent earthquake which has devastated her body (II.ii.34-43).[1] In the sequel to this play, Bussy's ghost returns to soliloquize about the prevalence of moral decrepitude:

> . . .as the thunder
> Seems, by men's duller hearing than their sight,
> To break a great time after lightning forth,
> Yet both at one time tear the labouring cloud,
> So men think penance of their ills is slow,
> Though th' ill and penance still together go.
> (*Revenge of Bussy*, V.i.9-14)

Here Chapman has created poetry from such unpromising material as the relative acuteness of sight and hearing, and the theory of

[1] Quoted pp. 130-131, above.

lightning formation. In fact, his interest in such matters is exceeded only by his desire to moralize.

As a classical scholar, Chapman could be expected to know the mythology dealing with meteors. He makes the usual allusions to Jove with his thunder,[2] to the Cyclopes preparing thunderbolts,[3] to the eagle as Jove's lightning bearer,[4] to Iris,[5] to the Winds.[6] But Chapman enjoyed exhibiting his learning; and although rarely presented with the officious pedantry of Jonson, his mythological references are often recondite. We find allusions to Typhon and his fight against Zeus,[7] to Orithyia and her rape by Boreas,[8] to Castor and Pollux in their role as guardians of sailors,[9] to the Milky Way as the highroad to Jove's place,[10] to the arrow shot at the scorching Sun by Hercules.[11] When Venus sends Leucote to warn the Winds against molesting Leander as he swims across the Hellespont, each Wind appears in the full regalia required by the extravagant mythological tradition:

First to black *Eurus* flies the white *Leucote*,
Borne mongst the *Negros* in the *Levant* Sea,
On whose curld head the glowing Sun doth rise,
And shewes the soveraigne will of Destinies,
To have him cease his blasts, and downe he lies.
Next, to the fennie *Notus* course she holds,
And found him leaning with his armes in folds
Upon a rock, his white hayre full of showres,
And him she chargeth by the fatall powres,
To hold in his wet cheekes his clowdie voyce.
To *Zephire* then that doth in flowres rejoyce.

[2] *Hymnus in Noctem*, 21-22; *Hymnus in Cynthiam*, 196; *Hero*, IV.207; *Andromeda*, 627-629; *Bussy*, I.i.37, IV.ii.36-37; *Caesar*, II.iv.101, II.v.3-4, V.i.171.

[3] *Hero*, IV.222; *Bussy*, IV.ii.36-37; *Caesar*, II.v.3-4.

[4] *Hymnus in Cynthiam*, 49; *Eugenia*, 742-744 and gloss; *Bussy*, III.ii.4-5.

[5] *Hero*, III.109-111; *Eugenia*, 131-132; *Widow's Tears*, IV.ii.171-172.

[6] Eurus: *Hero*, VI.35-37; "De Guiana," 104; *Beggar of Alexandria*, ix.83-84. Zephyrus: *Ovids Banquet*, xxviii.3, lxxxvi.5-6; *Hero*, V.235-236, VI.45; "Hymne to Hymen," 11. Notus: *Hero*, VI.40-44. Boreas: *Hero*, VI.46-49, 191-193. The Winds as a group: *Hymnus in Noctem*, 389; *Hymnus in Cynthiam*, 394-395; *Hero*, VI.12-14, 178-184; *Eugenia*, 128-129; "Hymne to Hymen," 60; *Byron's Conspiracy*, III.i.9-11.

[7] *Hymnus in Noctem*, 118-119; *Eugenia*, 1128-1130.

[8] *Hero*, VI.47-48, 191-193.

[9] *Widow's Tears*, II.iv.50-51.

[10] "Invective against Jonson," 121.

[11] *Hymnus in Noctem*, 257-259 and gloss; *Byron's Conspiracy*, I.ii.40-42; *Chabot*, II.ii.84-85.

> To snake-foote *Boreas* next she did remove,
> And found him tossing of his ravisht love,
> To heate his frostie bosome hid in snow,
> Who with *Leucotes* sight did cease to blow.[12]
> (*Hero,* VI.35-49)

This passage describing the Winds may trace its origin to the account of Creation in Ovid's *Metamorphoses* (I.61-66), and it owes much to the mythological handbooks compiled in Italy. We must note, however, that Chapman's allusions to mythology are not characterized by the insipid delicacy sought by Petrarchan pastoralists. In this passage from *Hero and Leander,* in fact, Zephyrus, the darling of the Italianate poets, is allotted but one line, whereas the less pleasant, more boisterous Winds receive much fuller treatment. Even amidst the decadent ornateness of *Hero and Leander,* Chapman manages to maintain an intellectual masculinity.

Chapman's refusal to indulge in the expected, pretty image is nowhere better shown than in his descriptions of dawn and sunset. Being such a conscious inheritor of the classical tradition, he could not avoid the standardized presentations of Aurora and Phoebus:

> As when the fierie coursers of the sunne,
> Up to the pallace of the morning runne,
> And from their nosthrills blow the spitefull day.
> (*Hymnus in Cynthiam,* 305-307)

But Chapman was aware of the artistic pitfalls hidden in the hackneyed mythology of these natural processes, and in *The Gentleman Usher* he gives an intentional parody of the traditional picture of dawn:

> The red-fac'd sun hath firk'd the flundering shades,
> And cast bright ammel[13] on Aurora's brow.
> . . . .
> The busky groves that gag-tooth'd boars do shroud
> With cringle-crangle horns do ring aloud.
> (I.i.185-186, 188-189)

When Prince Vincentio, the hero of the play, is asked for an opinion on this poetic effort, he replies with pointed irony: "It is strangely good, / No inkhorn ever did bring forth the like" (I.i.192-193).

[12] Note Figure 5.
[13] An archaic form of "enamel."

Chapman spurned the inkhorn-Muse, and his accounts of morning bear the imprint of his individual mind:

> Yet hath the morning sprinkled thr'out the clouds
> But half her tincture, and the soil of night
> Sticks still upon the bosom of the air.
> (*Day's Mirth*, i.1-3)

The image is largely traditional, but the phrasing is fresh. And a bit of scientific theory almost inevitably intrudes—"the soil of night" still hanging in the air is an accumulation of earthly exhalations which the Sun has not yet cleared away.

In his descriptions of nightfall, Chapman displays comparable individuality. He makes passing references to "Nights glorious mantle" which tenderly wraps the earth in darkness (*Hymnus in Noctem*, 336),[14] and once his imagination flags so that he tritely describes twilight as the time " when the light-crown'd monarch of the heavens / Shall quench his fire within the ocean's breast" (*Beggar of Alexandria*, i.274-275).[15] But balanced against this traditionalism are several passages in which Chapman creates entirely new mythology:

> . . .let him [the Sun] still be set
> In Somnus thickets: bound about the browes,
> With pitchie vapours, and with Ebone bowes [i.e., rainbows].
> (*Hymnus in Noctem*, 265-267)

> But dayes arme (tir'd to hold her torch. . .)
> Now let it fall within the Ocean streame,
> . . . .
> The windes made wing, into the upper light,
> And blew abroad the sparckles of the night.
> (*Hymnus in Cynthiam*, 390-391, 394-395)

> No longer could the day nor Destinies
> Delay the night, who now did frowning rise
> Into her throne; and at her humorous brests,
> Visions and Dreames lay sucking: all mens rests
> Fell like the mists of death upon their eyes.
> (*Hero*, VI.1-5)

In the last quotation echoes of Hesiod and Homer are insistent; but the total image, an icon of the goddess Night, is Chapman's own.

[14] Note also *Hymnus in Cynthiam*, 38.
[15] Cf. *Beggar of Alexandria*, i.247-248.

Chapman's most detailed presentation of Night and her attendants occurs when the goddess ascends her throne at the end of the *Hymnus in Noctem.* Chapman portrays the event as a triumphal procession or perhaps as a masque:

> Hence beasts, and birds to caves and bushes then,
> And welcome Night, ye noblest heires of men,
> Hence Phebus to thy glassie strumpets bed,
> And never more let Themis daughters spred,
> Thy golden harnesse on thy rosie horse,
> But in close thickets run thy oblique course.
> See now ascends, the glorious Bride of Brides,
> Nuptials, and triumphs, glittring by her sides,
> Juno and Hymen do her traine adorne,
> Ten thousand torches round about them borne:
> Dumbe Silence mounted on the Cyprian starre,
> With becks, rebukes the winds before his carre,
> Where she advanst; beates downe with cloudie mace,
> The feeble light to blacke Saturnius pallace:
> Behind her, with a brase of silver hynds,
> In ivorie chariot, swifter then the winds,
> Is great Hyperions horned daughter drawne
> Enchantresse-like, deckt in disparent lawne,
> Circkled with charmes, and incantations,
> That ride huge spirits, and outragious passions:
> Musicke, and moode, she loves, but love she hates,
> (As curious Ladies do, their publique cates)
> This traine, with meteors, comets, lightenings,
> The dreadfull presence of our Empresse sings.
> (lines 378-401)

Classical mythology provided most of the materials for this spectacular finale. Phoebus is banished eternally beneath the ocean, his "glassie strumpets bed," while Night arises in her greatest majesty. She is attended by Hymen and Juno, the god and goddess of marriage, and she is respectfully followed by Cynthia, the Moon. In the passage are obscure allusions characteristic of Chapman's mythology—in this case, allusions to "Themis daughters" and "Hyperions horned daughter," each of whom Chapman annotated in a gloss.[16]

[16] (1) "*Themis* daughters are the three houres, *viz. Dice*, *Irene*, and *Eunomia*, begotten by Jupiter. They are said to make ready the horse & chariot of the Sun every morning. *ut Orph*[eus, *Hymns*, xlii.1-2]." Cf. Hesiod, *Theogony*, 901-902; and Ovid, *Metamorphoses*, II.116-121. Chapman, however, is probably quoting from

In addition, Chapman created his own mythology by having Silence act as the gentleman-usher for Night; and he rides upon "the Cyprian starre," which must be Venus' star, or Hesperus. There are also hints of technical theory: the winds are calmed at sunset, Silence "with cloudie mace" excludes all light by overcasting the sky, and a host of other meteors attend Night's progress. Finally, a touch of moralizing satire appears in the comment that the Moon hates love "as curious Ladies do, their publique cates." This is description of scene and mood in the richest Renaissance manner; and not far behind we can already hear the ponderous tread of Milton, *il penseroso.*

Chapman derived much of his scientific information from Aristotle and Aratus, and many of his poetic ideas from Homer, Vergil, and Ovid. When Chapman read the classics, however, he did not stop with the natural philosophers or with the epic poets. Like every sixteenth-century savant, he diligently perused Pliny, the encyclopedist of the marvelous. During Elizabeth's reign, Pliny's fondness for the amazing statement and the incredible anecdote flowed in such channels as the chronicle-history, the bestiary, and the collection of assorted prodigies; and of course it received ever-renewed energy from its fountainhead in the master's own *Historia naturalis.* Furthermore, there was a strong folk tradition which paralleled this literary development. Chapman seems unusually well acquainted with beliefs about prodigious meteors, and many Pliny-like wonders pervade his poetry. In *Caesar and Pompey,* as a perfect example, Pompey recalls an incident which might well have been recorded by Pliny's own pen:

> Empedocles
> Recur'd a mortal plague through all his country
> With stopping up the yawning of a hill,
> From whence the hollow and unwholesome south
> Exhal'd his venom'd vapour.
> (V.i.217-221)

Although in this case the story has been traced to Plutarch's *De*

Natalis Comes, *Mythologiae,* IV.xvi, "De Horis." (2) "*Hesiodus* in *Theogonia* cals her [the Moon] the daughter of *Hyperion,* and *Thya* [371-374]." Chapman again could have found this erudition in Natalis Comes, *Mythologiae,* VI.ii, "De Aurore."

curiositate, it generates the sort of uncritical awe enjoyed by readers of the *Historia naturalis*.[17]

In *Caesar and Pompey* there is also a notable example of a wondrous meteor: multiple suns. In the best chronicle-history manner, Chapman opens his dramatization of the contention between the two Roman generals:

> Now will the two suns of our Roman heaven,
> Pompey and Caesar, in their tropic burning,
> With their contention all the clouds assemble
> That threaten tempests to our peace and empire,
> Which we shall shortly see pour down in blood,
> Civil and natural, wild and barbarous turning.
> (I.i.1-6)

Chapman here cites the meteor of double suns not only for the horror of the portent, but also because it provides him with an extremely functional image: Caesar and Pompey, the two Sun-rulers of the Roman heaven, will by their heat draw up the clouds which will condense into the bloody tempest of civil war. Chapman has taken the bare fact of the prodigy, and has created poetry by metaphorically expanding its prognosticative significance and meteorological consequences. The results are mighty lines worthy of Tamburlaine.

In addition to his knowledge of the lore pertaining to wondrous meteors, Chapman shows an exceptional ease in applying Elizabethan weather rules. He evidently read the almanacs. Chapman knew that a red Sun at rising foretells storms to come, and he introduced this portent as a mock-epic forecast of the disaster awaiting Hero:

> Her blushing het her chamber: she lookt out,
> And all the ayre she purpled round about,
> And after it foule black day befell,
> Which ever since a red morne doth foretell:
> And still renewes our woes for *Heros* wo.
> (III.175-179)

If the Sun appears without clouds at setting, however, good weather is indicated; and Chapman adapted this propitious sign to the mythology of the masque celebrating the marriage of Elizabeth, daughter of James I:

[17] For other noteworthy instances of Chapman's wonder-lore, see *Hero*, IV.76-79, 160-165; *Teares of Peace*, 1121-1125; *Bussy*, V.i.17-19; and *Caesar*, III.i.58-63.

See now the setting sun casts up his bank,
And shows his bright head at his sea's repair,
For sign that all days future shall be fair.
(*Masque*, 244-246)

Chapman must have consulted a mariner's handbook for the simile which describes Corinna rising from her couch when she becomes aware that Ovid has been spying upon her:

Rising as when (the sunne in *Leos signe*)
Auriga with the heavenly Goate upon her,
Shows her horn'd forehead with her Kids divine,
Whose rise kils vines, Heavens face with storms disguising;
No man is safe at sea, the Haedy rising.
(*Ovids Banquet*, lxxiv.5-9)

More homely weather signs depending upon the actions of animals also occur in Chapman's work:

Look how, against great rains, a standing pool
Of paddocks, toads, and water-snakes put up
Their speckled throats above the venomous lake,
Croaking and gasping for some fresh fall'n drops,
To quench their poison'd thirst, being near to stifle
With clotter'd purgings of their own foul bane.
(*Caesar*, I.i.18-23)

But this is not merely the unimaginative repetition of a weather sign. The belief that croaking frogs predict heavy rains is quite interestingly documented with a pseudoscientific explanation. Nor is each of the other weather signs quoted here without its effective poetical purpose, either as a forecast of future events or as a descriptive simile.

Many poetic conventions show up in Chapman's work, especially in his plays. Acceding to his penchant for the wondrous, Chapman reiterated all of the conventions concerning thunder and lightning. The commonplace about the swiftness of lightning provided the epithet "lightning haste" (*D'Olive*, IV.i.83).[18] The noise of drums and shot (*Hymnus in Cynthiam*, 344), of a trumpet (*Hero*, VI.257), of knocking at the door (*Beggar of Alexandria*, iv.161), of the hoofs of a boar (*Gentleman Usher*, I.ii.87), of the roaring of a lion (*Caesar*, II.ii.29)—all are presented as thunder. There are common-

[18] Cf. *Beggar of Alexandria*, x.129-131; *Bussy*, V.i.185-187.

places about winds: "words are but wind" (*D'Olive*, II.ii.245-246);[19] the wind provides a standard for the superlative of swiftness;[20] the winds are "not seene, but heard" (*Teares of Peace*, 503).[21] And there are numerous instances where strong emotions[22] or bad fortune[23] are figuratively expressed as tempests.

Yet, Chapman flaunted very few of the merely pretty conventions, such as the rain:tears metaphor. And when Chapman did use the rain:tears image, he developed it into an active, organic image which is much more than the repetition of a poetic convention:

> . . .love raiseth by his violent heat
> Moist vapours from the heart into the eyes,[24]
> From whence they drown his breast in daily showers.
> (*All Fools*, I.i.7-9)

> My anger's storm? Ah, poor Fortunio,
> One gentle word from thee would soon resolve
> The storm of my rage to a shower of tears.
> (*All Fools*, II.i.16-18)[25]

In the first quotation the lover's shower of tears falls from the clouds raised by the heat of his passion, a microcosmic repetition of the Aristotelian moisture cycle. In the second example the storm of anger could be distilled into a shower of tears by a gentle word, just as a cloud is condensed into rain by warm wind.[26] In both instances Chapman has given imagistic dimensions to the rain:tears convention by elaborating the scientific theory underlying the formation of rain.

We have now seen that Chapman enriched his poetry with ideas about meteors from many places: scientific theory, classical mythology, the wonder-tradition deriving from Pliny, folklore, and poetic

[19] Cf. *Widow's Tears*, I.ii.131-132; *Bussy*, III.ii.238; *Byron's Conspiracy*, V.ii.67-69; *Byron's Tragedy*, III.i.172-173, V.iii.114-116.

[20] Cf. *Hymnus in Noctem*, 393; *Hymnus in Cynthiam*, 250, 351; *Andromeda*, 115-119; "De Guiana," 104.

[21] Cf. *All Fools*, V.ii.269-272.

[22] Note as examples *Ovids Banquet*, xlvi.6, lxxiv.5-9; *Hero*, V.228-240; *Epicede*, 149-151; *All Fools*, II.i.15-18, III.i.230-231; *Bussy*, II.ii.140-141; *Byron's Tragedy*, I.ii.47-50; *Chabot*, III.i.129.

[23] Note as examples *Teares of Peace*, 1091; *D'Olive*, V.i.57; *Byron's Conspiracy*, II.ii.173-174; *Byron's Tragedy*, III.i.62-64, V.iii.213.

[24] Cf. *Beggar of Alexandria*, i.228-229.

[25] For the other two instances of the rain:tears convention in Chapman's work, note *Teares of Peace*, 1063-1064; and "Pro Vere," 1. Snow:whiteness images are also rare in Chapman; note *Ovids Banquet*, lix.5, cix.1-2; *Hero*, V.343, VI.8-10; *Gentleman Usher*, IV.ii.195-196.

[26] See p. 51, above.

convention. Imagery with religious connotation is almost totally lacking,[27] however, and so the charge that Chapman participated in an atheistic School of Night again demands consideration. For those who follow Caroline Spurgeon in reconstructing a poet's personal attitudes on the basis of imagery analysis, this absence of Biblical allusion may be convincing that Chapman was nonreligious. But to others, it may mean only that he excluded religious tropes from his work because such figures with their mystical implications would blunt the intellectual sharpness which he strove to maintain in his imagery. Even Chapman's "Hymne to Our Saviour on the Crosse," although an intensely religious poem, does not incorporate imagery taken from the Scriptures.

This discussion has repeatedly illustrated Chapman's distinctive technique: his habit of allowing the imagery to be the chief vehicle which conveys the intellectual content of the poetry. With Chapman, images are no longer mechanical devices from a handbook of rhetoric to adorn the surface of poetry. Nor are they useful as merely physical or emotional description. Instead, they are integrated segments which taken together make the poetic statement. The meaning is inherent in the image; and such an image, unlike Homeric similes and other rhetorical tropes, cannot be removed without also destroying the continuity of the thought itself.

This poetic technique which develops the argument through imagery demands a certain sort of image. It must be "witty"—that is, it makes its first appeal to the intellect. After we comprehend the image (which in many cases can be achieved only by conscious effort), then the meaning becomes apparent, followed by both ideas and feelings. The "witty" image may aim at the emotions as an ultimate goal, but it reaches the heart by going through the head.

A lucid instance of this sort of poetry occurs in *Ovids Banquet of Sence*. Although this example may seem somewhat frivolous because of the Ovidian excesses, the exaggeration resulting from these excesses reveals more clearly what Chapman is doing. Very early in the poem Chapman declares that Ovid has been drawn "like a fiery exhalation" toward Corinna, his "sun" (xiii.5-6). Ovid hides in a clump of bushes, and proceeds to indulge his senses of smell and hearing. Then, while he contemplates going on to his third course, *visus*, he

[27] One memorable exception is *Eugenia*, 742-744 and gloss.

is warned that the bushes may not be able to conceal him if his passion continues to grow at such a rapid rate:

> . . .the thicket *Floras* hands hath set
> To hide thy theft, is thinne and hollow harted,
> Not meete to have so high a charge imparted.
> (xlii.7-9)

These few lines introduce an image which is developed later: the bushes act as a screening vapor, and Ovid's fiery passion has built up just as exhalations accumulate within a hollow cloud. When exhalations become solidly compacted by the reaction of their Heat against the Cold of a cloud, they burst out in the form of thunderstones—and this is the precise imagistic form that Ovid assumes when his passion forces him to leave the thicket for his fourth course, *gustus*. When Ovid emerges from his hiding place, Corinna haughtily demands, "What savage boldnes hardned thee to this?" (lxxvi.2). To which Ovid replies:

> Love (sacred Madam) love exhaling mee
> (Wrapt in his sulphure) to this clowde of his
> Made my affections his artillerie,
> Shot me at you his proper Cytadell,
> And loosing all my forces, heere I fell.
> (lxxvi.5-9)

This is indeed "witty" poetry. It is based on a knowledge of the process by which thunderstones were produced through the interaction between hot exhalations and a cold cloud. The reader cannot follow what is happening in the poem unless he understands the image, and he cannot understand the image unless he knows his meteorology. Once he comprehends the rather farfetched comparison between Ovid and a thunderstone, however, he can then work out the relationship between Ovid, Love, and Corinna. The result is a clear and clever statement about Ovid's uncontrollable passion.

In his plays as well as poems Chapman relied upon the witty image to convey his meaning. In *The Revenge of Bussy d'Ambois*, for example, Aumale makes a cynical observation on friendship and a wry pun on the word "colours":

> And as through dewy vapors the sun's form
> Makes the gay rainbow girdle to a storm,[28]

[28] Cf. *Day's Mirth*, xi.67-69.

So in hearts hollow, friendship (even the sun
To all good growing in society)
Makes his so glorious and divine name hold
Colours for all the ill that can be told.
(III.i.53-58)

Just as the sun shines through a cloud to produce a rainbow as a false weather sign when a storm is gathering, Aumale says, so also does friendship shine falsely from hollow hearts, producing "colours" to hide evil deeds. In *Byron's Tragedy*, technical theory is the basis for a comparable witty image when Byron warns his fellow-conspirators about the need for stealth:

We must ascend to our intentions' top
Like clouds, that be not seen till they be up.
(I.ii.55-56)

As an example of the witty image derived from mythological meteorology, there is the comment of Ianthe to Sthenia, both waiting women to Eudora in *The Widow's Tears*. When Eudora is persistently wooed by a tiresome fop, Ianthe proposes to interrupt his suit:

We shall appear to her [Eudora] like the two fortunate stars in a tempest to save the shipwrack of her patience. (II.iv.50-51)

Castor and Pollux were signs of relief to storm-tossed sailors, and so will Ianthe and Sthenia appear to Eudora. Chapman could also adapt a Pliny-type wonder for witty imagery—as when Bussy, outlining the hypocritical action he will take to delude Monsieur, concludes:

A politician must like lightning melt
The very marrow, and not taint the skin.
(*Bussy d'Ambois*, IV.ii.188-189)

All of these images, so far as rhetorical classification is concerned, are nothing more than similes. But their distinctive characteristic is the shift in emphasis from antecedent to simile. The rhetorical simile of the epic poets has meaning only in relation to the thing or concept which it amplifies; the rhetorical simile is simply further elaboration of an idea already stated. But in the imagistic simile, the antecedent fuses with the simile; in fact, the antecedent is dependent upon the simile for its very meaning.

With the rhetorical simile, such as Spenser's extended conceits, both the simile and the thing it modifies stay on the literal level. An example of the poetic result is this stanza from *The Faerie Queene,* when Britomart removes her helmet and reveals her yellow hair:

> With that her glistring helmet she unlaced;
> Which doft, her golden lockes, that were up bound
> Still in a knot, unto her heeles downe traced,
> And like a silken veile in compasse round
> About her backe and all her bodie wound:
> Like as the shining skie in summers night,
> What time the dayes with scorching heat abound,
> Is creasted all with lines of firie light,
> That it prodigious seemes in common peoples sight.
> (IV.i.13.1-9)

Britomart's locks are compared to a silken veil which drapes down her back, and then to the bright but harmless lightning of a summer's night. These comparisons, however, are quite literal. The hair, the veil, and the lightning are literally hair, veil, and lightning. Furthermore, each is allowed to retain its individual identity and is not fused with any other element in the comparison. Finally, we should note that the two similes of the veil and the lightning are simply gratuitous elaborations of the ample description for the hair given in the first three lines of the stanza.

The last quotation from Chapman provides a definite contrast in technique:

> A politician must like lightning melt
> The very marrow, and not taint the skin.

At first glance, this may seem to be no more than a traditional simile. But we sense a difference; and upon closer examination, we can, I believe, cite a specific difference. In Chapman's comparison the simile and what it modifies do not retain their entities, but they indistinguishably coalesce. The politician becomes lightning. Futhermore, the attributes of the politician are expressed only in terms of the lightning, so that the politician must "melt / The very marrow, and not taint the skin." What Chapman has to say about politicians is intelligible only by interpreting what he says about lightning. So the statement is lifted off the merely literal level, where the elements in the simile would remain precisely what they are. The statement is transported to a higher, figurative level where lightning is politician and politician is lightning; and the attributes of one are the attributes of the other, irrespective of the terms in which these attributes are expressed. In a simile of Chapman's sort, as previously suggested, the emphasis is shifted from the antecedent to the simile, and the simile becomes the major means through which the poet conveys his meaning.

A technique that presents the argument through imagery clearly makes special demands upon the reader: he must know the particular idea (frequently abstruse) upon which the poet bases the image, and he must apply his knowledge and ingenuity in working out its significance. The reader cannot be passive, merely submitting himself to the poetry and permitting it to work upon him. On the contrary, he must actively engage in the intellectual activity; he must meet the poet at least half way, and together they work out the argument of the poem. So reading a poem of this sort is different from reading a poem in which the argument is expressed by direct statement and imagery serves only as superficial adornment or physical description. No longer is the reader *told* a poem; but starting with the materials and suggestions provided by the poet, he creates his own poem.

Chapman never learned to arrange his images so that the completed poem has a well-ordered structure. As a rule, his compositions are long and formless. He completely lacked Donne's genius for seeing each poem as a carefully integrated pattern of imagery. Chapman was a master at turning the individual image, however; and while we might wish that he had learned structural discipline for his poems from Donne and for his plays from Jonson, we would be loath to forfeit any of his Marlovian exuberance.

CHAPTER FIVE

JOHN DONNE

DONNE had also developed the "witty"-image[1] by the mid-1590's, about the same time that Chapman published his earliest works. Donne, however, exercised more rigorous control over his poetry; and while he does not excel Chapman in the forcefulness or aptness of individual images, he is much more effective in organizing his materials into an intelligible whole. Donne carried the witty-image technique to its extreme: his most successful poems are constructed of such images, arranged to produce a continuous pseudological argument.

"A Feaver," although not one of Donne's best poems, incorporates considerable meteorological theory and serves to demonstrate Donne's technique. In the poem Donne mock-seriously considers the significance of his mistress' malady, a fever. First he establishes a microcosm-macrocosm relationship, identifying her breath with the *spiritus mundi,* so that the lady becomes "the worlds soule" (line 9). She cannot die, he says; since she is his whole world, if she departed the whole world would turn to unsubstantial vapor (lines 6-8). If her breath passed from her body, the *spiritus mundi* would analogously desert the earth, and dissolution of the world would inevitably follow. But even if the world did not dissolve, Donne argues, when she died the earth would be no more than her "carkasse" without a soul; and "the worthyest men" who had intercourse with "the fairest woman" (of whom she is the prototype[2]) would be "but corrupt wormes," since they would be entering the dead carcass of the earth (lines 9-12). Next Donne recalls the widespread belief that Fire will be the agent to destroy the world on Judgment Day, and with assumed fearfulness he speculates "that this her feaver might be it" (line 16)—that is, the dreaded heat to effect the holocaust. Donne rejects this fear, though, by noting that

[1] See pp. 195 ff., above.
[2] This fact is established in the first stanza.

a fever strong enough to cause such havoc would require "much corruption" (lines 17-20), and she is but slightly ill. Therefore, he concludes:

> These burning fits but meteors bee,
> Whose matter in thee is soone spent.
> Thy beauty, and all parts, which are thee,
> Are unchangeable firmament.
> (lines 21-24)

Donne returns to the microcosm-macrocosm image, and he cites the Aristotelian postulate that meteors must be confined to the mutable sublunary region because the spheres beyond the Moon are incorruptible. Therefore the mistress' "burning fits" are only passing meteors which can have no permanent effect on her true self, which is "unchangeable firmament." In the poem one image leads to the next, and all are bound together by Donne's exaggeratedly pretentious references to the microcosm-macrocosm correspondence. The resolution comes in the penultimate stanza, which draws the playful parallel between her fever and ephemeral meteors, a syllogistic climax in keeping with the mock-serious tone of the entire poem.

Another example of a witty meteorological image, noteworthy for its incisiveness, appears near the end of "Satyre I." The "fondling motley humorist" with whom Donne has been walking suddenly spies his mistress in a window, "and like light dew exhal'd," the poet says, "he flings from mee" (line 107). Donne, characterized at length in the beginning of the poem as a melancholy man, equates himself with Earth, and he follows convention in seeing the mistress as the Sun. The silly lover, then, is irresistibly drawn up to the woman like a shapeless, senseless vapor exhaled by the Sun. By means of the simile, the narration of all this action, as well as the overtones of mockery and contempt, is compressed within one line of the poem.

As these witty images clearly show, Donne had been schooled in meteorological theory. In "The Storme" his description of the favorable wind (lines 13-16) and then the tempest's development (lines 25 ff.) is technically accurate. Yet, for all his meteorological knowledge, Donne made many fewer allusions to meteors than did most authors. This paucity of references to weather phenomena is difficult to explain, especially since Donne frequently drew from other scientific fields, such as cartography and alchemy. The answer, I believe, lies in Donne's indifference to the merely sensuous image. Unlike Marlowe, who gloried in the physical magnificence of meteors, Donne most often chose to base his imagery on experience appreciated by the intellect rather than by the senses. Actual meteors, being primarily visual experiences, did not interest Donne. Only the esoteric theories behind their formation, concealed from the eye but apparent to the mind, seemed suitable for his witty imagery.

Even the poetic conventions about meteors are absent—except when Donne consciously perverts them to satirize the tradition-bound Petrarchanists. Then Donne can lightly joke to his mistress about the "teare-floods" and "sigh-tempests" that unfailingly attend the parting of lovers ("Valediction: Forbidding Mourning," 6).[3] Donne also excluded mythological meteorology from his work, no doubt because it smacked too strongly of the excessively popular Ovidian tradition. There are no Junos presiding over the region of Air, no Irises, no Zephyrs, nor Cyclopes. In fact, the only reference to a Greek weather-god in all of Donne's poetry is an allusion to "wilde Boreas" and his rape of "faire Orithea" ("Elegy XVI," 21-23).

The only sort of meteorological imagery which Donne shared with the common poetic tradition were the Biblical motifs that impart sanctity to his Divine Poems. Although in these poems Donne still employed his witty-image technique, he managed to engender a tone of solemn sincerity, often by recalling a Scriptural passage or by echoing a Scriptural phrase. Donne refers to "the Crosse, which th' instrument / Of God dew'd on mee in the Sacrament" ("Crosse," 15-16); he recalls the earthquake and eclipse at Calvary ("Good-friday, 1613," 19-20); he interprets menacing clouds as God's anger ("Hymne to Christ," 5-6), and thunder as His threats (*Litanie*, 213). The Biblical phraseology, in fact, as much as the sacred subject matter itself, sets these Divine Poems apart from Donne's other work.

In conclusion, the functional imagery of Donne serves a different poetic purpose than the mainly ornamental imagery of Spenser. The author of *The Faerie Queene* narrated his poetry directly, pausing at times for Homeric similes or for other rhetorical decoration. But Donne developed his most characteristic poetry through the images

[3] Cf. "Lovers Infinitenesse," 1 ff.; "Canonization," 11-12; "Computation," 5.

themselves, so that the poem acquires meaning only as each image is interpreted and fitted into the over-all imagistic pattern. Spenser tells his poem, and the audience (if we had the information possessed by an average Elizabethan gentleman) need only listen. Indeed, too strenuous an effort to understand bars our entrance into Fairyland. Donne, on the other hand, demands the utmost exercise of the reasoning faculties, and insists that also the reader engage in the creative process.

CHAPTER SIX

WILLIAM SHAKESPEARE

SHAKESPEARE worked in every poetic genre popular with Elizabethans—the Ovidian verse-narrative, the sonnet, the chronicle-history play, the romantic comedy, the classic tragedy—and in each he produced unparalleled masterpieces. He brought every poetic skill to a new peak of effectiveness, and he persuasively reinterpreted existing knowledge, both human and Divine.

He had at his command all the meteorological information generally known in educated circles. He shows familiarity with technical theories, ancient mythology, Bibilical motifs, wonder lore, and of course poetic conventions. And to this bookish knowledge he added much that was available only through a rural boyhood and an appreciative observation of the outdoors. Finally, in creating poetry from this information he was master of all the techniques in which each of his contemporaries excelled.

Shakespeare was quite knowledgeable in Aristotelian meteorology, and his works abound in the technical terminology associated with it. His poetic vocabulary conspicuously includes such words as "meteor," "vapor," and "exhalation," without diminution of their scientific meanings. These terms, however, do not seem incongruous or indecorous; in fact, Shakespeare ingeniously worked them into memorably poetic phrases. For instance, the cold middle region of Air becomes the "thrilling region of thick-ribbed ice" (*M. for M.*, III.i.123); and Hamlet finds himself surrounded by inescapable evil, "a foul and pestilent congregation of vapours" (II.ii.314-315).

Shakespeare put into poetic service not only the terminology of Aristotelian science, but also its theories. As a matter of course he accepted the fundamental tenet that the Sun drew up the evaporations from which meteors formed. Therefore in *Love's Labour's Lost* Longaville offers this well-reasoned excuse for breaking his vow to pursue scholarship and ignore women:

Vows are but breath, and breath a vapour is:
Then thou, fair sun, which on my earth dost shine,
Exhalest this vapour-vow.
(IV.iii.68-70)

Longaville pleads that Maria has drawn forth his "earthly" vow (IV.iii.66) just as naturally as the Sun exhales earthly vapors, and therefore he is not guilty of wilfully breaking his pledge. Throughout the plays and poems Shakespeare created poetry from technical theories about many meteors, such as thunder and lightning,[1] hail,[2] and earthquakes.[3]

From the classical tradition Shakespeare derived much poetic material, and he made frequent allusions to the more common meteorological gods of ancient mythology. There are word pictures of "the ruffian Boreas" churning up a storm at sea (*Troilus*, I.iii.38 ff.); of "gentle" Zephyrus, "blowing below the violet" (*Cymbeline*, IV.ii.172); of "roaring Typhon" (*Troilus*, I.iii.160); of "tragic melancholy night" in her chariot bringing darkness (*2 Henry VI*, IV.i. 3-7); of "the all-cheering sun," who "in the furthest east begin[s] to draw / The shady curtains from Aurora's bed" (*Romeo*, I.i.140-142); of "many-colour'd Iris," the "distemper'd messenger of wet" (*All's Well*, I.iii.157-158). In *The Tempest* when Prospero commands an entertainment to celebrate the betrothal of Ferdinand and Miranda, a character representing Iris appears on stage and announces herself as the "watery arch and messenger" of Juno (IV.i.71).[4] The ensuing scene—involving Iris, Ceres, Juno, Nymphs, and rustic Reapers—is clearly patterned after the mythological masque then so much in vogue.

Many passages of Shakespeare echo references to weather phenomena found in the Bible. When Laertes warns Ophelia about the dangers which a false-hearted suitor presents to "the morn and liquid dew of youth" (I.iii.41), he is paraphrasing a line from the Psalms: "Thou hast the dew of thy youth" (110:3). When Shakespeare interrupts his sad tale of Lucrece to ponder "happiness," which is "as soon decay'd and done / As is the morning's silver

[1] Cf. *Shrew*, I.ii.95-96; *K. John*, I.i.24-28 [see p. 75, above]; *Coriolanus*, V.iii.151.
[2] Cf. *Antony*, III.xiii.159 ff. [see p. 56, above].
[3] Cf. *K. John*, V.iii.41-42; *Venus*, 1046-1048.
[4] See p. 141, above.

melting dew" (lines 23-24), he echoes Hosea: "Your goodness is as a morning cloud, and as the early dew it goeth away" (6:4). In *Henry V* Exeter portrays the young King as the vengeful Jehovah of the Apocalypse, and he warns the French monarch:

> . . .in fierce tempest is he coming,
> In thunder and in earthquake, like a Jove.
> (II.iv.99-100)

And Portia speaks eloquently about "the quality of mercy" which "droppeth as the gentle rain from heaven" (*Merchant*, IV.i.184-185).

Prodigious meteors occur prominently in Shakespeare's works, especially in historical plays where they foretell future political events. Unnatural transmutations in the heavens were generally interpreted as portents of analogous change in the commonweal: "These signs forerun the death or fall of kings" (*Richard II*, II.iv. 15). In addition to the soothsayer's warning to Julius Caesar, the entire gamut of ominous meteors are seen or reported before the assassination: thunder and lightning (*Caesar*, I.ii.1 [S. D.], II.ii.1 [S. D.]), an earthquake (I.iii.3-4), "a tempest dropping fire" (I.iii. 10), fiery impressions on men (I.iii.15-18, 25), thunderstones (I.iii. 49-52), burning exhalations (II.i.44-45), battles in the clouds (II.ii. 19-24), and rains of blood (II.ii.21). Horatio, troubled over the visitation by the ghost of Hamlet's father, recalls these prodigies which foretold disaster for the state of Rome (*Hamlet*, I.i.113-120); and Lennox reports that similar atmospheric disturbances accompanied Macbeth's treacherous murder of Duncan (*Macbeth*, II.iii. 59-66).

The prevalence of the belief in portents, and the growing Renaissance skepticism concerning their validity, are both attested by King John's complaint about the unrest in his realm:

> No natural exhalation in the sky,
> No scope of nature, no distemper'd day,
> No common wind, no customed event,
> But they will pluck away his natural cause
> And call them meteors, prodigies and signs,
> Abortives, presages and tongues of heaven,
> Plainly denouncing vengeance upon John.
> (*K. John*, III.iv.153-159)

In the next act of the play Shakespeare followed his sources[5] when Hubert, a murderer appointed by King John to kill Prince Arthur, fabricates a prodigy of multiple moons to give credence to his story that the kingdom's rightful heir has been slain (IV.ii.182-186). In *3 Henry VI* Princes Edward and Richard witness the equally portentous meteor of multiple suns, which prepares for the death of their father, the Duke of York (II.i.25-32).[6]

The fall of Richard II is likewise predicted by meteorological signs. Before Richard's dramatic return from Ireland, Shakespeare inserted a short conversation between Salisbury and a Welsh captain in Richard's army, the only purpose of which is to foretell the political strife immediately to follow. Displaying the Welshman's propensity for superstition, the captain enumerates the anomalies which have distracted his men:

> The bay-trees in our country are all wither'd
> And meteors fright the fixed stars of heaven;
> The pale-faced moon looks bloody on the earth
> And lean-look'd prophets whisper fearful change.
> (II.iv.8-11)

Salisbury sadly agrees that the signs are serious, and he expresses his fear for Richard's welfare by means of a simile based on the wondrous meteors presaging political change:

> Ah, Richard, with the eyes of heavy mind
> I see thy glory like a shooting star
> Fall to the base earth from the firmament.
> (II.iv.18-20)

After this scene, which affirms by meteorological portents that the present King has irrevocably lost his power, Richard's deposition is a *fait accompli.* Therefore when Richard returns from Ireland in Act III, he appears not as the Machiavellian confiscator of Bolingbroke's inheritance, but as the piteous victim of Fortune's fickleness. The transition from villain to tragic hero is achieved rapidly, though smoothly, by this short conversation about atmospheric anomalies between Salisbury and the Welsh captain.

All of this wonder lore in the historical plays can be found in the chronicles that Shakespeare consulted for his historical materials.

[5] See p. 138, n. 12, above.
[6] See p. 137, above.

Multiple suns, comets, and rains of blood were part of the chronicler's stock in trade. But Shakespeare also drew from the less formalized accounts of wondrous meteors that circulated as folklore. In his plays, for example, stage directions for thunder and lightning often intensify the mystery of marvelous events.[7] Both Caliban and Falstaff complain about the delusive vagaries of *ignis fatuus* (*Tempest*, II.ii.6-7; *1 Henry IV*, III.iii.44-50); and both Hamlet and Antony fix their attention on the spectacular permutation of cloud shapes (*Hamlet*, III.ii.393-399; *Antony*, IV.xiv.2-11). Juliet pretends that the dawning light is a fiery exhalation shaped like a torch, sent to guide Romeo to exile in Mantua (III.v.12-15). It was commonly thought that an infant's future was revealed through meteorological signs as well as the horoscope; and so Glendower, another Welshman, superstitiously contends that he was predestined for greatness:

> At my nativity
> The front of heaven was full of fiery shapes,
> Of burning cressets; and at my birth
> The frame and huge foundation of the earth
> Shaked like a coward.
> (*1 Henry IV*, III.i.13-17)

Shakespeare also worked into his plays many prodigies associated with the sea: storms at sea (*Tempest*, I.i.1 ff., V.i.41-44; *Othello*, II.i.2 ff.; *Pericles*, III.i.1 ff.); a waterspout (*Troilus*, V.ii.171-176); and Helena, the storm sign feared by mariners (*Tempest*, I.ii.196-203). This sort of wonder lore seldom received formal statement in books, but survived as the commonplace marvels of everyday life.

Another set of folk beliefs that show up in Shakespeare's poetry is the well-established list of weather rules.[8] Shakespeare knew that "men judge by the complexion of the sky / The state and inclination of the day" (*Richard II*, II.ii.194-195); and he himself was fully acquainted with the practice of prognosticating weather by signs, probably as a result of his upbringing in the country. So he described the "blue circles" like rainbows about Lucrece's eyes, and he predicted:

[7] Cf. *Tempest*, III.iii.53, 82; *Macbeth*, I.i.1, I.iii.1, III.v.1, IV.i.1, 68, 77, 87.
[8] See Appendix I.

These water-galls in her dim element
Foretell new storms to those already spent.
(*Lucrece,* 1588-1589)

Citing another rural commonplace, Shakespeare agreed that an unclouded Sun at setting foretold fair weather for the following day:

The weary sun hath made a golden set,
And, by the bright track of his fiery car,
Gives signal of a goodly day to-morrow.
(*Richard III,* V.iii.19-21)

At other times Shakespeare presumed his audience's knowledge that gnats swarming in the sunshine indicated continued fair weather, but conversely that the dispersal of these gnats accompanied rain. Therefore in *Comedy of Errors* he noted that "when the sun shines . . .foolish gnats make sport, / But creep in crannies when he hides his beams" (II.ii.30-31); and again in *Timon of Athens,* "one cloud of winter showers, / These flies are couch'd" (II.ii.180-181).

In his plays Shakespeare often depended upon weather signs to inform his audience what sort of weather—both actual and figurative —they could expect in the ensuing action. Blanch in *King John* dolefully observes that the Sun is unduly red and therefore stormy times are at hand: "The sun's o'ercast with blood: fair day, adieu!" (III.i.326). Similarly in *Richard II* Salisbury mourns for the misguided King, whose "sun sets weeping in the lowly west," and the audience would agree that the Sun clouded at setting predicted "storms to come, woe and unrest" (II.iv.21-22). Later in *Richard II* a weather portent based on the Sun's appearance at dawn repeats this forecast of imminent storms:

See, see, King Richard doth himself appear,
As doth the blushing discontented sun
From out the fiery portal of the east,
When he perceives the envious clouds are bent
To dim his glory and to stain the track
Of his bright passage to the occident.
(III.iii.62-67)

The weather sign is obvious: a "blushing" Sun, excessively red, foretold foul weather of wind and rain;[9] and the remainder of Richard's life is well described as stormy.

[9] Cf. *Venus,* 453-454.

The most extended instance of Shakespeare's dramatic use of weather tokens occurs just before the final battle in *1 Henry IV*. The King looking at the sky comments, "How bloodily the sun begins to peer / Above yon busky hill! the day looks pale / At his distemperature" (V.i.1-3). Prince Hal replies:

> The southern wind
> Doth play the trumpet to his purposes,
> And by his hollow whistling in the leaves
> Foretells a tempest and a blustering day.
> (V.i.3-6)

Here are several portents of severe storm: a bloody Sun, a pale sky, a southern wind, and leaves rustling among the trees. The southern wind, by stirring up the leaves, acts as herald to even stronger winds to follow. This dialogue between the King and Prince Hal achieves a double end: it forewarns the audience of impending violence; and coming as it does at the beginning of the terrible battle scenes, it serves the immediate purpose of setting the stage with cloudy heavens and howling winds.

Shakespeare's work contains numerous poetic conventions: comparisons to the whiteness and purity of snow;[10] frost and snow as tropes for old age;[11] dew as pearls;[12] similes based on the swiftness of lightning[13] and of the wind;[14] thunder as the metaphorical equivalent of a loud voice, usually wrathful;[15] clouds as frowns;[16] the adage

[10] *Tempest*, IV.i.55; *L.L.L.*, I.i.245, IV.ii.136; *M.N.D.*, III.ii.141; *W. Tale*, IV.iv.220; *Coriolanus*, V.iii.65-66; *T. Andron.*, II.iii.76; *Romeo*, I.v.50-51, III.ii.18-19; *Timon*, IV.iii.385-387; *Macbeth*, IV.iii.52-53; *Hamlet*, III.i.140-141, III.iii.45-46, IV.v.35; 195; *Othello*, V.ii.4; *Cymbeline*, II.v.13; *Venus*, 361-362; *Lucrece*, 196, 420, 1011; Sonnet cxxx.3.

[11] *Comedy of Errors*, V.i.311-312; *M.N.D.*, II.i.107-110; *A.Y.L.I.*, II.iii.52-53; *2 Henry VI*, V.i.166-168; *T. Andron.*, V.iii.77; *Hamlet*, IV.v.195; *Lear*, IV.vi.120-121.

[12] *M.N.D.*, I.i.209-211, II.i.14-15, IV.i.58-60; *K. John*, II.i.168-169; *Richard III*, IV.iv.321-322; *Lucrece*, 396.

[13] *Tempest*, I.ii.201-203; *M.N.D.*, I.i.145; *Richard II*, I.iii.79; *3 Henry VI*, II.i.129; *Romeo*, II.ii.118-120, III.i.177; *Lear*, IV.vii.34-35.

[14] *L.L.L.*, V.ii.260-261; *M.N.D.*, III.ii.94; *Cymbeline*, III.iv.37-39; *Venus*, 681.

[15] *M. for M.*, II.ii.110-113; *L.L.L.*, IV.ii.119; *M.N.D.*, IV.i.122-123; *Shrew*, I.ii.95-96; *Twelfth Night*, I.v.275; *K. John*, III.i.124, III.iv.38; *1 Henry VI*, III.ii.59; *3 Henry VI*, II.i.127; *Richard III*, I.iv.173; *Henry VIII*, V.iv.63-64; *Troilus*, II.iii.209; *Coriolanus*, I.iv.58-61, II.i.282-283; *T. Andron.*, II.i.58-59; *Hamlet*, I.ii.127-128; *Antony*, V.ii.83-86.

[16] *Tempest*, II.i.141-142; *Much Ado*, V.iv.40-42; *L.L.L.*, V.ii.203-204; *K. John*, V.ii.108-109; *1 Henry IV*, III.ii.82-83; *2 Henry VI*, III.i.154-155; *3 Henry*

that "words are but wind";[17] winds as the epitome of freedom,[18] even wantonness;[19] and conceits in which winds are sighs[20] and rain- or dew-drops are tears.[21] Sometimes Shakespeare simply repeated these conventions as he found them in the poetic tradition, so that we hear many commonplace similes: "white as driven snow" (*W. Tale,* IV.iv.220), "fresh as morning's dew" (*T. Andron.,* II.iii.201), "thick as hail" (*Macbeth,* I.iii.97), "free / As mountain winds" (*Tempest,* I.ii.498-499), "brief as the lightning" (*M.N.D.,* I.i. 145). In other instances, however, Shakespeare transformed a convention into his own complex sort of image. Here are two passages based on the whiteness-of-snow trope:

> . . .[Romeo] wilt lie upon the wings of night
> Whiter than new snow on a raven's back.
> (*Romeo,* III.ii.18-19)

> That pure congealed white, high Taurus' snow,
> Fann'd with the eastern wind, turns to a crow
> When thou hold'st up thy hand.
> (*M.N.D.,* III.ii.141-143)

In the first passage, Juliet is not satisfied merely to say that Romeo is fairer than snow. Instead, she states her hyperbole by means of a fanciful ratio:

Romeo : night > snow : raven

Shakespeare made this ratio mathematically acceptable by representing night as a bird with black wings, so that night and raven are common terms:

VI, II.iii.7, IV.i.73-74; *Richard III,* I.iii.267-269; *T. Andron.,* I.i.263, II.iii.33; *Hamlet,* I.ii.66; *Venus,* 971-972; *Lucrece,* 115-116; Sonnet xxxiii; *Pass. Pil.,* 311-312.

[17] *Comedy of Errors,* III.i.75; *Troilus,* V.iii.108-110.

[18] *Tempest,* I.ii.498-499; *A.Y.L.I.,* II.vii.47-49; *Coriolanus,* I.ix.88-89.

[19] *Tempest,* V.i.42; *M.N.D.,* II.i.129; *Merchant,* II.vi.16; *W. Tale,* I.ii.131-132; *Troilus,* III.ii.198-199; *Coriolanus,* V.iii.59; *Romeo,* I.iv.100-103; *Othello,* IV.ii.78.

[20] *Romeo,* III.v.135; *Antony,* I.ii.153; *Venus,* 51, 189-190, 965-966; *Lucrece,* 586; *Lov. Com.,* 7.

[21] *L.L.L.,* IV.iii.29, V.ii.819; *M.N.D.,* IV.i.58-61; *Shrew,* Ind.i.125; *K. John,* V.ii.45-53; *Richard II,* III.ii.146-147; *2 Henry IV,* I.iii.61, II.iii.59, IV.v.9; *2 Henry VI,* III.ii.339-340; *3 Henry VI,* I.iv.144-146, II.v.85-86; *Richard III,* V.iii.284; *Troilus,* IV.iv.55-56; *T. Andron.,* III.i.16-22, 222, V.i.116-117; *Romeo,* I.i.137-139, III.v.127 ff., V.iii.14-15; *Hamlet,* IV.v.166; *Lear,* III.vii.62, IV.iii. 19-20; *Antony,* I.ii.151-157, III.ii.50-51, V.ii.302-303; *Venus,* 82-83, 360, 955-960, 965-966; *Lucrece,* 560, 796, 1232, 1270-1271, 1676-1680, 1788-1790, 1829; *Lov. Com.,* 7.

∴ Romeo > snow

In the second passage Demetrius wishes to find a suitable standard against which to measure the whiteness of Helena's hand. He establishes the wonderful qualities of snow by a long list of modifiers ("pure congealed white"), and he particularizes the excellence of this special snow by exotic geography ("high Taurus" and "fann'd with the eastern wind"). This careful buildup heightens the hyperbole, which declares Helena's hand to be whiter than such snow. But underlying each of these passages, we should note, is the conventional hyperbole "whiter than snow."

Shakespeare rarely interrupted the movement of his poetry by a full-blown Homeric simile. He preferred the more closely integrated image, where the figure contained within itself the main thread of the poetic argument. The nearest Shakespeare came to an epic simile based on meteors is this comparison between the waterspout and a fatal sword stroke:

> . . .not the dreadful spout
> Which shipmen do the hurricano call,
> Constringed in mass by the almighty sun,
> Shall dizzy with more clamour Neptune's ear
> In his descent than shall my prompted sword
> Falling on Diomed.
>
> (*Troilus*, V.ii.171-176)

The tone of this image is not classical, however, despite the reference to Neptune. This is again Renaissance hyperbole rather than classical simile; and there is too great fusion between trope and antecedent for the image to be truly epic.

Although Shakespeare avoided Homeric similes, he nonetheless achieved some of his most impressive poetry by means of extended images. An example involving weather phenomena is Richard's speech at the opening of *Richard III*:

> Now is the winter of our discontent
> Made glorious summer by this sun of York;
> And all the clouds that lour'd upon our house
> In the deep bosom of the ocean buried.
>
> (I.i.1-4)

The late civil wars are figuratively described as a disagreeable winter whose cold has now been dispersed by a Sun-king. The wintry clouds which had blocked the Sun's warmth have been condensed into the ocean, and thereby removed. Richard expresses his changing fortune *in terms of* the seasonal variation in the Sun's heat; he does not *compare* his fortunes to seasonal changes. The trope (seasonal changes) has completely absorbed its antecedent (Richard's fortunes).

As another illustration of the extended image derived from weather changes, we may watch the King of France in *All's Well* granting pardon to Bertram:

> I am not a day of season,
> For thou mayst see a sunshine and a hail
> In me at once: but to the brightest beams
> Distracted clouds give way; so stand thou forth;
> The time is fair again.
>
> (V.iii.32-36)

Again, there is no simile. The King begins with the metaphorical premise that he *is* an unseasonable day, and he declares his attitude toward Bertram strictly in terms of good and bad weather. The King exists only as a changeable day; the antecedent again has no existence independent of the trope. These images resemble the epic in their grandness, and yet they are greatly different from Homeric similes. They expound no similarity between two mutually independent things; but rather they make a metaphorical statement in which the two components of the implicit comparison are indistinguishable. The sixteenth-century rhetorician would have put the label "allegorie" on such an extended image, noting that it is "a long and perpetuall Metaphore."[22] Perhaps it deserves the name "Homeric metaphor," because it combines the resounding grandeur of the classical epic with the metaphor's complete substitution of trope for antecedent.

The "Homeric metaphor" may be differentiated from the "witty" image by its mode of affecting the reader. The Homeric metaphor re-creates in our mind's eye some previous sense experience—the unpleasantness of winter, summer's warmth, alternate periods of hail and sunshine—and the new idea which the poet wishes to express about the antecedent is imagistically established by a recollection of these earlier sense impressions. The mind reacts responsively, but remains passive. Its response is largely unconscious. In contrast, the witty image demands that the intellect actively work through a

[22] George Puttenham, *The Arte of English Poesie,* ed. G. D. Willcock and Alice Walker (Cambridge Univ. Press, 1936), p. 187 [III.xviii].

thought pattern only suggested by the poet, often requiring esoteric information to clarify the intentionally obscure poetic statement. Conscious response is prerequisite. The witty image tends to be more terse, less grandiose; and comprehension of a witty image gives a feeling of participation in the activity of the poem.

A prime example of the witty image based on meteorology is this plaint from Romeo:

> Love is a smoke raised with the fume of sighs;
> Being purged, a fire sparkling in lovers' eyes.
> (*Romeo*, I.i.196-197)

Again, as with Homeric metaphors, we have an initial metaphorical premise: "Love is a smoke." But were we not acquainted with Aristotle's atmospheric cycle, we could not understand this image, because Romeo is talking about the vapors and exhalations which the Sun draws up. Love, he says, is a hot and dry exhalation, "a smoke." Always raised with exhalations are hot and moist vapors, a "fume of sighs." The Sun exhales these two sorts of evaporations simultaneously, just as a mistress inevitably evokes both Fiery love and Watery sighs. When the Sun-mistress disperses "the fume of sighs" by the proximity of her favor, however, then the bright love, purged of cloudy discontent, can sparkle clearly in the suitor's eyes. This elaborate metaphor, implying a detailed analogy between macrocosm and microcosm, can be compressed within two lines because Shakespeare need state only the initial postulate that "love is a smoke." The exposition of the image, dependent upon application of the proper meteorological principles, is left to the reader. The result is a conceit with the precision and conciseness of the best metaphysical poetry.

Shakespeare's genius thus expressed itself through many outlets. Like Chapman, he could base his imagery on scientific principles; like Jonson, he could successfully reconstruct the beauties of meteorological mythology; and like Nashe, he could expound the wondrous commonplace. As regards technique, he could turn an extended conceit like Spenser, or a compact metaphysical image like Donne. Of all his contemporaries, Shakespeare used the widest range of meteorological information, he used it most frequently, and he used it most effectively. Like Marlowe, he could fill the heavens with awe-inspiring splendor.

APPENDIXES

APPENDIX ONE

WEATHER PROGNOSTICATION

THE study of meteors had a strained connection with astrology through the applied pseudo science of weather forecasting. Since the Moon was mistress of all things compounded of Water (including clouds, rain, and dew), and since the Sun and other planets controlled the generation and dissipation of meteors, it was believed that the future state of the weather could be foretold through scrutiny of the heavenly bodies. Moreover, various animals, more sensitive than human beings to certain celestial influences, frequently gave advance hints about approaching rain, wind, or tempest.

The practice of weather prognostication by means of empirical rules dates back to Theophrastus' *De signis aquarum et ventorum* and Aratus' *Diosemea.*[1] But in Renaissance England the best known tracts on forecasting were Vergil's *Georgics* (I.351 ff.) and the catalogue of "signes to prognosticate what weather is toward" in Pliny's *Historia naturalis* (XVIII.xxxv). All the classical rules for weather forecasting were based on simple observations of the heavens or of common animals.

The authority for astrological weather prediction came primarily from Ptolemy's *Tetrabiblos.* During the early Middle Ages the tradition was furthered by Arabic pens, the most important being those of Alkindus, Albumasar, and Albohazen Haly. These men saw meteorology as merely an adjunct to astrology. In Europe works on weather prediction were composed during the late medieval period by many prominent astrologers, such as Leopold of Austria, Guido Bonatti da Forli, Firmin de Beauval, and John Eschuid of Ashendon. Fourteenth-century England nurtured a notable group of writers on forecasting—Richard of Wallingford, Robert of York, and William Merle—who recognized the value of weather records and current observations in making plausible predictions. Throughout

[1] See p. 11, above. See also Gillespie, *Vergil, Aratus and Others.*

the Renaissance, however, the domination of astrology over weather prognostication was complete. The weather predictions of the astrologers were widely sold in the form of annual forecasts, and they greatly enhanced the reputations of such men as Luca Gaurico and Agostino Nifo in Italy, Antoine Mizauld in France, and Johann Carion and Johann Müller (Regiomontanus) in Germany. Some of the most popular prognosticators in England were Anthony Ascham, Leonard Digges, John Securis, Thomas Hill, Thomas Buckmaster, Robert Watson, Gabriel Frende, and Thomas Bretnor.[2]

The layman could usually depend upon the multiannual almanac not only for weather predicitions, but also for a list of weather signs by which he could make his own short-range forecasts. Below are tabulated the weather signs recommended by ten authorities easily available to Elizabethans. To make the summary representative, it includes four classical sources, four Renaissance astrologers, a handbook of navigation, and a handbook of husbandry. Unless a sign is listed by at least two of these ten authorities, it has not been catalogued. The authorities for the inclusion of each sign are indicated by the following code:

T Theophrastus, *De signis aquarum et ventorum*

A Aratus, *Diosemea*

V Vergil, *Georgics*

P Pliny, *Historie of the World*

D Leonard Digges, *A Prognostication of Right Good Effect* (1555)

M Philip Moore, *A Fourtie Yeres Almanacke* (*ca.* 1567)

F *Perpetuall and Naturall Prognostications of the Change of Weather* (1591), trans. I. F[armery?]

G Godfridus, *Knowledge of Things Unknowne* (1619)

C Martin Cortes, *The Arte of Navigation* (1561), trans. Richard Eden

H Thomas Hill, *The Profitable Arte of Gardening* (1568)

The weather signs are listed according to what they portend, under the main headings of "Fair Weather," "Rain," "Wind," and "Tem-

[2] See Eustace F. Bosanquet, *English Printed Almanacks and Prognostications* (London, 1917); *Corrigenda and Addenda* (London, 1928); and *Notes on Further Addenda* (London, 1937).

pest." Within each of these main headings are also grouped together those signs dependent upon (1) the actions of animals, (2) the appearance of the sky or heavenly bodies, and (3) miscellaneous observations.

Fair Weather

(1)

1. Cranes flying out to sea and not returning	T	A					F			H
2. Gnats flying in sunshine							F			H
3. Owl hooting during storm or at night	T	A	V	P			F			
4. Oxen lying on left side	T						F			H
5. Rooks or ravens crying softly and repeatedly	T	A	V	P						H

(2)

1. Sun unclouded at rising, but not fiery	T	A	V	P	D		F	G	C	H
2. Sun unclouded at setting	T	A	V	P	D		F			H
3. Red sky in evening	T	A		P	D		F	G	C	H
4. Clear sky on fourth rising of new Moon	T	A	V	P	D		F	G	C	H
5. One circle around Moon quickly vanishing	T	A			D	M	F	G	C	
6. Rainbow during foul weather				P	D		F	G		H
7. Mist or low clouds in valleys	T	A	V	P			F			H
8. Low clouds over seacoast	T	A								

Rain

(1)

1. Ants storing up provisions					D		F		C	
2. Ants bringing out eggs from nest	T	A	V	P	D					
3. Centipedes crawling on walls	T	A								
4. Chickens crowing more than usual		A			D		F			
5. Cormorants crying loudly, diving, or flying in circles	T	A		P			F			
6. Cranes flying inland	T	A	V	P	D					
7. Crows, ravens, or rooks agitating their wings	T	A	V	P	D		F			
8. Crows or ravens uttering two or three notes quickly	T	A	V	P	D		F			H
9. Dogs pawing the earth	T	A								
10. Dolphins or porpoises diving near land	T			P			F			
11. Ducks flapping wings	T	A					F			
12. Flies biting more viciously than usual	T	A					F			
13. Frogs croaking	T	A	V	P			F			H

14. Land birds taking baths	T	A	V				F			H
15. Mice squeaking and skipping about	T	A								
16. Oxen sniffing wind	T	A	V	P	D		F			
17. Oxen licking their hoofs	T	A		P	D		F			H
18. Peacocks making noise					D		F			
19. Ravens, hawks, or chickens searching their feathers for lice	T						F			
20. Salamanders appearing	T						F			
21. Sheep frisking wantonly		A		P						
22. Swallows skimming over ponds	T	A	V	P	D		F			
23. Swine tossing or hiding hay	T[3]	A	V	P			F			H
24. Worms coming out of earth	T	A		P	D		F			

(2)

1. Sun having dark marks or appearing hollow at rising	T	A	V	P	D		F	G		H
2. Sun hidden in cloud at rising	T	A	V	P	D	M		G		H
3. Unduly red Sun or red clouds at dawn	T	A		P	D	M	F	G	C	H
4. Rays preceding Sun at rising	T	A	V	P				G		
5. Mock or multiple suns	T	A				M				
6. Solar halos	T	A		P						
7. Sun hidden in cloud at setting	T	A	V	P						
8. Red sky at sunset	T			P						
9. Dark mist over Moon	T	A	V	P	D		F	G	C	H
10. Horns of Moon appearing blunt		A		P		M			C	H
11. Clouds like wool	T	A		P	D		F			H
12. Rainbows in clear weather	T	A	V	P	D		F	G		H
13. Thunder in evening	T			P	D	M	F			
14. Thunder in summer	T	A								

(3)

1. Bells heard farther than usual				P	D		F			H
2. Bubbles on surface of rivers and springs	T			P			F			
3. Many sparks in kitchen fire	T	A		P			F			
4. Oil sputtering in lamps	T	A	V	P			F			
5. Snuff gathering on lampwick	T	A	V	P						

Wind

(1)

1. Dog rolling on ground	T						F			H
2. Ducks, wild or tame, flapping wings	T	A					F			

[3] Theophrastus states: ὅταν μῦες περὶ φορυτοῦ μάχωνται καὶ φέρωσιν (*De signis*, 49). Μῦες is probably a scribal error for σύες (Aratus, *Phaenomena*, 1123).

3. Herons crying and rising above clouds	T	A	V	P	D		F			
4. Sea birds flying from ocean	T	A	V	P						
5. Spider webs in air	T	A					F			H

(2)

1. Fiery or blood-red Sun at rising	T	A		P	D	M	F			H
2. Divided rays from Sun at rising	T	A	V	P		M	F			
3. Rays preceding Sun at rising	T	A		P		M		G		
4. Multiple suns	T	A								
5. Solar halos	T	A		P	D	M	F	G	C	H
6. Fiery Sun at setting			V	P	D	M		G		H
7. Reddish Moon	T	A	V	P	D	M	F	G	C	H
8. Imperfect halos around Moon	T	A		P		M				
9. Halos around Moon	T	A		P	D			G	C	
10. Comets	T			P	D	M				
11. Shooting stars	T	A	V	P	D	M	F	G		H
12. Stars sparkling more brightly than usual					D	M		G		H
13. Thunder in the morning	T			P	D	M	F	G		

(3)

1. Leaves rustling in forest			V	P			F			H
2. Sea surging	T	A	V	P	D	M	F			
3. Thistledown or feathers floating on bodies of water	T	A	V	P						

Tempest

(1)

1. Asses shaking ears	T					F		
2. Bees not venturing far from hive	T	A			D	F		H
3. Birds fleeing from sea	T	A		P	D			
4. Cattle lying on right side	T	A				F		H
5. Dog lying on right side						F		H
6. Dog rolling on ground	T				D	F		H
7. Dog digging a hole	T	A						
8. Dolphins playing near land	T		V	P		F		
9. Earthworms appearing	T	A		P	D	F		
10. Finches or sparrows chirping at dawn	T	A			D	F		
11. Hedgehog closing both his holes[4]	T					F		H
12. Land birds taking baths	T	A	V					

[4] "The hedgehogge where he lyeth, maketh two holes, the one opening toward the Northe, and the other toward the South, and which of them he stoppeth, from the same parte the winde ariseth, and if both at once, then great store of wind to follow" (Hill, "Certaine Husbandly Conjectures" [appended to *Profitable Arte of Gardening*], p. 73). Cf. Theophrastus, *De signis*, 30.

13. Mice squeaking and skipping about	T	A								
14. Wasps swarming in autumn	T	A								
15. Wolf howling	T	A					F			
16. Wolf near human settlement	T	A					F			
(2)										
1. Sun pale at rising			V	P				G	C	
2. Solar halos		A		P		M		G	C	H
3. Spots on Sun at setting	T	A	V							
4. Sun rays divided at setting	T	A		P		M				
5. Red halo around Moon		A		P		M		G		
6. Two or more halos around Moon		A		P		M	F		C	
7. Mist over "Asses' Manger"[5]	T	A		P						
8. Shooting stars	T	A		P	D	M	F	G		H
9. Comets						M	F			
10. Thunder in evening					D		F			

Two contradictory cautions must be noted in dealing with Renaissance weather rules. First, the lists were taken almost wholesale from Greek and Latin authorities, and little allowance was made for the difference between the climate and topography of the Mediterranean area and that of England. Consequently several signs which had originally possessed some degree of plausibility for Greece and Rome were inapplicable in England. However, a counterwarning against complete incredulity must also be given. Many of these signs were the results of an empirical method—they worked because they had been observed to precede certain weather conditions on many previous occasions.

In addition to weather rules, other miscellaneous criteria were often used to prognosticate atmospheric conditions. John Taylor, for instance, recounted the common practice of predicting weather by aches and pains in the body. Men's backs, he said, are "prognosticating aking Almanacks":

> Some by a painefull elbow, hip, or knee,
> Will shrewdly guesse, what wether's like to be:
> Some by their cornes are wondrous weather-wise,
> And some by biting of lice, fleas, or flies:

[5] "Within the signe Cancer, there be two pretie stars which the Mathematicians call Aselli, (*i.* little Asses) betweene which there seemeth to be a small clowd taking up some little roome, and this they name in Latine Praesepia (*i.* a Crib, Crarch, Bowzey, or Manger:)" (Pliny, *Historie of World*, p. 612 [XVIII.xxxv]).

The gowt, sciatica, the Gallian *Morbus,*
Doth oft foretell if tempests shall disturbe us;
For though these things converse not with the stars,
Yet to mans griefe they are Astronomers.[6]

Applying other rules, Godfridus in his *Knowledge of Things Unknowne* gave a table "to know the weather that shall be all the yeere, after the change of every Moone, by the prime dayes":

Sunday Prime, drie weather.
Munday Prime, moist weather.
Tuesday Prime, cold and windy.
Wednesday Prime, marvellous.
Thursday Prime, faire and cleere.
Friday Prime, faire and foule.
Saturday Prime, raine.[7]

In "The Husband Mans Practice" Godfridus added that the day of the week upon which Christmas fell was indicative; for example, "if Christmasse day fall on the Sunday, that yeere shall be a warme Winter."[8] For Leonard Digges, New Year rather than Christmas was the significant day, so he gave a table to prognosticate the weather "by the fallyng of Newyears daye."[9]

Allusions to empirical rules for predicting weather occur frequently in Elizabethan and Jacobean literature,[10] although they might easily remain unnoticed by the modern reader uninformed about Renaissance weather signs. What no reader could fail to see, however, is a bald list of storm tokens such as that inserted by Chapman in *Eugenia* (lines 55-127). Nor could anyone miss the point of

[6] *Drinke and Welcome* (London: A. Griffith, 1637), Ciii^v^. Theophrastus had noted certain pains which foretold weather changes (*De signis*, 30). On this persistent belief, see Brand and Hazlitt, *Popular Antiquities*, III.215.

[7] Pp. 44-45. This table was repeated in various almanacs; for instance, in Leonard Digges, *Prognostication of Right Good Effect*, Bii^v^, and in Erra Pater, *Pronostycacion for Ever*, Bi^v^.

[8] P. 100. The tradition of forecasting the year's weather from the day upon which Christmas came was inherited from the Middle Ages; see "Christmas Day Prognostications," *Secular Lyrics of the XIVth and XVth Centuries*, ed. R. H. Robbins (Oxford, 1952), pp. 63-67.

[9] *Prognostication of Right Good Effect*, Ciii^v^-Civ. Thomas Hill also predicted the year's weather from the day of the week upon which New Year fell ("Certaine Husbandly Conjectures" [appended to *Profitable Arte of Gardening*], pp. 51-53).

[10] There was considerable burlesque literature lampooning both the inaccuracy and the fantastic claims of the prognosticators. See Carroll Camden, Jr., "Elizabethan Almanacs and Prognostications," *The Library*, XII (1931), 100-108; and Allen, *Star-Crossed Renaissance*, pp. 190-246.

such direct allusions to weather signs as references to "a red morn, that ever yet betoken'd /Wreck to the seaman, tempest to the field" (Shakespeare, *Venus*, 453-454), or to "the caryon Crowe, that lothsome beast, / Which cryes agaynst the rayne" (Gascoigne, "Gascoignes Good Morrow," 57-58). Neither could anyone misunderstand such forthright statements of weather lore as the following:

> What tydings doe the dauncing dolphins bring,
> But that some dangerous storme approcheth nere?
> (Davies, *Orchestra*, ci.3-4)
>
> . . .*bees* in stormes unto their hives returne.
> (Davies, "Of Humane Knowledge,"
> *Nosce Teipsum*, p. 22)
>
> . . .beasts licking 'gainst the hayre
> Fore-shew some storme.
> (Dekker, *Match Me in London*, IV.202)

But the modern reader might be puzzled by this line: "He lifts up's nose, like a fowle Por-pisse before / A storme" (*Dutchesse of Malfy*, III.iii.63-64).[11] Or he might not see the point of this cynical observation: ". . .rain is fair weather when the ground is dry and barren, especially when it rains humour, for then do men, like hot sparrows and pigeons, open all their wings ready to receive them" (Chapman, *Humorous Day's Mirth*, ii.5-8). Certainly, if he did not know that swallows skimming the ground predicted rain, he would not understand Jonson's lament that virtue must now "like a swallow (preying towards stormes) / Fly close to earth" (*Poetaster*, IV.ix.50-51).

[11] Cf. Jonson, *Sejanus*, V.621-624.

APPENDIX TWO

INDEX OF AUTHORITIES BEFORE 1558

THIS list of pre-Elizabethan authorities gives the following information under each entry: (1) name of authority; (2) his dates; (3) his works directly concerned with meteors. For each work listed, the entry includes the place and date of the earliest printed edition that I have been able to identify. Those books which I have not actually seen, I have marked with an asterisk (*); in describing them, I have relied upon the following sources of bibliographical information:

Gesner *B* = Conrad Gesner, *Bibliotheca universalis* (Zurich, 1545)
Gesner *P* = Conrad Gesner, *Pandectae* (Zurich, 1548)
Brunet = J.-C. Brunet, *Manuel du Libraire* (7 vols.; Paris, 1860-1878)
Hain = Ludwig Hain, *Repertorium bibliographicum* (2 vols.; Berlin, 1925)
Copinger = W. A. Copinger, *Supplement to Hain's Repertorium bibliographicum* (2 vols.; Berlin, 1926)
Schwab = Moise Schwab, *Bibliographie d'Aristote* (Paris, 1896) [lithographed]

Under major authorities (such as Aristotle and Pliny) I have listed as separate titles the earliest edition of the more important commentaries and translations.

Abiosi, Giovanni Battista (*fl.* 1494)
**Trutina rerum coelestium et terrestrium* (Trevisa, 1498) [Hain 25].
Abū Ma'shar, *see* Ja'far ibn Muhammad
Adelard of Bath (*fl.* 1130)
Quaestiones naturales perdifficiles ([Louvain, *ca.*1475]) [Hain 85].
Agobard, Saint, Archbishop of Lyons (779-840)
Contra insulsam vulgi opinionem de grandine & tonitruis [first printed in *Opera* (Paris, 1605)].

Ailly, Pierre d' (*ca.*1350-1422)
Tractatus brevis. . .que in prima secunda atque tercia regionibus aeris fiunt (Leipzig, [*ca.*1495]) [Hain 846].

Albertus Magnus (1193-1280)
Philosophia pauperum ([Toulouse, *ca.*1485]) [British Museum IA.42443].
Liber methaurorum ([Venice], 1488) [Hain 513].
De natura locorum, ed. Georg Tannstetter (Vienna, 1514).

Albohazen Haly, *see* 'Alī ibn 'Abī al-Rajjāl

Albumasar, *see* Ja'far ibn Muhammad

Alcionio, Pietro (*ca.*1487-1527)
Aristotelis. . .meteoron. . .[et] de mundo [Latin text by Alcionio] et al. (Venice, 1521).

Alemann, Konrad von (called von Megenberg, 1309-1374)
Das Puch der Natur [German paraphrase of Thomas de Cantimpré, *De natura rerum*] (Augsburg, 1475) [Hain 4041].

Alexander of Aphrodisias (*fl.* 193-217)
'Εις τὰ μετεωρολογικά ['Αριστοτέλους] [with Greek text] et al. (Venice, 1527).
In quatuor libros meteorologicorum Aristotelis commentatio [Latin text by Alessandro Piccolomini, with Latin text of Aristotle by Piccolomini] et al. (Venice, 1540) [cf. Copinger 237].

Alfred of Sareshel (*fl.* 1215)
Meteorologica [comm. on Aristotle], no early eds.

Alighieri, Jacopo di Dante (d. <1349)
Il Dottrinale, no early eds.

'Alī ibn 'Abī al-Rajjāl (called Albohazen Haly, *fl.* 11th century)
In iudiciis astrorum [Latin text] (Venice, 1485) [Hain 8349].

Alkindus, *see* Yakub b. Ishāk al-Kindi

Anaxagoras (*ca.*500-426 B.C.)
Known only through citation by subsequent writers, such as Plutarch (*De placitis philosophorum*, passim) and Diogenes Laertius (*Eminent Philosophers*, II.9).

Angeli de Ulma, Jacobus, *see* Engelhart, Jacob

Apuleius, Lucius (*ca.*126->173)
Epitoma. . .de mundo [Latin paraphrase of Aristotle] (Vienna, [*ca.* 1497]) [Hain 1321].

Aquaeus, Stephanus, *see* Laigue, Etienne de

Aquinas, St. Thomas (*ca.*1227-1274)
Expositiones textuales. . .in libros. . .metherologorum [Aristotelis] [with Latin text] et al. (Cologne, 1497) [Hain 6813].
**De principiis rerum naturalium* (Leipzig, 1498) [Hain 1524].

Meteorologicorum [*libri quatuor*] [Latin text by Alessandro Piccolomini] et al. (Venice, 1540), with comm. Alexander of Aphrodisias [Latin text by Piccolomini].

Meteora [Greek text] (Venice, 1551), with comms. Olympiodorus of Alexandria and John of Alexandria.

Meteora [Latin text by G. B. Camozzi] (Venice, 1551), with comms. Olympiodorus of Alexandria and John of Alexandria [Latin text by Camozzi].

Meteorologicorum libri quatuor [Latin text by Joachim Périon] (Paris, 1552).

[*Meteorologica*] [Greek and Latin texts] (Paris, 1556), with comm. Francesco Vicomercato.

La Meteora [Italian text by Antonio Bruccioli] (Venice, 1555).

De mundo [Latin paraphrase by Apuleius] (Vienna, [*ca.* 1497]) [Hain 1321].

De mundo [Latin text by Pietro Alcionio] et al. (Venice, 1521).

De mundo [Greek text, and Latin text by Guillaume Budé] et al. (Basle, 1533), with comm. Simon Grynaeus.

Du Monde [French text, anon.] et al. (Lyons, 1542).

Atacinus, *see* Varro, Publius Terentius

Auvergne, Pierre d'[1]

**Super libros metheororum* [*Aristotelis*] (Salamanca, 1497) [Hain 12852].

Averroës (1120-1198)

[*Commentarius in libros meteororum Aristotelis*] [with Latin text] (Padua, 1474) [Hain 1696].

Avicenna, *see* Husain ibn 'Abd Allāh

Avienus, Rufus Festus (*fl.* 366-372)

Arati phaenomena [Latin paraphrase by Avienus] (in *Opera,* ed. Vittore Pisano) (Venice, 1488), with the *Aratea* of Germanicus Caesar and Cicero [Hain 2224].

Bacon, Roger (*ca.*1214-1294)

In meteora [comm. on Aristotle], no early eds. [Bodleian MS Digby 190].

Barbaro, Ermolao (1454-1493)

Castigationes Plinianae (Rome, 1493) [Hain 2421].

Compendium scientiae naturalis ex Aristotele, ed. Daniello Barbaro (Venice, 1545).

Bartholomaeus Anglicus (*fl.* 1220-1250)

De proprietatibus rerum [Latin text] ([Cologne, *ca.*1472]) [Hain 2498].

De proprietatibus rerum [English text by John of Trevisa] ([London, 1495]) [Hain 2520].

[1] Unidentified, but not to to be confused with the troubadour, d. 1307.

Bartholomaeus Arnoldi von Usingen (d. 1532)
Compendium naturalis philosophiae [*Aristotelis*] (Erfurt, [*ca.* 1505]).

Batrachus, *see* Frosch, Johann

Beda Venerabilis (673-735)
De natura rerum et temporum ratione (Basle, 1529).

Beroaldo, Filippo (1453-1505)
Caii Plynii Secundi naturalis historiae libri, ed. Beroaldo (Parma, 1476) [Hain 13091].
Opusculum de terraemotu et pestilentia (Bologna, 1505).

Beucer, Caspar, *see* Peucer, Caspar

Blemmidas, *see* Nicephorus Blemmidas

Boccaccio, Giovanni (1313-1375)
Genealogiae deorum gentilium (Venice, 1472) [Hain 3315].

Boccadiferro, Lodovico (1482-1545)
Lectiones super primum librum meteorologicorum Aristotelis [first printed in Venice, 1565].

Bocfeld, Adam (*fl.* 1350)
Notabilia super libri Metheororum [*Aristotelis*], no early eds.

Bonatti, Guido (<1223-*ca.*1297)
Decem continens tractatus astronomiae (Augsburg, 1491) [Hain 3461].

Bricot, Thomas
Textus abbreviatus Aristotelis super octo libris physicorum et tota naturali philosophia [including *Meteorologica,* Books I-III, and comm. by Bricot] (Paris, 1494) [Hain 3971].

Brossier, Simon (*fl.* 1536)
Totius philosophiae naturalis [*Aristotelis*] *epitome* (Paris, 1536).

Bruccioli, Antonio (*fl.* 1522-1554)
Historia Naturale di C. Plinio Secondo [Italian text by Bruccioli] (Venice, 1548).
La Meteora di Aristotile [Italian text by Bruccioli] (Venice, 1555).

Buccaferea, Lodovico, *see* Boccadiferro, Lodovico

Budé, Guillaume (1467-1540)
Plutarchi Cheronei de placitis philosophorum [Latin text by Budé] (Paris, 1505).
Aristotelis. . .de mundo libellus [Latin text by Budé] (Paris, 1526).

Buridan, Jean (*ca.*1297-*ca.*1358)
Quaestiones in libros metheororum [comm. on Aristotle], no early eds. [Bodleian MS Canon. Misc. 462].

Burley, Walter (1275-1357)
Compendium super libros metheororum [comm. on Aristotle], no early eds. [Bodleian MSS Digby 98, Add. A.370].

Calcagnini, Celio (1479-1541)

Paraphrasis trium librorum meteororum Aristotelis (in *Opera aliquot*) (Basle, 1544).

Camerarius, Joachim, Sr. (1500-1574)

In hoc libello. . .Æolia. In qua exponuntur nomina locaque ventorum Graeca & Latina. . .Prognostica. Ubi supra trecenta & triginto indicia tempestatum memorantur et al. (Nuremberg, 1535).

Κλαυδίου Πτολεμαίου. . .τετρβιβλος σύνταξις [Greek text, and Latin text by Camerarius], ed. Camerarius, et al. (Nuremberg, 1535).

De eorum qui cometae appellantur nominibus, natura, caussis, significatione (Leipzig, 1558).

Camozzi, Giovanni Battista (1515-1591)

Olympiodori philosophi Alexandrini in meteora Aristotelis commentarii. Ioannis Grammatici Philoponi scholia in I. meteorum Aristotelis [Latin text by Camozzi] (Venice, 1551).

Cardano, Girolamo (1501-1576)

De subtilitate libri xxi (Nuremberg, 1550).

De la subtilité, & subtiles inventions [French text by Richard le Blanc] (Paris, 1556).

De rerum varietate (Basle, 1557).

Carion, Johann (1499-1538)

Prognosticatio und Erklerung der grossen Wesserung (Leipzig, 1522).

Cartari, Vincenzo (*fl.* 1551)

Le imagini con la spositione de i dei degli antichi (Venice, 1556).

Castrovol, Pedro da

**Commentarius in libros meteororum* [comm. on Aristotle] ([Lerida], 1488) [Hain 4650].

Caxton, William (*ca.*1422-1491)

The Mirrour of the World [trans. from French] ([Westminster, 1481]) [Hain 11656].

Champier, Claude (*ca.*1520-?)

**Brief et facile commentaire de toutes choses engendrées en l'ain* (Lyons, 1558) [Brunet I.1777-1778].

Cicero, Marcus Tullius (106-43 B.C.)

Arati fragmenta [Latin paraphase by Cicero] (in Avienus, *Opera*, ed. Vittore Pisano) (Venice, 1488), with the *Aratea* of Germanicus Caesar and Avienus [Hain 2224].

Cleomedes (*fl.* 2nd century)

Circularis inspectionis meteororum [*libri duo*] [Latin text by Giorgio Valla] et al. (Venice, 1498) [Hain 11748].

Κυκλικὴ θεωρία ἐις βιβλία β′ [Greek text] (Paris, 1539).

Collimitius, *see* Tannstetter, Georg

Comes, Natalis (*ca.*1520-1582)
Mythologiae sive explicationum fabularum libri decem (Venice, 1551).
Conrad von Megenburg, *see* Alemann, Konrad von
Constantius (perhaps Antonio Costanzio, d. 1490)
**Liber de naturis liquidorum* [Gesner *P*].
Contarini, Gasparo (1483-1542)
De elementis & eorum mixtionibus (Paris, 1548).
Degen, Jakob (called Schegk, 1511-1587)
In reliquos naturalium Aristotelis libros commentaria. . .videlicet. . . meteoron lib. IIII et al. (Basle, 1550).
Democritus (*ca.*460-357 B.C.)
Known only through citation by subsequent writers, such as Plutarch (*De placitis philosophorum,* passim) and Diogenes Laertius (*Eminent Philosophers,* IX.34-49).
Digges, Leonard (d. 1574)
A Prognostication of Right Good Effect (London, 1555).[2]
Douglas, David
De naturae mirabilibus opusculum (Paris, 1524).
Dullaert, Jan (*ca.*1470-1513)
Librorum metheororum Aristotelis [Book I only] *facilis expositio et quaestiones super eosdem* [with Latin text] (Paris, 1514).
Duns Scotus, John (*ca.*1265-*ca.*1308)
Questiones super tres libros Metheororum [*Aristotelis*], no early eds.
Eck, Johann (1486-1543)
Aristotelis. . .libri meteororum .IIII. [Latin text]. . .*adiectis Eckii commentariis* et al. (Augsburg, 1519).
Engelhart, Jacob (caled Jacobus Angeli de Ulma, *fl.* 1402)
Tractatus de cometis ([Memmingen, 1490]) [Hain 1099].
Epicurus (342-270 B.C.)
Known only through citation by subsequent writers, such as Diogenes Laertius (*Eminent Philosophers,* X.98-116).
Eschuid, John, of Ashendon (*ca.*1325->1368)
Summa astrologiae iudicialis de accidentibus mundi (Venice, 1489) [Hain 6685].
Faber, Jacob, *see* Lefèvre d'Etaples, Jacques
Fausto, Sebastiano (*fl.* 1532-1560)
Meteorologia, cioè discorso de le impressioni humide & secche (Venice, 1542).
Ferrari, Antonio de (called Galateo, 1444-1516)
Liber de situ elementorum (Basle, 1558).

[2] F. R. Johnson notes that this 1555 edition is actually a revision of an *editio princeps* of 1553 (*Astronomical Thought in Renaissance England* [Johns Hopkins Press, 1937], p. 123).

Firmin de Beauval (*fl.* 1338-1345)

Opusculum repertorii pronosticon in mutationes aeris tam via astrologica quam metheorologica et al. (Venice, 1485) [Hain 13393].

Fortunatus, Matthaeus (*fl.* early 16th century)

L. Annei Senecae naturalium quaestionum libri VII. . . .in eosdem libros annotationes [with text] (Venice, 1522).

Frosch, Johann (called Batrachus, *fl.* 1514-1535)

De origine et principiis naturalibus impressionum in singulis aeris regionibus (Strasbourg, 1532).

Frytsche, Marcus

Meteororum, hoc est, impressionum aerearum et mirabilium naturae operum (Nuremberg, 1555).

Gaetano da Thiene, *see* Thiene, Gaetano da

Galateo, *see* Ferrari, Antonio de

Gaphar, *see* Ja'far ibn Muhammad

Gaurico, Luca (1476-1558)

Ephemerides (Venice, 1533).

Geminus Rhodius (*fl.* 77 B.C.)

Isagoge in meteora [comm. on Aristotle], no early eds.

Germanicus Caesar (B.C. 16-19 A.D.)

Arathus [Latin paraphrase of Aratus] et al. (Bologna, 1474) [Hain 10707].

Ghelen, Siegmund (1497-1554)

C. Plinii Secundi historia mundi, ed. with annotations by Ghelen (Basle, 1535).

Gower, John (*ca.*1325-1408)

Confessio amantis (Westminster, 1483) [Hain 7835].

Grataroli, Guglielmo (1516-1568)

Prognostica naturalia de temporum mutatione perpetua (Basle, [1552]).

Grosseteste, Robert (*ca.*1175-1253)

"De impressionibus aeris," "De aeris intemperia prognostica," "De iride," "De cometis," etc., no early eds. [Bodleian MSS Digby 48, Digby 98].

Grynaeus, Simon (1493-1541)

Scholion. . .in Aristotelis libellum de mundo [with Greek text and Latin text by Guillaume Budé] et al. (Basle, 1533).

Guillaume de Conches (1080-*ca.*1154)

De philosophia mundi [often attributed to Honoré d'Autun], no early eds.

Hieronymus de Sancto Marco[8]

Opusculum de universali mundi machina ac de metheoricis impressionibus ([London, 1505]).

[8] On the probable identity of this name, see Lynn Thorndike, *A History of Magic and Experimental Science* (6 vols.; New York, 1923-1941), IV.703 ff.

Hippocrates of Cos (*ca.*460-*ca.*377 B.C.)
De aere et aqua et regionibus [Latin text] et al. (Milan, 1481) [Hain 13891].
Honoré d'Autun (called Solitarius, d. >1130)
Ymago mundi ([Nuremberg, *ca.*1472]) [Hain 8800].
Hrabanus Maurus, *see* Rabanus Maurus
Husain ibn 'Abd Allāh (called Avicenna, 980-1037)
Canonis [*libri V*] [Latin text by Gerard of Cremona] ([Strasbourg, *ca.*1475]) [Hain 2197].
Isidore of Seville (*ca.*570-636)
Ethimologiarum [*libri XX*] ([Strasbourg, *ca.*1470]) [Hain 9270].
De responsione mundi & astrorum ordinatione [i.e., *De natura rerum*] (Augsburg, 1472) [Hain 9302].
Jacobus Angeli de Ulma, *see* Engelhart, Jacob
Jacobus d'Amorsfordia, *see* Tymaeus, Jacob, van Amersfoort
Ja'far ibn Muhammad (called Gaphar = Abū Ma'shar, called Albumasar, 805-885)
Astrorum iudices. . .de pluviis imbribus et ventis: ac aeris mutatione (Venice, 1507).
Javelli, Crisostomo (*ca.*1471-1538)
**Epitome in philosophiam naturalem Aristotelis* (Venice, 1547) [Schwab 1024].
John of Alexandria (called Philoponus, *fl.* 6th century)
Scholia in primum meteorum Aristotelis [with Greek text] (Venice, 1551), with comm. Olympiodorus of Alexandria.
Scholia in I. meteorum Aristotelis [Latin text by G. B. Camozzi, with Latin text of Aristotle by Camozzi] (Venice, 1551), with comm. Olympiodorus of Alexandria.
John of Ashendon, *see* Eschuid, John
John of Damascus, St. (*ca.*700-754)
De orthodoxa fide liber [Latin text by Jacques Lefèvre d'Etaples] (Paris 1507).
Konrad von Megenberg, *see* Alemann, Konrad von
Laigue, Etienne de (called Aquaeus, d. 1537)
In omnes C. Plinii Secundi naturalis historiae. . .libros. . .commentaria (Paris, 1530).
Landino, Cristoforo (1424-1504)
Historia naturale di C. Plinio Secondo [Italian text by Landino] (Venice, 1476) [Hain 13105].
Latini, Brunetto (*ca.*1220-1294)
El tesoro, trans. [from French] B. Giamboni (Trevisa, 1474) [Hain 4009].

Laurentius, Joannes, *see* Lydus, Joannes Laurentius

Lavater, Ludwig (1527-1586)

Cometarum omnium fere catalogus (Zurich, 1556).

Lefèvre d'Etaples, Jacques (called Jacob Faber, *ca.*1455-1537)

Littere librorum P C G M. . .liber metheororum et al. [Latin *paraphrases* (Paris, 1501), with comm. Lefèvre d'Etaples.

In hoc opere continentur totius philosophiae naturalis [*Aristotelis*] *paraphrases* (Paris, 1501), with comm. Le Fèvre d'Etaples.

Leopold of Austria (*fl.* 13th century)

Compilatio. . .de astrorum scientia decem continens tractatus (Augsburg, 1489) [Hain 10042].

Lonicer, Johann (1499-1569)

De meteoris compendium, ex Aristotele, Plinio, et Pontano (Frankfurt, 1548).

Lucretius Carus, Titus (98-55 B.C.)

**De rerum natura* ([Brescia, *ca.*1473]) [Hain 10281].

Luther, Martin (1483-1546)

Uber das erst buch Mose (Wittenberg, 1527).

Lycosthenes, *see* Wolffhardt, Conrad

Lydus, Joannes Laurentius (490-*ca.*565)

De signis tempestatum, no early eds.

Macrobius (*fl.* 395-423)

In somnium Scipionis [with text of Cicero] et al. (Venice, 1472) [Hain 10426].

Maerlant, Jacob van (*ca.*1235-*ca.*1300)

Der naturen bloeme [Flemish adaptation of Thomas de Cantimpré, *De natura rerum*], no early eds.

Maffei, Raffaele (called Volaterranus, 1451-1522)

Commentariorum urbanorum [*libri XXXVIII*] (Rome, 1506).

Magistris, Jean de (1432-1482)

Questiones perutiles super tota philosophia [comms. on Aristotle] (Parma, 1481) [Hain 10447].

Magnus, Olaus (*ca.*1490-1568)

Historia de gentibus septentrionalibus (Rome, 1555).

Mahieu le Vilain (*fl.* late 13th century)

Les Metheores [French text of Aristotle], no early eds.

Manilius, Marcus (*fl.* A.D. 1)

Astronomicon (Nuremberg, [*ca.*1472]) [Hain 10703].

Manuzio, Paolo (1512-1574)

De gli elementi, e di molti loro notabili effetti (Venice, 1557).

De elementis, et variis eorum effectis [Latin trans. by Jacob Carpenter of the preceding work] (Paris, 1558).

Megenberg, Konrad von, *see* Alemann, Konrad von

Merle, William (d. 1347)
De futura aëris intemperie, no early eds. [Bodleian MS Digby 176].

Mexia, Pedro (1496-1552)
**Silva de varia leccion* (Seville, 1542) [Brunet III.1688].

Meygret, Louis (*ca.*1510->1560)
Le second livre de Caius Plinius Secundus, sur l'histoire des œuvres de nature [French text by Meygret] (Paris, 1552).

Milich, Jacob (1501-1559)
Liber II. C. Plinii de mundi historia, cum commentariis (Frankfurt, 1543).

Mizauld, Antoine (*ca.*1510-1578)
Phaenomena, sive aeriae ephemerides (Paris, 1546).
Le mirouer du temps, autrement dict, Ephemerides perpetuelles de l'air [French trans. of the preceding work] (Paris, 1547).
Meteorologia, sive rerum aeriarum commentariolus (Paris, 1547).
Le mirouer de l'air [French trans. of the preceding work] (Paris, 1548).
Cometographia (Paris, 1549).

Monheim, Johann (1509-1564)
Elementorum physiologiae, seu philosophiae naturalis libri septem (Cologne, 1542).

Müller, Johann (called Regiomontanus, 1436-1476)
De cometae magnitudine, longitudineque ac de loco eius vero, problemata XVI (Nuremberg, 1531).

Neckam, Alexander (1157-1217)
De natura rerum, no early eds.

Nicephorus Blemmidas (*ca.*1197-1272)
Epitome physica [Greek text], ed. Johann Wegelin [first printed in Augsburg, 1605].

Nicoletti, Paolo (called Paulus Venetus, 1372-1429)
Liber methaurorum [comm. on Aristotle] (in *Summae naturalium [Aristotelis]*) (Venice, 1476) [Hain 12515].
De compositione mundi et al. (Venice, 1498) [Hain 12518].

Nifo, Agostino (1473-1538)
**In libris Aristotelis meteorologicis commentaria* [with Latin text by Nifo] (Venice, 1531) [Gesner *B*].
De verissimis temporum signis commentariolus (Venice, 1540).

Olympiodorus of Alexandria (*fl.* 6th century)
In meteora Aristotelis commentarii [with Greek text] (Venice, 1551), with comm. John of Alexandria.
In meteora Aristotelis commentarii [Latin text by G. B. Camozzi, with Latin text of Aristotle by Camozzi] (Venice, 1551), with comm. John of Alexandria.

Orbellis, Nicolaus de (d. 1455)

Cursus librorum philosophiae naturalis [comms. on Aristotle] (printed with *Summulae philosophiae rationalis*) (Basle, 1494) [Hain 12044].

Oresme, Nicole (*ca.*1320-1382)

Questiones super libros Metheororum Aristotelis, no early eds.

Paulus Venetus, *see* Nicoletti, Paolo

Peckham, John (*ca.*1240-1292)

Prospectiva ([Milan, *ca.*1482]) [Hain 9425].

Périon, Joachim (*ca.*1499-1559)

Aristotelis meteorologicorum libri quatuor [Latin text by Périon] (Paris, 1552).

Perscrutator, *see* Robert of York

Peucer, Caspar (1525-1602)

De meteorologia (in *Commentarius de praecipuis divinationum generibus*) (Wittenberg, 1553).

Philoponus, *see* John of Alexandria

Piccolomini, Alessandro (1508-1578)

Alexandri Aphrodisiensis. . .in quatuor libros meteorologicorum Aristotelis commentatio [Latin text by Piccolomini, with Latin text of Aristotle by Piccolomini]. . .*Accedit. . .tractatus de iride* (Venice, 1540).

Pierre d'Auvergne, *see* Auvergne, Pierre d'

Pitati, Pietro (*fl.* middle 16th century)

Tractatus. . .[de] mutatione aeris (in *Almanach novum*) (Tübingen, 1544).

Pliny, the Elder (23-79)

Libros naturalis historiae (Venice, 1469) [Hain 13087].

Naturalis historiae libri, ed. Filippo Beroaldo (Parma, 1476) [Hain 13091].

Historia mundi (Basle, 1535), with comm. Siegmund Ghelen.

De naturali historia [Book II only] et al. (Basle, 1531), with comms. Jacob Ziegler and Georg Tannstetter.

Liber II. . .de mundi historia (Frankfurt, 1543), with comm. Jacob Milich.

Historia naturale [Italian text by Cristoforo Landino] (Venice, 1476) [Hain 13105].

Le second livre. . .sur l'histoire des œuvres de nature [French text by Louis Meygret] (Paris, 1552).

Plutarch of Chaeronea (*ca.*46-120)

De placitis philosophorum [Latin text by Guillaume Budé] (Paris, 1505).

Περὶ τῶν ἀρεσκόντων τοῖς φιλοσοφοῖς [Greek text, with Latin text by Budé] (Basle, 1531).

Poliziano, Angelo (1454-1494)
Silva cui titulus Rusticus (Florence, 1483) [Hain 13233].
Pontano, Giovanni Gioviano (1426-1503)
Meteororum liber (in *Opera*) ([Venice, 1505]).
Posidonius of Rhodes (*ca.*135-51 B.C.)
Known only through citation by subsequent writers, such as Plutarch (*De placitis philosophorum*, passim) and Diogenes Laertius (*Eminent Philosophers*, VII.151-155). The *De mundo* traditionally ascribed to Aristotle seems to be a redaction of two lost works by Posidonius, the Μετεωρολογικὴ στοιχείωσις and the Περὶ κόσμου.
Ptolemaeus, Claudius (*fl.* 139-161)
Liber quadripartiti [Latin text] (Venice, 1484) [Hain 13543].
Τετράβιβλος σύνταξις [Greek text, and Latin text by Joachim Camerarius], ed. Camerarius, et al. (Nuremberg, 1535).
Inerrantium stellarum significationes [Latin text by Nicolaus Leonicus] et al. (Venice, 1516).
Rabanus Maurus (*ca.*776-856)
De sermonum proprietate & mistica rerum significacione [i.e., *De universo*] ([Strasbourg, *ca.*1465]) [Hain 13669].
In Genesim libri IIII et al. (Cologne, 1532).
Rastell, John (d. 1536)
A New Interlude and a Mery of the Nature of the .iiii. Elements (London, [*ca.*1520]).
Regiomontanus, *see* Müller, Johann
Reisch, Gregor (d. 1525)
**Margarita philosophica* (Heidelberg, 1496) [Hain 13852].
Reynman, Leonhard (*fl.* early 16th century)
**Von warer Erkanntnus des Weters* (Augsburg, 1505).
Richard of Wallingford (*ca.*1292-1336)
Exafrenon pronosticorum temporis, no early eds., but trans. into English *ca.*1385 [Bodleian MS Digby 180; and for the English trans., Bodleian MS Digby 67].
Robert of York (called Perscrutator, <1312-*ca.*1348)
De impressionibus aeris, no early eds.
Schegk, Jakob, *see* Degen, Jakob
Seneca, Lucius Annaeus (B.C. 4-65 A.D.)
Libri de naturalibus questionibus (in *Opera omnia*) (Venice, 1492) [Hain 14594].
De questionibus naturalibus (Leipzig, [*ca.*1493]) [Hain 14613].
Naturalium quaestionum libri VII (Venice, 1522), with comm. Matthaeus Fortunatus.
Simon of Faversham (*ca.*1270-*ca.*1306)
Quaestiones in meteora [comm. on Aristotle], no early eds.
Solitarius, *see* Honoré d'Autun

Stobaeus, Joannes (*fl.* 4th century)
Eclogarum libri duo: quorum prior physicas, posterior ethicas complectitur [first printed in Antwerp, 1575; Greek text, and Latin text by Willem Canter, et al.].

Sydrach (anonym)
**La fontaine de toutes sciences* (Paris, 1486) [Hain 15190].

Tannstetter, Georg (called Collimitius, 1482-1535)
De natura locorum [*Alberti Magni*], ed. Tannstetter (Vienna, 1514).
Artificium de applicatione astrologiae ad medicinam. . .canones aliquot (Strasbourg, 1531).
In C. Plinii de naturali historia librum secundum commentarius [with text] et al. (Basle, 1531), with comm. Jacob Ziegler.
*Vitellionis. . .*περὶ ὀπτικῆς, ed. Tannstetter and Peter Apian (Nuremberg, 1535).

Tartaglia, Niccolo (*ca.*1500-1559)
Regola generale da sulevare. . .ogni affondata nave. . .[*ed*] *un trattato di segni delle mutationi dell'aria* ([Venice, 1551]).

Tartareto, Pietro (d. >1509)
Totius philosophiae necnon metaphisicae Aristotelis. . .expositio [including *Meteorologica*, Books I-III, and comm. by Tartareto] (Paris, 1494) [Hain 15344].

Themon Judaeus (d. >1361)
Quaestiones quarti methaurorum [comm. on Aristotle] ([Pavia, *ca.* 1482]) [British Museum IB.31329].

Theon of Alexandria (*fl.* 365-395)
Phaenomena [Greek text of Aratus] *cum Theonis scholiis* (in *Scriptores astronomici veteres*) (Venice, 1499), with the *Aratea* of Cicero, Germanicus Caesar, and Avienus [Hain 14559].

Theophrastus (374-287 B.C.)
De ventis. . .de signis aquarum et ventorum [Greek text] (in Aristotle, *Opera*, Vol. II) (Venice, 1495-1498) [Hain 1657].
De signis tempestatum, ventorum et aquarum [Latin text] et al. [attributed to Aristotle] (Bologna, 1501) [Bibliothèque Nationale Rés. R.54(2)].

Thiene, Gaetano da (1387-1465)
In quattuor Aristotilis metheororum libros expositio (Padua, 1476) [Hain 15506].

Thomas Aquinas, *see* Aquinas, St. Thomas

Thomas de Cantimpré (1201-<1280)
De natura rerum, no early eds.; *see* Alemann, Konrad von, and Maerlant, Jacob van.

Werner, Johann (1468-1528)

Canones. . .complectentes praecepta & observationes de mutatione aurae (Nuremberg, 1546).

Wildenberg, Hieronymus (1465-1558)

Totius naturalis philosophiae in physicam Aristotelis epitome, cuius haec est facies:. . .meteororum IIII (Basle, 1544).

Willich, Jodocus (1501-1552)

**Isagoge in Aristotelis, Alberti Magni et Pontani meteorologica* (Frankfort, 1549) [Schwab 1329].

Dialysis quatuor librorum in georgicis Vergilii. . .[et] signorum prognosticorum de tempestatibus aeris physica explicatio (Frankfurt, 1551).

Wolffhardt, Conrad (called Lycosthenes, 1518-1561)

Prodigiorum ac ostentorum chronicon (Basle, 1557).

Yakub b. Ishāk al-Kindi (called Alkindus, *ca.*810-*ca.*873)

Astrorum iudices. . .de pluviis imbribus et ventis: ac aeris mutatione et al. (Venice, 1507).

Ziegler, Jacob (*ca.*1470-1549)

In C. Plinii de naturali historia librum secundum commentarius [with text]et al. (Basle, 1531), with comm. Georg Tannstetter.

LIST OF EDITIONS USED IN CITATIONS

1. *Elizabethan and Jacobean Authors*

Beaumont, Francis, and Fletcher, John. *Plays*, ed. Felix E. Schelling. New York, 1905.
Chapman, George. *Tragedies*, ed. Thomas M. Parrott. London, 1910.
———. *Comedies*, ed. Thomas M. Parrott. London, 1914.
———. *Poems*, ed. Phyllis B. Bartlett. MLA; Oxford Univ. Press, 1941.
Daniel, Samuel. *Works*, ed. Alexander B. Grosart. 5 vols. Huth Library; London, 1885-1896.
Davies, Sir John. *Poems*, ed. Alexander B. Grosart. 2 vols. Early English Poets; London, 1876.
Dekker, Thomas. *Non-Dramatic Works*, ed. Alexander B. Grosart. 5 vols. Huth Library; London, 1884-1886.
Donne, John. *Poems*, ed. Herbert J. C. Grierson. 2 vols. Oxford Univ. Press, 1912.
Drayton, Michael. *Works*, ed. J. William Hebel. 5 vols. Oxford, 1931-1941.
Gascoigne, George. *Works*, ed. John W. Cunliffe. 2 vols. Cambridge Univ. Press, 1907.
Greene, Robert. *Works*, ed. Alexander B. Grosart. 15 vols. Huth Library; London, 1881-1886.
Hall, Joseph. *Poems*, ed. A. Davenport. Liverpool Univ. Press, 1949.
Jonson, Ben. *Works*, ed. C. H. Herford and Percy Simpson. 10 vols. Oxford Univ. Press, 1925-1950.
Kyd, Thomas. *Works*, ed. Frederick S. Boas. Oxford Univ. Press, 1901.
Marlowe, Christopher. *Works*, ed. C. F. Tucker Brooke. Oxford Univ. Press, 1910.
Marston, John. *Works*, ed. A. H. Bullen. 3 vols. London, 1887.
Nashe, Thomas. *Works*, ed. Ronald B. McKerrow. 5 vols. London, 1904.
Peele, George. *Works*, ed. A. H. Bullen. 2 vols. London, 1888.
Raleigh, Sir Walter. *Poems*, ed. Agnes M. C. Latham. London, 1929.
Sackville, Thomas. *The Mirror for Magistrates*, ed. Lily B. Campbell. Cambridge Univ. Press, 1938.
Shakespeare, William. *Works*, ed. William G. Clark and William Aldis Wright. Globe ed.; London, 1864.

Sidney, Sir Philip. *Works*, ed. Albert Feuillerat. 3 vols. Cambridge Univ. Press, 1912-1923.

Spenser, Edmund. *Works*, ed. Edwin Greenlaw, et al. 10 vols. Johns Hopkins Press, 1932-1949.

Tourneur, Cyril. *Works*, ed. Allardyce Nicoll. London, 1930.

Watson, Thomas. *Poems*, ed. Edward Arber. London, 1870.

Webster, John. *Works*, ed. F. L. Lucas. 4 vols. London, 1927.

2. *Greek and Latin Authors*

Apollodorus. *The Library*. Trans. Sir James G. Frazer. 2 vols. Loeb; London, 1921.

Apollonius Rhodius. *The Argonautica*. Trans. R. C. Seaton. Loeb; London, 1912.

Aratus. *Phaenomena* [including the *Diosemea*]. Trans. G. R. Mair. Loeb; London, 1921.

Aristotle. *Meteorologica*. Trans. H. D. P. Lee. Loeb; London, 1952.

Bartholomaeus Anglicus. *Batman uppon Bartholome, His Booke De Proprietatibus Rerum*, ed. Stephen Batman. London, 1582.

Beda Venerabilis. *De natura rerum* (*PL*, Vol. XC, ed. J.-P. Migne). Paris, 1862.

Boccaccio, Giovanni. *Genealogiae*. Venice, 1511.

Cartari, Vicenzo. *Le imagini de i dei degli antichi*. Venice, 1571.

———. *Imagines deorum, qui ab antiquis colebantur*. Trans. [into Latin] A. Verdier. Lyons, 1581.

Comes, Natalis. *Mythologiae, sive explicationum fabularum*. Paris, 1583.

Diodorus Siculus. *The Library of History*. Trans. C. H. Oldfeather. 10 vols. Loeb; London, 1933-1954.

Diogenes Laertius. *Lives of Eminent Philosophers*. Trans. Robert D. Hicks. 2 vols. Loeb; London, 1925.

Epicurus. *The Extant Remains*. Trans. Cyril Bailey. Oxford, 1926.

Hesiod. *Hesiod, the Homeric Hymns, and Homerica*. Trans. Hugh G. Evelyn-White. Loeb; London, 1914.

Homer. *The Iliad*. Trans. Augustus T. Murray. 2 vols. Loeb; London, 1924.

———. *The Odyssey*. Trans. Augustus T. Murray. 2 vols. Loeb; London, 1919.

Hyginus, Caius Julius. *Fabularum liber* [*et al.*]. Basle, 1570.

Isidore of Seville. *De natura rerum* (*PL*, Vol. LXXXIII, ed. J.-P. Migne). Paris, 1850.

———. *Etymologiae* (*PL*, Vol. LXXXII, ed. J.-P. Migne). Paris, 1850.

Lactantius, Placidus. *Narrationes Fabularum* (in *Auctores Mythographi Latini*, ed. A. van Staveren). Leyden and Amsterdam, 1742.

Lucian. *The Dialogues*. Trans. William Tooke. London, 1930.
Lucretius. *De rerum natura*. Trans. H. A. J. Munro. 2 vols. 2d ed.; Cambridge, 1866.
Macrobius, Ambrosius Theodosius. [*Works*], ed. Francis Eyssenhardt. Teubner; Leipzig, 1868.
Manilius, Marcus. *Astronomicon*, ed. A. E. Housman. 5 vols. Cambridge Univ. Press, 1903-1930.
Ovid. *Fasti*. Trans. Sir James G. Frazer. Loeb; London, 1931.
———. *Metamorphoses*. Trans. Frank J. Miller. 2 vols. Loeb; London, 1916.
Philostratus the Elder. *Imagines*. Trans. Arthur Fairbanks. Loeb; London, 1931.
Plato. *Cratylus* [*et al.*]. Trans. H. N. Fowler. Loeb; London, 1926.
———. *Timaeus* [*et al.*]. Trans. R. G. Bury. Loeb; London, 1952.
Pliny. *The Historie of the World*. Trans. Philemon Holland. 2 books. London, 1601.
———. *Natural History*. Trans. H. Rackham. Loeb; London, 1938.
Plutarch. *The Philosophie Commonlie Called the Morals*. Trans. Philemon Holland. London, 1603.
———. ΠΕΡΙ ΤΩΝ ΑΡΕΣΚΟΝΤΩΝ ΦΙΛΟΣΟΦΟΙΣ ΦΥΣΙΚΩΝ ΔΟΓΜΑΤΩΝ (in *Moralia*, Vol. V), ed. G. N. Bernardakis. Teubner; Leipzig, 1893.
Rabanus Maurus. *Allegoriae in Sacram Scripturam* (*PL*, Vol. CXII, ed. J.-P. Migne). Paris, 1878.
———. *De universo* (*PL*, Vol. CXI, ed. J.-P. Migne). Paris, 1864.
Seneca, Lucius Annaeus. *The Workes Both Morrall and Natural*. Trans. Thomas Lodge. London, 1614.
———. *Naturalium questionum libri VII* (in *Opera*, Vol. II), ed. F. Haase. Teubner; Leipzig, 1898.
Servius. *Commentarii in Virgilium*, ed. H. A. Lion. 2 vols. Göttingen, 1826.
Theophrastus. *Weather Signs* [*et al.*]. Trans. Sir Arthur Hort. Loeb; London, 1916.
Valerius Flaccus. *Argonautica*. Trans. J. H. Mozley. Loeb; London, 1936.
Vergil. *Eclogues, Georgics, Aeneid*. Trans. H. Rushton Fairclough. 2 vols. Loeb; London, 1916-1918.
Vitruvius. *De architectura*, ed. F. Krohn. Teubner; Leipzig, 1912.

SELECTED BIBLIOGRAPHY

1. *Primary Sources*[1]

Abenezrah, Kinki. *An Everlasting Prognostication of the Change of Weather*. London: for M. S[parke, 1620?].
Apian, Peter. *Cosmographicum*. Landshut, 1524.
Babington, Gervase. *Certaine Plaine, Briefe, and Comfortable Notes upon Everie Chapter of Genesis*. London: for T. Charde, 1592.
Bacon, Francis. *Historia naturalis et experimentalis*. London, 1622.
Bainbridge, John. *An Astronomicall Description of the Late Comet from the 18. of Novemb. 1618 to the 16. of December Following*. London: E. Griffin for J. Parker, 1619.
Batman, Stephen. *The Doome Warning All Men to the Judgemente*. London: R. Newberry for H. Bynneman, 1581.
Bohun, Ralph. *A Discourse Concerning the Origine and Properties of Wind*. Oxford: W. Hall for T. Bowman, 1671.
Bonaventura, Federigo. *Anemologia*. Urbino, 1593.
Bourne, William. *An Almanacke and Prognostication for X. Yeeres*. London: R. Watkins and J. Roberts, 1581.
Brerewood, Edward. *Tractatus duo quorum primus est de meteoris, secundus de oculo*. Oxford, 1631.
Calvin, John. *A Commentarie. . .upon the First Booke of Moses Called Genesis*. Trans. Thomas Tymme. London: for J. Harrison and G. Bishop, 1578.
Churchyard, Thomas. *A Warning for the Wise*. London: J. Allde and N. Lyng, 1580.
Cortes, Martin. *The Arte of Navigation*, Trans. Richard Eden. London: R. Jugge, 1561.
Cuningham, William. *The Cosmographical Glasse*. London: J. Day, 1559.
Descartes, René. *Discours de la méthode. . .Plus la dioptrique, les météores, et la géométrie*. Paris, 1637.
Erra Pater. *Pronostycacion For Ever*. London: T. Colwell, [*ca.*1562].
Everard, John. *Somewhat: Written by Occasion of Three Sunnes Seene at Tregnie in Cornewall*. London: [for T. Walkeley], 1622.
Fenton, Edward. *Certaine Secrete Wonders of Nature*. London: Henry Bynneman, 1569.

[1] I have not repeated texts included in Appendix II or in the "List of Editions Used in Citations."

Ideler, Julius L. *Meteorologia veterum Graecorum et Romanorum.* Berlin, 1832.

Johnson, Francis R. *Astronomical Thought in Renaissance England.* Johns Hopkins Press, 1937.

Kocher, Paul H. *Science and Religion in Elizabethan England.* San Marino [California], 1953.

Sarton, George. *Introduction to the History of Science.* 3 vols. Baltimore, 1927-1948.

Thorndike, Lynn. *A History of Magic and Experimental Science.* 6 vols. New York, 1923-1941.

———. "Oresme and Fourteenth Century Commentaries on the Meteorologica," *Isis,* XLV (1954), 145-152.

———. "More Questions on the Meteorologica," *Isis,* XLVI (1955), 357-360.

Wolf, Abraham. *A History of Science, Technology, and Philosophy in the 16th and 17th Centuries.* London, 1935.

Fleming, Abraham. *A Bright Burning Beacon.* London: Henry Denham, 1580.

———. *A Treatise of Blazing Starres in Generall,* adapted from Frederick Nausea. London: B. Alsop, 1618.

Fludd, Robert. *Philosophia sacra & vere Christiana, seu meteorologia cosmica.* Frankfurt, 1626.

Fraunce, Abraham. *The Third Part of the Countesse of Pembrokes Ivychurch: Entituled, Amintas Dale.* London: for T. Woodcocke, 1592.

Fromondus, Libertus. *Meteorologicorum libri sex.* Antwerp, 1627.

Fulke, William. *A Goodly Gallery with a Most Pleasaunt Prospect, into the Garden of Naturall Contemplation, to Beholde the Naturall Causes of All Kind of Meteors.* London: William Griffith, 1571.

Gartze, Johann. *Meteorologia.* Wittenberg, 1568.

Gibbens, Nicholas. *Questions and Disputations Concerning the Holy Scripture.* London: Felix Kyngston, 1601.

Giraldi, Lilio Gregorio. *De deis gentium libri.* Lyons, 1565.

Godfridus. *The Boke of Knowledge of Thynges Unknowen Apperteynynge to Astronomye.* London: R.Wyer, [1530?].

———. *The Knowledge of Things Unknowne. . .with the Husbandmans Practise.* London: J. B[eale] for Roger Jackson, 1619.

Golding, Arthur. *A Discourse upon the Earthquake. . .the Sixt of Aprill .1580.* London: Henry Bynneman, 1580.

Harvey, Gabriel. *Three Proper, and Wittie, Familiar Letters.* London: Henry Bynneman, 1580.

Harward, Simon. *A Discourse of the Severall Kinds and Causes of Lightnings.* London: J. Windet, 1607.

Havenreuter, Johann Ludwig. *Commentarii. . .in Aristotelis. . .Meteorologicorum libros quatuor.* Frankfurt, 1605.

Hill, Thomas. *A Contemplation of Mysteries.* London: Henry Denham, [1571].

———. *The Profitable Arte of Gardening.* London: Henry Bynneman, 1574.

Hooke, Robert. "A Method for Making a History of the Weather," in *The History of the Royal-Society,* by Thomas Sprat. London, 1667.

K., F. *Of the Crinitall Starre, Which Appeareth This October and November. 1580.* London: [R. Watkins, 1580].

Kalender of Sheepeherds. London: J. Wally, [1560?].

Kalender of Shepherdes [Paris, 1503; London, 1506], ed. H. Oskar Sommer. London, 1892.

Keckermann, Bartholomaeus. *Systema physicum* (in *Operum omnium. . . tomus primus,* col. 1657-1756). Geneva, 1614.

La Primaudaye, Pierre de. *The Third Volume of the French Academie*. Trans. R. Dolman. London: George Bishop, 1601.

Leopold of Austria. *Li Compilacions de le Science des Estoilles, Books I-III*, ed. Francis J. Carmody. Univ. of California Publications in Modern Philology; Univ. of California Press, 1947.

Maplet, John. *The Diall of Destiny*. London: Thomas Marsh, 1581.

Merle, William. *Consideraciones temperiei pro 7 annis*, reproduced and trans. S. J. Symons. London, 1891.

Meurer, Wolfgang. *Meteorologia, quaestionibus informata*. Leipzig, 1587.

Monardes, Nicolas. *The Boke Which Treateth of the Snow* [dated 1574], appended to *Joyfull Newes out of the New-found Worlde*. Trans. John Frampton. London: E. Allde, 1596.

Moore, Philip. *A Fourtie Yeres Almanacke*. London: John Kingston for Henry Saunderson, [*ca.*1567].

Nicholas of Lyra. *Biblia sacra cum glossa ordinaria. . .et Postilla Nicolai Lyrani*. 6 vols. Lyons, 1589.

Paduani, Fabricio. *Tractatus duo, alter de ventis, alter perbrevis de terraemotu*. Bologna, 1601.

Perpetuall and Naturall Prognostications of the Change of Weather. Trans. [from Italian] I. F[armery?]. London: J. Wolfe, 1591.

Pond, Edward. *Enchiridion. . .1604*. London: E. Allde, 1604.

Rao, Cesare. *I Meteori*. Venice, 1582.

Reisacher, Wilhelm. *Disputatio philosophica, de meteoris*. Ingolstadt, 1588.

Reisch, Gregor. *Margarita philosophica*. [Strasbourg], 1515.

Rodrigues de Castro, Stephano. *De meteoris microcosmi libri quatuor*. Florence, 1621.

Saluste du Bartas, Guillaume de. *Bartas His Devine Weekes & Workes*. Trans. Joshua Sylvester. London: H. Lownes, 1605.

Scribonius, Gulielmus Adolphus. *Naturall Philosophy*. Trans. Daniel Widdowes. London, 1621.

Shakelton, Francis. *A Blazyng Starre or Burnyng Beacon, Seene the 10. of October Laste*. London: John Kingston for Henry Kirkham, 1580.

Stanhuf, Michèle. *De meteoris libri duo*. Wittenberg, 1562.

Telesio, Bernardino. *De his, quae in aëre fiunt; & de terraemotibus*. Naples, 1570.

Twyne, Thomas. *A Shorte and Pithie Discourse Concerning. . .Earthquakes*. London: Richard Jones, 1580.

———. *A view of Certain Wonderful Effects. . .of the Comete, or Blasing Star, Which Appered in the Southwest upon the .X. Day of Novemb. . . .1577*. London: Richard Jones, 1578.

Verro, Sebastian. *Physicorum libri .X*. London: Henry Bynneman, 1581.

Willsford, Thomas. *Natures Secrets, or, The Admirable and Wonderfull History of the Generation of Meteors*. London: for N. Brook, 1658.

2. *Secondary Sources*

Allen, Don Cameron. *The Star-Crossed Renaissance*. Duke Uni 1941.

Bosanquet, Eustace F. *English Printed Almanacks and Prognos A Bibliographical History to the Year 1600*. London, 19 *rigenda and Addenda*. London, 1928. *Notes on Further* London, 1937.

Buell, Llewellyn M. "Arthur Golding and the Earthquake *PQ*, XXIV (1945), 227-232.

———. "Elizabethan Portents: Superstition or Doctrine?" *Es cal and Historical Dedicated to Lily B. Campbell* (Uni fornia Press, 1950), pp. 27-41.

Camden, Carroll, Jr. "Elizabethan Almanacs and Prognosticat *Library*, XII (1931), 83-108, 194-207.

Campbell, Lily B. "Richard Tarlton and the Earthquake of 15 IV (1940-41), 293-301.

Collins, D. C. "Exhalations," *TLS*, 2 October 1930, p. 782.

Fassig, Oliver Lanard. *Bibliography of Meteorology*. Washin 1889-1891.

Fobes, F. H. "Medieval Versions of Aristotle's Meteorolog *Philology*, X (1915), 297-314.

Gillespie, William E. *Vergil, Aratus and Others*. Princeton,

Gunther, Robert W. T. *Early Science in Oxford*, Vol. I. C

Hellmann, Gustav. *Die Anfänge der meteorologischen E und Instrumente*. Berlin, 1890.

———. *Contribution to the Bibliography of Meteorology Magnetism in the Fifteenth, Sixteenth, and Sevente* (extract from Part II of the Report of the Chicago Congress, August 1893, pp. 352-394).

———. *Neudrucke von Schriften und Karten über M Erdmagnetismus* (nos. 1-12). Berlin, 1893-1899.

———. *Meteorologische Volksbücher*. Berlin, 1895.

———. *Beiträge zur Geschichte der Meteorologie*. B 1914; nos. 6-10, 1917.

———. *Beiträge zur Erfindungsgeschichte meteorologis* (in *Abhandlungen der preussischen Akademie der Jahrgang 1920. Physikalisch-Mathematische Klass* 1920.

———. *Die Meteorologie in den deutschen Flugsch blättern des XVI. Jahrhunderts* (in *Abhandlunge Akademie der Wissenschaften. Jahrgang 19 Mathematische Klasse*, nr. 1). Berlin, 1921.

LIST OF PASSAGES CITED

SPENSER

MARLOWE

JONSON

CHAPMAN

DONNE

SHAKESPEARE

GENERAL INDEX

This General Index does not duplicate entries in the Index of Authorities Before 1558, the Selected Bibliography, and the List of Passages Cited.